1969

THIS BOOK HAS BEEN SENT TO YOU
AT THE SUGGESTION OF

LYLE D. LINDER

Please accept it with our compliments

McGRAW-HILL BOOK COMPANY

Ex Libris:_____

VECTOR ANALYSIS

INTERNATIONAL SERIES IN
PURE AND APPLIED MATHEMATICS

William Ted Martin and E. H. Spanier
CONSULTING EDITORS

VECTOR ANALYSIS

HOMER E. NEWELL, Jr.

Physicist, Naval Research Laboratory
Lecturer in Mathematics, University of Maryland

McGRAW-HILL BOOK COMPANY, INC.

New York   Toronto   London

1955

VECTOR ANALYSIS

Library of Congress Catalog Card Number 55–5693

VII

46398

THE MAPLE PRESS COMPANY, YORK, PA.

To My Wife

PREFACE

Vector analysis, when used with skill and understanding, can be a useful and powerful tool for the engineer and physicist. The subject is not especially difficult, and with a moderate amount of effort, one can acquire facility in the application of vector methods to physical problems. Yet many students who have been exposed to a course in vector analysis, once released from the disciplines of the course, fail to apply vector techniques even where the benefits are most obvious. I have not made any genuine study of why this should be, but it appears quite likely that a major cause is the failure of teacher and text to get the student to think in terms of vectors.

If vector analysis remains to the student simply a mathematical discipline, then it is likely also to remain sterile. On the other hand, if vectors and vector concepts become an integral part of the physical and intuitive reasoning of the student, then the mathematics falls into its proper perspective as a framework for that reasoning. More than that, the mathematics enriched with physical meaning becomes easier to remember and to manipulate, and applications become more apparent.

It is the intent of this text to develop the algebra and calculus of vectors in the way in which the physicist and engineer will want to use them. From the outset the student is encouraged to think of vectors as physical or geometric quantities. The exercises are designed not only to furnish practice in manipulation but also to establish vectors and vector concepts in the physical and geometric intuition of the student.

Part I, the basic portion of the text, is devoted to a fairly thorough treatment of vector algebra and the vector calculus. It can be used, at what is often called the undergraduate-graduate level, as the basis for a three-hour one-semester course. The text is purposely concise, and much of the meat of the course will be found to reside in the exercises, to which the student should devote a considerable portion of his time. By so doing he will complete the text for himself. Only by a generous application of effort to the doing of problems can he hope to gain the skill and insight needed in the practical use of vector techniques.

The first chapter covers the algebra of vectors. Chapter 2 contains a

survey of the ordinary calculus. While the chapter reviews material
with which the student is assumed to be familiar, the opportunity is
taken to recast much of it in vector form, preparatory to plunging into
the vector calculus. Differentiation of vectors, and the gradient of a
vector, are discussed in Chap. 3, while Chap. 4 continues the development
of the vector calculus with a treatment of divergence, circulation, curl,
Gauss' theorem, and Stokes' theorem. The operator ∇ is introduced in
Chap. 5 and discussed in Chaps. 5 and 6. A rather thorough treatment
of curvilinear coordinates appears in Chap. 7. Finally, Chap. 8 provides
a general discussion of vector fields and potential theory.

Practical applications of vector analysis are given in Part II. Chapter 9 is devoted to miscellaneous applications. Motions in space are
considered in Chap. 10, and a brief sketch of electromagnetic theory
appears in Chap. 11.

The reader will perhaps note that tensors are not taken up in Part I.
This is an indirect consequence of a decision to limit the size of Part I to
what could be covered in a three-hour one-semester course. From many
years of experience, I have found that the material which is included
amply fills such a course, and I would not wish to displace any of it for
the usual treatment of dyadics given in vector analysis courses.

The material of Part II is provided as illustrative matter. The teacher
can use it, or chosen parts of it, to supplement the basic theory contained
in Part I. The subjects covered are those which have been appropriate
to classes that I have taught, and represent only a modest selection from
the wide choice open to the teacher. There are many other subjects,
such as hydrodynamics and elasticity, which might well have been
included.

The principal criterion for this text has been that it should be understandable and useful to the serious student, and in this connection I
should like to express my thanks to those many students in my classes
who took the time and interest to think about the problems of organiza-
tion and presentation, and to give me their thoughts. I should also
like to thank Dr. J. W. Siry for checking the manuscript and Elizabeth
Mooney for typing it.

HOMER E. NEWELL, JR.

CONTENTS

PART II. APPLICATIONS

PART I

THEORY

CHAPTER 1

SCALARS AND VECTORS

1-1. Scalars

A quantity which can be represented by a single number is known as a *scalar*. The elementary charge on an electron is a particularly simple example of such a quantity. The speed of light in a vacuum is another.

Let $f(x,y,z,t)$ be a single-valued function of the parameters x, y, z, and t within some domain of definition for f. To every admissible set of values for the parameters there corresponds a single number. Thus $f(x,y,z,t)$ is a scalar function of x, y, z, and t. If x, y, and z are cartesian coordinates and t is time, the quantity f is a scalar function of position in space and of time. A familiar example of such a scalar function is the temperature within a material substance. In the most general case the temperature varies from point to point, and at each point it may vary with time. Likewise, both pressure and mass density within a region through which a compressible fluid is flowing depend upon position and time.

The number of parameters upon which a scalar function depends varies from case to case. Within an incompressible fluid at rest and under the influence of gravity, for example, the pressure depends solely upon depth below the surface. When a hard rubber object is charged by rubbing with fur, the density of charge in general varies from point to point on the surface of the object and is a function of the two parameters necessary to specify position on the surface. The temperature of the earth's atmosphere, on the other hand, depends upon a rather large number of variables. Among these are the three coordinates of position, the time of day, the season of the year, and an unknown number of parameters needed to specify conditions in the sun.

Scalar functions are those with which one meets in the differential and integral calculus. It is assumed that the reader is familiar with such functions, and with the concepts of limit and continuity and the processes of differentiation and integration.

Finally, a region throughout which a scalar function is defined will often be referred to as a *scalar field*.

EXERCISES

1. Give examples of well-known mathematical scalar constants.

2. Give additional examples of physical scalar constants.

3. Give additional examples of scalar fields.

4. Consider the three-dimensional scalar field

$$\phi = x^2 + 2y^2 + 3z^2$$

where x, y, z are rectangular cartesian coordinates.   What are the "equipotential surfaces" of ϕ; that is, what are the surfaces $\phi =$ constant?

5. Under the assumption that density ρ is proportional to pressure p, show that the pressure in a fluid at rest in the earth's gravitational field is given by

$$p = p_0 e^{-\frac{gh}{K}}$$

where h is height above some reference level, p_0 is pressure at the reference level, g is the acceleration of gravity, and K is an appropriate constant.

Step 1: The difference in pressure dp between height h and height $h + dh$ is the weight of a column of air of unit cross-sectional area contained between the levels h and $h + dh$.   Write a relation expressing this fact, noting that pressure decreases as height increases.

Step 2: Replace ρ by an expression in p.

Step 3: Integrate with respect to h.

6. In an ideal gas, pressure p, absolute temperature T, and density ρ are related by the equation of state

$$p = \rho \frac{R}{M} T$$

where R is the universal gas constant, and M is the molecular mass of the gas in question.   It has been shown by rocket and other measurements that up to 70 miles altitude the pressure in the earth's atmosphere is divided by 10 for every 10-mile increase in height.   Assuming a constant atmospheric temperature (which is not a correct assumption), use the result of Exercise 5 to calculate an average temperature for the earth's atmosphere from the ground to 70 miles altitude.   Take $g = 980.1$ cm/sec^2, $R = 8.314 \times 10^7$ ergs/°K mole, and $M = 28.97$.

7. In Exercise 5 it was tacitly assumed that the acceleration of gravity g was constant.   Actually g varies inversely as the square of the distance from the center of the earth.   Let g_0 be the value of g at the surface of the earth, and let h denote height above the ground. Taking the radius of the earth as 3,963 miles, write an expression for g in terms of g_0 and h. Using this expression for g, rework Exercise 5 to obtain p as a function of height.

8. Using the result of Exercise 7, rework Exercise 6. How much error was introduced into the calculation of Exercise 6 by using the value of g existing at the earth's surface?

1-2. Vectors

The essential feature of a scalar is its magnitude. Some quantities, however, possess a characteristic direction as well as magnitude. Among these, for example, are forces, velocities, accelerations, and current densities.

To specify such quantities it is necessary to state both the magnitude and the direction. Geometrically this can be done by representing the quantity in question as an arrow of suitable length and appropriate direction. Arithmetically such a quantity can be specified by three ordered numbers, for if the representative arrow be placed with its tail at the origin of a fixed coordinate system, then the three numbers comprising the coordinates of the arrow tip uniquely specify both the length and direction of the arrow. These three numbers may, of course, be the cartesian coordinates, spherical coordinates, cylindrical coordinates, or any other set of coordinates of the arrow tip.

It is a familiar fact that when two forces act upon a mass with a common point of application, their combined effect is that which would be produced by a single force of a uniquely determined magnitude and direction acting alone. This single resultant force can be obtained by applying the familiar parallelogram rule. Thus, if in Fig. 1-1 OA and OB represent two forces acting at a point O, then the diagonal OR of the parallelogram, of which OA and OB are adjacent sides, represents the force which is the resultant of OA and OB acting together. The magni-

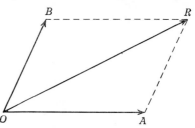

Fig. 1-1. The parallelogram rule for addition of forces.

tude of the resultant force is represented by OR on the same scale as that used in drawing OA and OB, and the direction of the resultant force is that of OR. Both the magnitude and direction of OR can be calculated from the corresponding quantities for OA and OB graphically using the parallelogram construction, or analytically by simple trigonometric means.

Quantities which possess magnitude and direction and which combine according to the parallelogram law are known as vectors.

It is important to note that all three of the properties listed above are essential parts of the vector concept. Analytical processes involving vector quantities must take into account the parallelogram law as well as the directional properties of vectors. Magnitude and direction alone do not make a vector quantity. For example, finite rotations of a body possess a magnitude, namely, the total angle of rotation, and a characteristic direction, namely, that of the axis of rotation. But a little reflection will show that the parallelogram law cannot be used in general to obtain the resultant of two such rotations performed in succession.

There is another fundamental point here which must be emphasized. Throughout this text vectors are thought of as physical or geometric entities. As such, each vector quantity has a meaning completely independent of any coordinate system which may be introduced for the purposes of calculation or mathematical analysis. One must use the physical or geometric meaning of any given vector quantity as the ultimate basis from which to derive a mathematical expression for the vector in terms of whatever coordinates are used. Also, in changing from one set of coordinates to another set, the physical or geometric meaning is unaltered by the transformation, even though the representative expression may change markedly. This invariance in physical or geometric meaning forms the basis from which to derive the mathematical transformation from the old to the new expression.

Often it is convenient, sometimes essential, to think of a vector as localized in space. A force vector, for example, is thought of as attached to the point of application of the physical force itself. Again, within a moving fluid the velocity of flow can be represented by what is called a *field of vectors*. With each point in the region of flow may be associated a vector representing the speed and direction of flow. In the general case this velocity vector varies from point to point in space and at each point may vary with time. Such vector fields are constantly met with in physics and engineering.

EXERCISES

1. Give additional examples of vectors and vector fields.

2. Prove, by presenting a suitable counterexample, that the finite rotations in space are not vector quantities.

3. Prove that the positions of points in space relative to a fixed origin are vector quantities. (*Hint:* Think of the positions as displacements from the origin, and show that such displacements combine according to the parallelogram law.)

1-3. Notation

It is customary to represent a vector quantity by means of a letter in boldface type. The boldface character signifies both the magnitude and the directional properties of the vector. Ordinary absolute value signs are often used to indicate the magnitude alone. Thus the vector **A** has the magnitude $|\mathbf{A}|$. A simpler method, which will be used throughout this text, is to denote the magnitude by the italic form of the letter used in boldface to denote the vector quantity.

Often it will be convenient to speak of "points **r**, **A**, **B**, . . . ," meaning thereby the tips of the vectors **r**, **A**, **B**, . . . when the vectors are placed with their tails at the origin of coordinates. This convention will be adopted henceforth.

1-4. Addition of Vectors

Let **A** and **B** denote two vectors. The resultant vector obtained from **A** and **B** by the parallelogram rule is called the sum of **A** and **B**. The addition of two vectors is denoted in the usual fashion by **A** + **B**. But it is to be remembered that the plus sign in this expression calls for the operation of combining the two vectors by the parallelogram method and has, therefore, a different meaning from that of ordinary scalar addition.

The sum of two vectors **A** and **B** can be obtained geometrically by placing the tail of **A** at the tip of **B** as in Fig. 1-2. Then the arrow, the tail of which coincides with that of **B** and the tip of which coincides with that of **A**, represents the sum **A** + **B**. Similarly, the tail of **B** can be placed at the tip of **A** and the triangle completed to obtain **A** + **B**. Frequently it is convenient to visu-

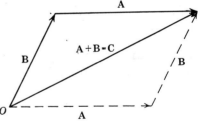

Fig. 1-2. The triangle law for addition of vectors.

alize the addition of two vectors in terms of this triangle law rather than in terms of the parallelogram rule. Plainly the two methods are equivalent.

Often in the course of an analysis it is desirable to resolve a vector into a sum of two or more other vectors. This can be done by a single or repeated application of the triangle law. Figure 1-2, which earlier was regarded as illustrating the addition of **A** and **B** to give **A** + **B**, can also be thought of as showing the resolution of a vector **C** into the two

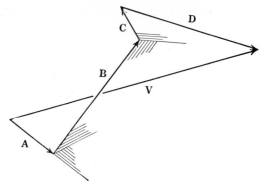

FIG. 1-3. Resolution of a vector into four noncoplanar vectors.

vectors **A** and **B**.   Resolution of a vector **V** into the sum of four non-coplanar vectors is shown in Fig. 1-3.

The vector obtained by projecting a vector **A** orthogonally onto a line

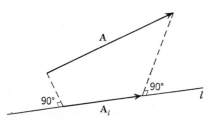

FIG. 1-4. The component of a vector along a direction different from that of the vector.

of specified direction is known as the *component* of **A** in the specified direction.   In Fig. 1-4 the component of **A** in the direction of line l is the vector $\mathbf{A}_l$.   If θ is the acute angle between **A** and l, then the magnitude of $\mathbf{A}_l$ is $A \cos \theta$.   The resolution of a vector into mutually perpendicular components is of especial importance both in the plane and in three dimensions.   In the former case the vector is resolved into two perpendicular components; and in the latter case into three mutually orthogonal components.

EXERCISES

In the following exercises let (x,y) and (x,y,z) denote rectangular coordinates in the plane and in space respectively.

1. A vector in the plane is three units long and makes an angle of 135° with the positive x axis.   What are its components along the positive x and positive y directions?

2. A vector in space is four units long and makes angles of 45° and 60° with the x and y axes respectively.   What is its component along the positive z direction?

3. A vector in the xy plane extends from $(0,0)$ to the point $(3,-4)$.   Find its length and the angle it makes with the positive x axis.

4. A vector in space has the components $(-3,4,-12)$. What is its length, and what angle does it make with the positive y axis?

5. A vector in the xy plane is 13 units long, and has the component -5 along the x axis. What is its direction?

6. A vector in space of unit length has the component $\frac{1}{2}$ along the x axis and makes an angle of 120° with the positive z axis. What is its y component?

Do Exercises 7 to 15 graphically.

7. Vectors **A** and **B** in the xy plane have the components $(5,4)$ and $(-3,2)$ respectively. Obtain **A** + **B**.

8. **A** and **B** are unit vectors in the xy plane making angles 30° and 120° respectively with the positive x axis. Find **A** + **B**.

9. Vectors **A** and **B** in the xy plane have the components $(3,-6)$ and $(2,1)$. Resolve **A** into **B** plus a third vector **C**, obtaining the components of **C**.

10. **A** lies in the xy plane and has the components $(7,-2)$. Find the component of **A** along the line $y = x$.

11. The true air speed of a plane is 150 knots; its heading is 35° east of north. The wind is 30 knots from the southeast. What are the plane's speed and direction of motion over the ground?

12. A ship is steaming due south at 20 knots. The ocean currents, however, are moving to the northwest at 2 knots. In what direction, and at what speed in that direction, is the ship actually moving?

13. The true air speed of an airplane is 250 knots. At the level at which the plane is flying the wind is from north-northeast at 70 knots. What heading must the plane assume in order that its track over the ground be due east, and what will the plane's speed over the ground be?

14. As the sun is setting, a train is moving along a straight track heading 20° west of south (S 20° W). To the east of the train is a straight wall running from S 10° E to N 10° W. If the train is going 70 miles/hr, how fast is the train's shadow moving along the wall?

15. A mass of 20 g is sliding down a perfectly smooth inclined plane which makes an angle of 25° with the horizontal. (*a*) How fast is the mass accelerating? (*b*) How long after starting from rest will it be traveling at 10 m/sec? (Use Newton's law: **F** = m**a**; **F** = force, **a** = acceleration, m = mass. Determine **F** from the fact that it is the component along the plane of the weight m**g** of the mass, **g** being the acceleration of gravity.)

16. A weight w hangs vertically, supported by a string which could support twice w but no more. By means of a second (sufficiently strong) string the weight is pulled always horizontally, moving the original string away from the vertical. At what angle to the vertical will the first string break?

17. According to Coulomb's law, the force **F** on a charge e' placed in the field of an electron, of charge e, is

$$\mathbf{F} = \frac{ee'}{kr^2} \mathbf{r}^0$$

Due regard must be paid to the signs of the charges. The quantities r and $\mathbf{r}^0$ are respectively the distance and the unit vector, i.e., vector of unit length, from the electron to the other charge, while k is the dielectric constant of the surrounding medium. Compute the magnitude (in dynes) and the direction of the force exerted by two electrons fixed 3 cm apart in free space ($k = 1$) upon a proton located 4 cm from one electron and 5 cm from the other. Take $e = 4.8 \times 10^{-10}$ esu.

1-5. Properties of Addition for Vectors

The addition of two vectors is a commutative operation. That is, for all pairs of vectors **A** and **B**:

$$\mathbf{A} + \mathbf{B} = \mathbf{B} + \mathbf{A}$$

This fact is plain from the definition of addition.

The summation of vectors is also an associative process, which is to say that any three vectors **A**, **B**, and **C** satisfy the relation

$$\mathbf{A} + (\mathbf{B} + \mathbf{C}) = (\mathbf{A} + \mathbf{B}) + \mathbf{C}$$

This is seen by reference to Fig. 1-5, which shows the parallelepiped constructed from **A**, **B**, and **C** as a set of adjacent edges. The diagonal of the

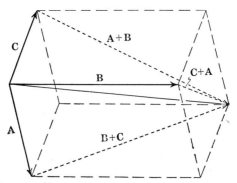

Fig. 1-5. The associative law for vector addition.

parallelepiped is plainly any one of $\mathbf{A} + (\mathbf{B} + \mathbf{C})$, $\mathbf{C} + (\mathbf{A} + \mathbf{B})$, and $\mathbf{B} + (\mathbf{C} + \mathbf{A})$. As a consequence the parentheses need not be used in indicating the sum of three vectors **A**, **B**, and **C**. It suffices to write **A** + **B** + **C**.

For the sake of completeness one introduces the concept of a null vector, the magnitude of which is zero. The direction of a null vector is indeterminate, and is usually specified in any analyses by suitable limiting processes. It is common to use the ordinary cipher to denote the null vector. Whether the scalar zero or the vector zero is meant is usually plain from the context.

Any vector **A** satisfies the relation

$$\mathbf{A} + 0 = \mathbf{A}$$

Also every vector equation

$$\mathbf{A} + \mathbf{X} = 0$$

has a unique solution for **X**. The solution, called the inverse of **A** with respect to addition, is simply that vector which has the same magnitude as **A**, but which is oppositely directed.

1-6. Groups

A group is a set of elements a, b, c, . . . , with an operation $\oplus$ which can be performed upon pairs of elements from the set, which obey the following laws:

1. For every pair of elements a and b, the result $a \oplus b$ of operating upon a and b is another element of the set.

2. The associative law holds for the operation $\oplus$.

3. Every linear equation

$$a \oplus x = b$$

or

$$x \oplus a = b$$

where a and b are elements of the set, has a solution for x.

If in addition the operation $\oplus$ obeys the commutative law the group is said to be *commutative* or *abelian*.

The rational fractions, real numbers, and complex numbers are all examples of commutative groups with respect to the operation of ordinary addition. The operation symbolized by $\oplus$, however, does not have to be interpreted as addition. It can, for example, be ordinary multiplication. Thus, without the number zero any one of the sets of numbers listed above forms a commutative group relative to ordinary multiplication.

A review of the properties of vectors relative to the addition operation discussed in Sec. 1-5 shows that vectors form a commutative group with respect to addition. The significance of this is that as far as addition is concerned, the algebra of vector symbols is the same as the algebra of ordinary real numbers.

EXERCISES

1. Prove that every group possesses a right-hand identity element R and a left-hand identity element L such that for every element a of the set

$$a \oplus R = L \oplus a = a$$

(*Hint:* From law 3 there is an R and there is an L corresponding to any chosen element a. Use laws 3 and 2 to show that R and L also work with every other element b of the group.)

2. Show that all right and left identity elements of a group are one and the same element I. (*Hint:* Let R be any right identity element and L any left identity element. Then consider $L \oplus R$.)

3. Let I be the identity element for a given group. Prove that for each element a of the group there is an inverse element a^{-1} such that

$$a^{-1} \oplus a = a \oplus a^{-1} = I$$

(*Hint:* From law 3 there are right- and left-handed inverses a_r^{-1} and a_l^{-1}. Consider $(a_l^{-1} \oplus a) \oplus a_r^{-1} = a_l^{-1} \oplus (a \oplus a_r^{-1})$ to show that all the inverses are equal.)

4. Show that the rational integers form a group with respect to ordinary addition. What is the identity element of the group? What is the inverse element to -10?

5. Show that the set of complex numbers $1, i, -1, -i$ forms a group with respect to multiplication. What is the identity element of the group? Determine the inverse to each element.

6. Show that the totality of rotations about a fixed point in the plane forms a group with respect to the operation of addition, defined for two rotations as applying the one rotation to the plane and thereafter the second. What is the identity element? What is the inverse element to a given rotation? Devise a means of representing each element of this group by a single real number, and using ordinary addition of real numbers for the group operation.

7. Show that vectors in space form a group with respect to vector addition.

1-7. Subtraction of Vectors

As for scalars, subtraction of vectors is defined as the inverse of addition. If the expression $\mathbf{A} - \mathbf{B}$ be used to denote the difference between

A and **B**, the defining relation becomes

$$(\mathbf{A} - \mathbf{B}) + \mathbf{B} = \mathbf{A}$$

In words, **A** − **B** is that vector to which **B** must be added to give **A**. The triangle rule can be used to give a very simple geometrical construction for **A** − **B** when **A** and **B** are placed so that their tails coincide. Then **A** − **B** is the vector directed from the tip of **B** to the tip of **A** as shown in Fig. 1-6.

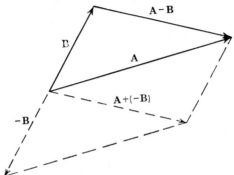

Fig. 1-6. Subtraction of vectors.

The vector **A** − **B** may also be obtained by reversing the direction of **B** and adding the resulting vector to **A**. This operation is indicated by the dashed lines in Fig. 1-6. For this reason the vector of magnitude B which is directed oppositely to **B** is denoted by −**B**. Thus, **A** − **B** and **A** + (−**B**) are the same.

EXERCISES

1. Vectors **A** and **B** in the xy plane have the components (5,4) and (−3,2). Find **A** − **B** graphically.

2. Vectors **A** and **B** are unit vectors in the xy plane making angles of 30° and 120° respectively with the positive x axis. Find **A** − **B** graphically.

3. A plane is moving over the ground in the due west direction at a speed of 130 knots. If the wind is from the northeast at 20 knots, what are the true air speed and heading of the plane?

1-8. Multiplication of a Vector by a Scalar

Let m be any real number, and let **A** be any vector. Then the quantity $m\mathbf{A}$ is defined to be the vector of magnitude $|m|A$ which has the direction of **A** if m is positive or which is directed oppositely to **A** if m is negative. It will be noted that for any positive integer n and any vector

A the quantity n**A** as defined and the sum **A** + **A** + · · · + **A** (with n terms) are equal. In fact, precisely the reasoning which leads from the positive integers through the negative integers and zero, to the rational fractions, and finally to the concept of real numbers, also leads directly from the addition of an integral number of equal vectors to the definition of m**A** given above.

One can readily show that for any real numbers m and l, and for any vectors **A** and **B**, the following relations hold:

$$m\mathbf{A} + l\mathbf{A} = (m + l)\mathbf{A} \tag{1-1}$$
$$m\mathbf{A} + m\mathbf{B} = m(\mathbf{A} + \mathbf{B}) \tag{1-2}$$

EXERCISES

1. Prove relations (1-1) and (1-2) geometrically.

2. Show that the mid-point of the parallelogram formed from vectors **A** and **B** as adjacent edges is the point $\frac{1}{2}(\mathbf{A} + \mathbf{B})$.

3. Show geometrically that if **A** and **B** are nonparallel vectors, then

$$l\mathbf{A} + m\mathbf{B} = 0$$

if and only if both l and m are zero.

4. Show geometrically that if vectors **A**, **B**, and **C** are noncoplanar when placed with their tails in coincidence, then

$$l\mathbf{A} + m\mathbf{B} + n\mathbf{C} = 0$$

if and only if all of l, m, and n are zero.

5. Let **A** and **B** be any pair of nonparallel vectors, and let **C** be any vector in the plane of **A** and **B**. Show that **C** can be written uniquely in the form

$$\mathbf{C} = l\mathbf{A} + m\mathbf{B}$$

where l and m are real scalar constants.

6. Let **A**, **B**, and **C** be any set of vectors which are noncoplanar when placed with their tails in coincidence, and let **D** be any vector. Show that **D** can be written uniquely in the form

$$\mathbf{D} = l\mathbf{A} + m\mathbf{B} + n\mathbf{C}$$

where l, m, and n are real scalar constants.

7. A body at rest is acted upon by three forces **A**, **B**, and **C**. What equation must these vectors satisfy? What geometrical condition must they satisfy?

8. What is the locus of points **P** given by

$$\mathbf{P} = \mathbf{A} + k\mathbf{B}$$

where **A** and **B** are fixed vectors and k is a variable real scalar?

9. Show that the straight line through the distinct points **A** and **B** has the equation

$$\mathbf{r} = \mathbf{A} + t(\mathbf{B} - \mathbf{A})$$

where t is a real variable, and **r** is the general point of the line.

10. Let **A** be a fixed vector with its tail at the origin of coordinates, and let **r** be a variable vector of constant magnitude. What is the locus of points **R** given by

$$\mathbf{R} = \mathbf{A} + \mathbf{r}$$

11. Show geometrically that for any two vectors **A** and **B**

$$A - B \le |\mathbf{A} + \mathbf{B}| \le A + B$$

12. Show that a necessary and sufficient condition that three distinct points **A**, **B**, and **C** be collinear is that

$$l\mathbf{A} + m\mathbf{B} + n\mathbf{C} = 0$$

where

$$l + m + n = 0$$

(*Hint:* Points **A**, **B**, and **C** are collinear if and only if vectors **C** − **A** and **C** − **B** are parallel.)

13. Show that four distinct points **A**, **B**, **C**, and **D** are coplanar if and only if

$$k\mathbf{A} + l\mathbf{B} + m\mathbf{C} + n\mathbf{D} = 0$$

where

$$k + l + m + n = 0$$

14. Show by vector means that the medians of the triangle of vertices **A**, **B**, and **C** intersect in the common point

$$\frac{\mathbf{A} + \mathbf{B} + \mathbf{C}}{3}$$

1-9. The Scalar Product of Two Vectors

Let **A** and **B** be any two vectors and denote the angle between their directions by θ. The scalar, or inner, product of the two vectors is defined as $AB \cos \theta$, and is designated by either of the two notations (**A,B**) and $\mathbf{A} \cdot \mathbf{B}$. There are other notations for scalar product, but the two listed here are by far the most frequently used. Both the parenthesis notation and the dot notation are sufficiently common that it is well to develop an equal familiarity with the two.

Write $\mathbf{A} \cdot \mathbf{B}$ in the form $(A \cos \theta)B$. From this it is plain that the scalar product of $\mathbf{A}$ and $\mathbf{B}$ is simply the magnitude of the projection of $\mathbf{A}$ onto $\mathbf{B}$, multiplied by the magnitude of $\mathbf{B}$. Likewise $\mathbf{A} \cdot \mathbf{B}$ is the magnitude of the projection of $\mathbf{B}$ onto $\mathbf{A}$ multiplied by the magnitude of $\mathbf{A}$. In the case in which $\mathbf{B}$ is a unit vector, that is, a vector of unit magnitude, $\mathbf{A} \cdot \mathbf{B}$ is simply the magnitude of the component of $\mathbf{A}$ in the direction of $\mathbf{B}$. The product $\mathbf{A} \cdot \mathbf{B}$ vanishes not only when A or B does, but also when $\cos \theta$ vanishes. Thus, it is possible for $\mathbf{A} \cdot \mathbf{B}$ to be zero when neither $\mathbf{A}$ nor $\mathbf{B}$ is the null vector. In such a case $\mathbf{A}$ must be perpendicular to $\mathbf{B}$.

Since the factors in the product $AB \cos \theta$ are real numbers, their order is immaterial. Thus

$$\mathbf{A} \cdot \mathbf{B} = AB \cos \theta = BA \cos \theta = \mathbf{B} \cdot \mathbf{A}$$

The factors in the scalar product may be commuted without altering the value of the product; hence, the operation of forming the scalar product of one vector with another is a commutative operation.

The component of the vector sum $\mathbf{B} + \mathbf{C}$ in the direction of a vector $\mathbf{A}$ is the sum of the individual components of $\mathbf{B}$ and $\mathbf{C}$ in that direction. This fact is illustrated in Fig. 1-7, which is drawn for the general case in

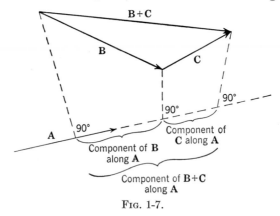

FIG. 1-7.

which $\mathbf{B}$, $\mathbf{C}$, and $\mathbf{A}$ are not coplanar. Recalling the fact that the scalar product of $\mathbf{A}$ and another vector is just the product of the magnitude of $\mathbf{A}$ and the component of the other vector in the direction of $\mathbf{A}$, it is plain that

$$\mathbf{A} \cdot (\mathbf{B} + \mathbf{C}) = \mathbf{A} \cdot \mathbf{B} + \mathbf{A} \cdot \mathbf{C}$$

That is, the dot operation giving the scalar product is distributive with respect to vector addition.

By simple iteration this rule can be extended to sums of more than two terms. Thus,

$$\mathbf{A} \cdot (\mathbf{B} + \mathbf{C} + \mathbf{D} + \cdots) = \mathbf{A} \cdot \mathbf{B} + \mathbf{A} \cdot \mathbf{C} + \mathbf{A} \cdot \mathbf{D} + \cdots$$

EXERCISES

1. The notation $\mathbf{A}^2$ is used to denote $\mathbf{A} \cdot \mathbf{A}$. What value does $\mathbf{A}^2$ have?

2. Consider vectors $\mathbf{A}$, $\mathbf{B}$, and $\mathbf{C}$ such that

$$\mathbf{A} = \mathbf{B} - \mathbf{C}$$

From

$$\mathbf{A}^2 = (\mathbf{B} - \mathbf{C})^2$$

prove the law of cosines.

3. Let II be a plane passing at a distance p from the origin of coordinates, and let $\mathbf{n}$ be the vector of unit length normal to II and directed from the origin toward the plane. Show that the equation of II can be put in the form

$$\mathbf{r} \cdot \mathbf{n} = p$$

4. Let $\mathbf{R}$ be the vector from the origin of coordinates to a point in space. Obtain an expression for the distance of the point $\mathbf{R}$ from the plane

$$\mathbf{r} \cdot \mathbf{n} = p$$

5. Obtain a vector equation for a sphere.

6. By vector means show that the diagonals of a parallelogram are perpendicular if and only if the parallelogram is a rhombus or a square.

7. What does the equation

$$(\mathbf{r} - \mathbf{a}) \cdot \mathbf{r} = 0$$

where $\mathbf{a}$ is a constant and $\mathbf{r}$ is a variable, represent?

8. Let $\mathbf{A}$ and $\mathbf{B}$ be two vectors. Show that the component of $\mathbf{A}$ in the direction of $\mathbf{B}$ is given by

$$\frac{\mathbf{A} \cdot \mathbf{B}}{B^2} \mathbf{B}$$

What is the component of $\mathbf{A}$ normal to $\mathbf{B}$?

9. Given the three points $\mathbf{A}$, $\mathbf{B}$, and $\mathbf{C}$. Obtain analytically the unit vector in the direction of the bisector of the angle subtended at $\mathbf{B}$ by $\mathbf{A}$ and $\mathbf{C}$.

1-10. Right- and Left-handed Sets of Vectors

Before proceeding to the definition of vector product it is well to describe what is meant by a right-handed set of vectors. Let $\mathbf{A}$, $\mathbf{B}$, and $\mathbf{C}$

be three noncoplanar vectors. Imagine these vectors placed so that their tails coincide and think of this common origin as lying on the surface of the earth, with the vector **A** pointing northward along a meridian and with vector **C** underground in the meridian plane containing **A**. If, with this arrangement, vector **B** lies to the east of the meridian plane containing **A** and **C**, then the set **A**, **B**, and **C** in that order is said to be a right-handed set. If, however, **B** lies to the west, the set **A**, **B**, and **C** is said to be left-handed.

Once the concept of a right-handed set of vectors is clearly in mind, it is a simple matter to devise a great number of mnemonics. One of the most frequently used is the familiar screw driver rule. Consider a set of mutually orthogonal vectors **A**, **B**, and **C**. Imagine a right-handed screw driven into the tail end of the shaft of an arrow representing **C**, and think of **A** as attached to the screw. Now turn the screw in such a direction that **A** will come to coincide with **B** after turning through an angle of 90°. If, to do this, the screw must be driven farther into the shaft of **C**, the set **A**, **B**, **C** in that order is right-handed; otherwise it is left-handed. The reader can quickly extend the rule to take care of the cases in which **A**, **B**, and **C** are not mutually perpendicular.

Still another test can be applied by placing the tails of **A**, **B**, and **C** at a common origin and viewing the plane of **A** and **B** from the tip of **C**. Then if, as viewed from the tip of **C**, a counterclockwise rotation of less than 180° in the plane of **A** and **B** will bring **A** around to the direction of **B**, the set is right-handed; otherwise it is left-handed.

1-11. The Vector Product of Two Vectors

The operation of forming a scalar product is a means of associating a characteristic scalar value with every pair of vectors. The vector, or outer, product of two vectors, on the other hand, is itself a vector; and the operation of forming the vector product serves to associate a definite vector with every pair of vectors.

Let **A** and **B** be two vectors and denote the angle between them by θ. The vector product **A** × **B**, or [**A**,**B**], of **A** and **B** is that vector which satisfies the following conditions:

(a) $$|\mathbf{A} \times \mathbf{B}| = AB \sin \theta$$

(b) $$(\mathbf{A} \times \mathbf{B}) \cdot \mathbf{A} = (\mathbf{A} \times \mathbf{B}) \cdot \mathbf{B} = 0$$

(c) **A**, **B**, and **A** × **B** in that order form a right-handed set

The first relation gives the magnitude of the vector product in terms of those of the two factors **A** and **B**. The second relation states that the vector product is perpendicular to the plane of **A** and **B**, but does not specify which of the two possible directions is to be chosen. The last condition removes this ambiguity of direction.

The vector product of **A** and **B** vanishes not only when **A** or **B** is a null vector but also when $\sin \theta$ is zero. The latter happens if **A** and **B** are parallel, whether similarly or oppositely directed.

From the definition it is seen that although **A** $\times$ **B** and **B** $\times$ **A** are of equal magnitude, nevertheless they are oppositely directed. Thus

$$\mathbf{A} \times \mathbf{B} = -\mathbf{B} \times \mathbf{A}$$

Hence, the formation of the vector product of two vectors is not a commutative operation. Similarly, by comparing (**A** $\times$ **A**) $\times$ **B** with **A** $\times$ (**A** $\times$ **B**), where **A** $\times$ **B** is assumed not to vanish, it is apparent that the associative law also does not hold for vector products. In the special case considered here the first method of grouping yields the null vector since (**A** $\times$ **A**) vanishes, whereas the second method of grouping does not yield the null vector.

EXERCISES

1. Show that the magnitude of **A** $\times$ **B** equals the area of the parallelogram of which **A** and **B** are adjacent sides.

2. The magnitude of **A** is 5; that of **B** is 2. Evaluate

$$(\mathbf{A} \times \mathbf{B})^2 + (\mathbf{A} \cdot \mathbf{B})^2$$

3. Show that (**A** $\times$ **B**) $\times$ **C**, where **A** and **B** are not parallel, can be written as a linear combination of **A** and **B**.

4. Show that

$$[(\mathbf{A} \times \mathbf{B}) \times \mathbf{A}] \cdot \mathbf{A} = 0$$
$$[(\mathbf{A} \times \mathbf{B}) \times \mathbf{A}] \cdot \mathbf{B} = A^2 B^2 \sin^2 \theta$$

where θ is the angle between **A** and **B**.

5. Use the results of Exercise 4 to evaluate l and m in the relation

$$(\mathbf{A} \times \mathbf{B}) \times \mathbf{A} = l\mathbf{A} + m\mathbf{B}$$

1-12. The Distributive Law for Vector Products

The operation of forming the vector product of two vectors is distributive with respect to addition; that is, if **A**, **B**, and **C** are three arbitrary vectors,

$$\mathbf{A} \times (\mathbf{B} + \mathbf{C}) = \mathbf{A} \times \mathbf{B} + \mathbf{A} \times \mathbf{C}$$

This fact can be established by visualizing the formation of the vector product in the following way. Let **A** and **B** be any two vectors and let the angle between them be θ. As in Fig. 1-8, project the vector AB normally onto a plane perpendicular to **A**, and within that plane rotate the new vector through 90° in the counterclockwise direction as viewed from the tip toward the tail of **A**. The final result is a vector **V** which

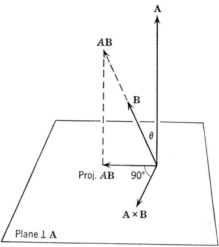

Fɪɢ. 1-8. Geometric method of obtaining the vector product of two vectors.

has the magnitude $AB \sin \theta$ and which is perpendicular to the plane of **A** and **B**, so directed that **A**, **B**, and **V** form a right-handed set. Hence **V** is **A** × **B**.

Now consider the three vectors **A**, **B**, and **C**. Think of the vectors **B**, **C**, and **B** + **C** as forming the sides of a triangle in accordance with the familiar triangle law. Apply simultaneously to all three vectors of the triangle the geometric operation described above for forming the vector product with the vector **A**. The result is a new triangle of sides **A** × **B**, **A** × **C**, and **A** × (**B** + **C**), with the last plainly the sum of the first two. Hence

$$\mathbf{A} \times (\mathbf{B} + \mathbf{C}) = \mathbf{A} \times \mathbf{B} + \mathbf{A} \times \mathbf{C}$$

EXERCISES

1. Obtain in vector form an equation for the plane through three noncollinear points $\mathbf{r}_1$, $\mathbf{r}_2$, and $\mathbf{r}_3$.

2. Multiply out and simplify

$$(\mathbf{A} + \mathbf{B}) \times \mathbf{C} + (\mathbf{B} + \mathbf{C}) \times \mathbf{A} + (\mathbf{C} + \mathbf{A}) \times \mathbf{B}$$

3. Multiply out and simplify

$$(\mathbf{A} + \mathbf{B}) \times (\mathbf{A} - \mathbf{B})$$

Use the result to prove that the product of the diagonals of a parallelogram multiplied by one-half the sine of the angle between them equals the area of the parallelogram.

1-13. Some Important Vector Relationships

A familiarity with a number of important algebraic vector identities is essential to skill in the handling of vector problems. The following three should be memorized:

$$\mathbf{A} \times (\mathbf{B} \times \mathbf{C}) = (\mathbf{A} \cdot \mathbf{C})\mathbf{B} - (\mathbf{A} \cdot \mathbf{B})\mathbf{C} \qquad (1\text{-}3)$$

A simple proof of this identity can be given as follows. Let $\mathbf{i}$ be a unit vector lying along $\mathbf{C}$ and let $\mathbf{j}$ be a second unit vector in the plane of $\mathbf{B}$ and $\mathbf{C}$ perpendicular to $\mathbf{i}$. Similarly, let $\mathbf{k}$ be the unit vector $\mathbf{i} \times \mathbf{j}$. Then $\mathbf{A}$, $\mathbf{B}$, and $\mathbf{C}$ can be written in the form

$$\mathbf{A} = A_1\mathbf{i} + A_2\mathbf{j} + A_3\mathbf{k}$$
$$\mathbf{B} = B_1\mathbf{i} + B_2\mathbf{j}$$
$$\mathbf{C} = C_1\mathbf{i}$$

where the coefficients of $\mathbf{i}$, $\mathbf{j}$, and $\mathbf{k}$ in the above relations are appropriate scalar constants. Using these relations it can be shown that

$$\mathbf{A} \times (\mathbf{B} \times \mathbf{C}) = A_1 B_2 C_1 \mathbf{j} - A_2 B_2 C_1 \mathbf{i}$$

and that

$$(\mathbf{A} \cdot \mathbf{C})\mathbf{B} - (\mathbf{A} \cdot \mathbf{B})\mathbf{C} = A_1 B_2 C_1 \mathbf{j} - A_2 B_2 C_1 \mathbf{i}$$

The truth of (1-3) is immediately apparent.

$$|\mathbf{A} \times \mathbf{B} \cdot \mathbf{C}| = \text{volume of parallelepiped formed from } \mathbf{A}, \mathbf{B}, \text{ and } \mathbf{C}$$
$$\text{as adjacent edges} \qquad (1\text{-}4)$$

The quantity $\mathbf{A} \times \mathbf{B} \cdot \mathbf{C}$ often is called the triple scalar product of $\mathbf{A}$, $\mathbf{B}$, and $\mathbf{C}$ and is written as $(\mathbf{ABC})$.

The proof of (1-4) lies simply in noting that the magnitude of $\mathbf{A} \times \mathbf{B}$ is the area of the base of the parallelepiped in question, while the projection of $\mathbf{C}$ upon the direction of $\mathbf{A} \times \mathbf{B}$ is the altitude of the parallelepiped. Thus

$$|(\mathbf{A} \times \mathbf{B}) \cdot \mathbf{C}| = |\mathbf{A} \times \mathbf{B}| \,|\text{projection of } \mathbf{C} \text{ onto } \mathbf{A} \times \mathbf{B}|$$
$$= (\text{area of base}) \cdot (\text{altitude}) = \text{vol. of parallelepiped}$$

The value of $\mathbf{A} \times \mathbf{B} \cdot \mathbf{C}$ is positive or negative accordingly as $\mathbf{A}$, $\mathbf{B}$, and $\mathbf{C}$ do or do not form a right-handed set in the order given. It is plain that

$$\mathbf{A} \cdot \mathbf{B} \times \mathbf{C}$$

also gives the volume of the parallelepiped so that

$$\mathbf{A} \times \mathbf{B} \cdot \mathbf{C} = \mathbf{A} \cdot \mathbf{B} \times \mathbf{C}$$

The third relation is

$$(\mathbf{A} \times \mathbf{B}) \cdot (\mathbf{C} \times \mathbf{D}) = (\mathbf{A} \cdot \mathbf{C})(\mathbf{B} \cdot \mathbf{D}) - (\mathbf{A} \cdot \mathbf{D})(\mathbf{B} \cdot \mathbf{C}) \qquad (1\text{-}5)$$

This is the generalized identity of Lagrange. The proof follows directly from (1-3) and (1-4) above.

$$\begin{aligned}
(\mathbf{A} \times \mathbf{B}) \cdot (\mathbf{C} \times \mathbf{D}) &= \mathbf{A} \cdot (\mathbf{B} \times (\mathbf{C} \times \mathbf{D})) \\
&= \mathbf{A} \cdot [(\mathbf{B} \cdot \mathbf{D})\mathbf{C} - (\mathbf{B} \cdot \mathbf{C})\mathbf{D}] \\
&= (\mathbf{A} \cdot \mathbf{C})(\mathbf{B} \cdot \mathbf{D}) - (\mathbf{A} \cdot \mathbf{D})(\mathbf{B} \cdot \mathbf{C})
\end{aligned}$$

When $\mathbf{C} = \mathbf{A}$ and $\mathbf{D} = \mathbf{B}$, this reduces to the more familiar identity of Lagrange

$$(\mathbf{A} \times \mathbf{B})^2 = \mathbf{A}^2\mathbf{B}^2 - (\mathbf{A} \cdot \mathbf{B})^2$$

where, for example, the notation $\mathbf{A}^2$ has been used to denote the quantity $\mathbf{A} \cdot \mathbf{A}$.

EXERCISES

1. Express $(\mathbf{A} \times \mathbf{B}) \times (\mathbf{C} \times \mathbf{D})$ as a linear combination of $\mathbf{C}$ and $\mathbf{D}$; as a linear combination of $\mathbf{A}$ and $\mathbf{B}$. What is the direction of $(\mathbf{A} \times \mathbf{B}) \times (\mathbf{C} \times \mathbf{D})$?

2. Show that

$$\mathbf{A} \times \mathbf{B} + \mathbf{B} \times \mathbf{C} + \mathbf{C} \times \mathbf{A}$$

is perpendicular to the plane of the points $\mathbf{A}$, $\mathbf{B}$, and $\mathbf{C}$.

3. Show that

$$(\mathbf{A} \times \mathbf{B}) \cdot (\mathbf{B} \times \mathbf{C}) \times (\mathbf{C} \times \mathbf{A}) = (\mathbf{A} \times \mathbf{B} \cdot \mathbf{C})^2$$

4. By means of products express a condition that vectors $\mathbf{A}$, $\mathbf{B}$, and $\mathbf{C}$ be parallel to a plane.

5. By means of products write a condition that the plane parallel to $\mathbf{A}$ and $\mathbf{B}$ be normal to that parallel to $\mathbf{C}$ and $\mathbf{D}$.

6. By means of products write a condition that four vectors, all of different directions, be parallel to a plane.

1-14. Analytical Representation of Vectors

Let $\mathbf{i}$ and $\mathbf{j}$ be two perpendicular unit vectors, and let $\mathbf{k}$ be the unit vector $\mathbf{i} \times \mathbf{j}$. The three vectors $\mathbf{i}$, $\mathbf{j}$, and $\mathbf{k}$ form a mutually perpendicular right-handed set. They satisfy the relationships

$$\mathbf{i} \cdot \mathbf{i} = \mathbf{j} \cdot \mathbf{j} = \mathbf{k} \cdot \mathbf{k} = 1$$
$$\mathbf{i} \cdot \mathbf{j} = \mathbf{j} \cdot \mathbf{k} = \mathbf{k} \cdot \mathbf{i} = 0$$
$$\mathbf{i} \times \mathbf{j} = \mathbf{k} \qquad \mathbf{j} \times \mathbf{k} = \mathbf{i} \qquad \mathbf{k} \times \mathbf{i} = \mathbf{j}$$

An arbitrary vector $\mathbf{A}$ can be represented very conveniently in terms of $\mathbf{i}$, $\mathbf{j}$, and $\mathbf{k}$. Such a vector can be written uniquely in the form

$$\mathbf{A} = A_1\mathbf{i} + A_2\mathbf{j} + A_3\mathbf{k}$$

The coefficients A_1, A_2, and A_3 are simply the magnitudes of the components of $\mathbf{A}$ in the directions of $\mathbf{i}$, $\mathbf{j}$, and $\mathbf{k}$ respectively.

If the vectors $\mathbf{i}$, $\mathbf{j}$, $\mathbf{k}$, and $\mathbf{A}$ be thought of as emanating from a common origin, then (A_1, A_2, A_3) are just the cartesian coordinates of the tip of $\mathbf{A}$ referred to coordinate axes lying along $\mathbf{i}$, $\mathbf{j}$, and $\mathbf{k}$.

If $\mathbf{A}$ and $\mathbf{B}$ are vectors $A_1\mathbf{i} + A_2\mathbf{j} + A_3\mathbf{k}$ and $B_1\mathbf{i} + B_2\mathbf{j} + B_3\mathbf{k}$, then it is a simple matter to verify, using relations and vector properties already established, that in rectangular coordinates

$$a\mathbf{A} = aA_1\mathbf{i} + aA_2\mathbf{j} + aA_3\mathbf{k}$$
$$\mathbf{A} + \mathbf{B} = (A_1 + B_1)\mathbf{i} + (A_2 + B_2)\mathbf{j} + (A_3 + B_3)\mathbf{k}$$
$$\mathbf{A} \cdot \mathbf{B} = A_1B_1 + A_2B_2 + A_3B_3$$
$$\mathbf{A} \times \mathbf{B} = (A_2B_3 - A_3B_2)\mathbf{i} + (A_3B_1 - A_1B_3)\mathbf{j} + (A_1B_2 - A_2B_1)\mathbf{k}$$

The last relation can be written symbolically in the form

$$\mathbf{A} \times \mathbf{B} = \begin{vmatrix} \mathbf{i} & \mathbf{j} & \mathbf{k} \\ A_1 & A_2 & A_3 \\ B_1 & B_2 & B_3 \end{vmatrix}$$

Finally, if $\mathbf{C} = C_1\mathbf{i} + C_2\mathbf{j} + C_3\mathbf{k}$, one has

$$\mathbf{A} \times \mathbf{B} \cdot \mathbf{C} = (A_2B_3 - A_3B_2)C_1 + (A_3B_1 - A_1B_3)C_2$$
$$+ (A_1B_2 - A_2B_1)C_3 = \begin{vmatrix} A_1 & A_2 & A_3 \\ B_1 & B_2 & B_3 \\ C_1 & C_2 & C_3 \end{vmatrix}$$

EXERCISES

1. Prove that in rectangular coordinates

$$\mathbf{A} \cdot \mathbf{B} = A_1B_1 + A_2B_2 + A_3B_3$$

2. Prove that in rectangular coordinates

$$\mathbf{A} \times \mathbf{B} = \begin{vmatrix} \mathbf{i} & \mathbf{j} & \mathbf{k} \\ A_1 & A_2 & A_3 \\ B_1 & B_2 & B_3 \end{vmatrix}$$

For Exercises 3 to 21, use

$$A = i + j - k$$
$$B = i - j + 2k$$
$$C = 2i + j + 2k$$
$$D = i - j$$

3. Find $A + B - 2C$.

4. Find $A \cdot C$.

5. Evaluate $A \times B \cdot D$.

6. Give the unit vector, i.e., the vector of unit length, in the direction of B.

7. Give the unit vector directed oppositely to C.

8. Find the angle between A and B.

9. Resolve D into two components, one along and the other perpendicular to C.

10. Find a unit vector normal to the plane of A and B.

11. Find the angle between the plane of A and B and the plane of C and D.

12. Find a unit vector in the direction of the intersection of the plane of A and B with the plane of C and D.

13. Find the center of gravity of the triangle of vertices A, B, and C.

14. Write a vector equation for the straight line through points C and D.

15. Obtain the equation of the plane through the point A and perpendicular to the vector B.

16. Find the distance of D from the plane of Exercise 15. Is D on the same side of the plane as the origin?

17. Find the area of the parallelogram with A and C as sides.

18. Verify that (1-3) is satisfied by A, B, C.

19. Find the volume of the parallelepiped with B, C, and D as edges.

20. Verify that (1-5) is satisfied by A, B, C, and D.

21. Find the unit vector which bisects the angle between $A - B$ and $C - B$.

22. Under the assumption that A, B, C, are in the order given a left-handed set, where

$$A = i + 2j$$
$$B = j - 2k$$
$$C = 2i - k$$

the set i, j, k being a set of mutually orthogonal unit vectors, tell whether the set i, j, k is right-handed or left-handed.

23. Let $B = k \times A$. Prove that $B_1 = -A_2$, $B_2 = A_1$.

24. Let the vector $\mathbf{R}$ make angles α, β, γ with the base vectors $\mathbf{i}$, $\mathbf{j}$, $\mathbf{k}$. Show that

$$\mathbf{R} = R(\mathbf{i}\cos\alpha + \mathbf{j}\cos\beta + \mathbf{k}\cos\gamma)$$

The angles α, β, and γ, and their cosines are called direction angles and direction cosines of $\mathbf{R}$.

1-15. Reciprocal Sets of Vectors

Let $\mathbf{A}_1$, $\mathbf{A}_2$, $\mathbf{A}_3$ and $\mathbf{B}_1$, $\mathbf{B}_2$, $\mathbf{B}_3$ be two sets of vectors which satisfy the relations

$$\mathbf{A}_\alpha \cdot \mathbf{B}_\beta = \delta_{\alpha\beta} \qquad \alpha, \beta = 1, 2, 3 \tag{1-6}$$

where the $\delta_{\alpha\beta}$ are defined as follows:

$$\delta_{\alpha\beta} = \begin{cases} 1 & \alpha = \beta \\ 0 & \alpha \neq \beta \end{cases} \tag{1-7}$$

The expression (1-6) stands for the nine equations

$$\begin{array}{lll} \mathbf{A}_1 \cdot \mathbf{B}_1 = 1 & \mathbf{A}_2 \cdot \mathbf{B}_1 = 0 & \mathbf{A}_3 \cdot \mathbf{B}_1 = 0 \\ \mathbf{A}_1 \cdot \mathbf{B}_2 = 0 & \mathbf{A}_2 \cdot \mathbf{B}_2 = 1 & \mathbf{A}_3 \cdot \mathbf{B}_2 = 0 \\ \mathbf{A}_1 \cdot \mathbf{B}_3 = 0 & \mathbf{A}_2 \cdot \mathbf{B}_3 = 0 & \mathbf{A}_3 \cdot \mathbf{B}_3 = 1 \end{array} \tag{1-6a}$$

The sets $\mathbf{A}_1$, $\mathbf{A}_2$, $\mathbf{A}_3$ and $\mathbf{B}_1$, $\mathbf{B}_2$, $\mathbf{B}_3$ are said to be reciprocal sets of vectors. Such sets of vectors will turn out to be important in the study of general coordinate systems.

At this point it may be well to caution the reader against confusing the subscripts in (1-6) and (1-6a) with the subscripts hitherto used to denote the different cartesian components of a vector. Here the subscripts serve to differentiate among the vectors of a set of vectors. The point may be clarified by writing out some of the above relations in component form. Thus, in cartesian coordinates, $\mathbf{A}_\alpha$ would be

$$\mathbf{A}_\alpha = A_{\alpha 1}\mathbf{i} + A_{\alpha 2}\mathbf{j} + A_{\alpha 3}\mathbf{k}$$

relation (1-6):

$$A_{\alpha 1}B_{\beta 1} + A_{\alpha 2}B_{\beta 2} + A_{\alpha 3}B_{\beta 3} = \delta_{\alpha\beta}$$

and the second of equations (1-6a):

$$A_{11}B_{21} + A_{12}B_{22} + A_{13}B_{23} = 0$$

The determinants $a = \mathbf{A}_1 \cdot \mathbf{A}_2 \times \mathbf{A}_3$ and $b = \mathbf{B}_1 \cdot \mathbf{B}_2 \times \mathbf{B}_3$ cannot vanish. Suppose, on the contrary, that a does vanish. Then $\mathbf{A}_1$, $\mathbf{A}_2$, and $\mathbf{A}_3$ are coplanar and one can be expressed as a linear combination of the other two. Suppose

$$\mathbf{A}_3 = k_1\mathbf{A}_1 + k_2\mathbf{A}_2$$

where k_1 and k_2 are not both zero. Then

$$1 = \mathbf{A}_3 \cdot \mathbf{B}_3 = k_1\mathbf{A}_1 \cdot \mathbf{B}_3 + k_2\mathbf{A}_2 \cdot \mathbf{B}_3 = 0$$

which is absurd. Hence, $a \neq 0$; likewise $b \neq 0$.

There can be only one set of vectors reciprocal to $\mathbf{A}_1$, $\mathbf{A}_2$, and $\mathbf{A}_3$. If $\mathbf{C}_1$, $\mathbf{C}_2$, $\mathbf{C}_3$ are also reciprocal to $\mathbf{A}_1$, $\mathbf{A}_2$, $\mathbf{A}_3$, then

$$\mathbf{A}_\alpha \cdot \mathbf{B}_\beta = \delta_{\alpha\beta}$$
$$\mathbf{A}_\alpha \cdot \mathbf{C}_\beta = \delta_{\alpha\beta}$$

whence

$$\mathbf{A}_\alpha \cdot (\mathbf{B}_\beta - \mathbf{C}_\beta) = 0$$

for all α and β. None of the vectors $\mathbf{B}_\beta - \mathbf{C}_\beta$ can fail to vanish. For, if so, it would be perpendicular to all of the $\mathbf{A}_\alpha$, all of which would accordingly be coplanar. But it was shown above that the $\mathbf{A}_\alpha$ cannot be coplanar. Hence

$$\mathbf{C}_\beta = \mathbf{B}_\beta$$

for all β.

Since $\mathbf{B}_1$ is normal to $\mathbf{A}_2$ and $\mathbf{A}_3$, $\mathbf{B}_1$ must be parallel to $\mathbf{A}_2 \times \mathbf{A}_3$. Similarly $\mathbf{B}_2$ and $\mathbf{B}_3$ are parallel to $\mathbf{A}_3 \times \mathbf{A}_1$ and $\mathbf{A}_1 \times \mathbf{A}_2$ respectively.

One can readily see that

$$\mathbf{B}_1 = \frac{\mathbf{A}_2 \times \mathbf{A}_3}{a}$$

$$\mathbf{B}_2 = \frac{\mathbf{A}_3 \times \mathbf{A}_1}{a} \qquad (1\text{-}8)$$

$$\mathbf{B}_3 = \frac{\mathbf{A}_1 \times \mathbf{A}_2}{a}$$

Likewise

$$\mathbf{A}_1 = \frac{\mathbf{B}_2 \times \mathbf{B}_3}{b}$$

$$\mathbf{A}_2 = \frac{\mathbf{B}_3 \times \mathbf{B}_1}{b} \qquad (1\text{-}9)$$

$$\mathbf{A}_3 = \frac{\mathbf{B}_1 \times \mathbf{B}_2}{b}$$

Using (1-9),

$$a = \mathbf{A}_1 \cdot \mathbf{A}_2 \times \mathbf{A}_3 = \frac{1}{b^3}[(\mathbf{B}_2 \times \mathbf{B}_3) \cdot (\mathbf{B}_3 \times \mathbf{B}_1) \times (\mathbf{B}_1 \times \mathbf{B}_2)]$$

$$= \frac{1}{b^3}[(\mathbf{B}_2 \times \mathbf{B}_3) \cdot (\mathbf{B}_3 \times \mathbf{B}_1 \cdot \mathbf{B}_2)\mathbf{B}_1]$$

$$= \frac{b^2}{b^3} = \frac{1}{b}$$

EXERCISES

1. Establish relations (1-8) and (1-9).

2. Given $\mathbf{A}_1 = 4\mathbf{i}$, $\mathbf{A}_2 = 3\mathbf{j}$, $\mathbf{A}_3 = 2\mathbf{k}$, find the reciprocal set of vectors.

3. Given $\mathbf{A}_1 = \mathbf{i} + \mathbf{j}$, $\mathbf{A}_2 = \mathbf{j}$, $\mathbf{A}_3 = \mathbf{i} + \mathbf{j} + \mathbf{k}$, find the reciprocal set.

4. Given $\mathbf{A}_1 = 2\mathbf{i} - \mathbf{j} + 3\mathbf{k}$, $\mathbf{A}_2 = -\mathbf{i} + 3\mathbf{j} + 3\mathbf{k}$, $\mathbf{A}_3 = \mathbf{i} + \mathbf{j} - 2\mathbf{k}$. Find the reciprocal set $\mathbf{B}_1$, $\mathbf{B}_2$, $\mathbf{B}_3$.

5. For Exercise 4 verify that

$$\mathbf{A}_1 \cdot \mathbf{A}_2 \times \mathbf{A}_3 = [\mathbf{B}_1 \cdot \mathbf{B}_2 \times \mathbf{B}_3]^{-1}$$

REFERENCES

Graustein, W. C.: "Differential Geometry," The Macmillan Company, New York, 1935.

Joos, G.: "Theoretical Physics," translated by I. M. Freeman, G. E. Stechert & Company, New York, 1934.

Phillips, H. B.: "Vector Analysis," John Wiley & Sons, Inc., New York, 1933.

CHAPTER 2

A REVIEW OF SOME MATHEMATICAL CONCEPTS

The intent of this text is to present vector analysis in such a way as to keep the underlying physics and geometry clearly in mind. With such an approach it is hoped that the reader will find the subject an understandable and useful tool. To this end, however, it is absolutely essential that the student also understand clearly the geometry which underlies the concepts and techniques of the differential and integral calculus. The present chapter outlines the material with which it is assumed the reader is familiar and can serve as a basis for review. It is, however, intentionally sketchy, and the student should fill in the gaps by referring to texts on the calculus. Also, the emphasis herein is upon concepts, although it must be pointed out that manipulative skill is required in their application to the vector calculus. It is, therefore, urged that the student supplement his review with manipulative drill as needed.

2-1. Point Sets. Curves. Region

A collection of points is called a point set. For the present discussion consider sets of points in ordinary space. A point is an *interior point* of a given set if it is the center of some sphere which contains only points of the set. A point is an *exterior point* of a given set if it is the center of some sphere which contains no points of the set. A point is a *boundary point* of a given set if every sphere of which the point is center contains both points of the set and points not of the set.

A set of points is *open* if all of the points of the set are interior points. A set of points is *closed* if the set includes all of its boundary points.

Let $\mathbf{r}(t)$ be the vector from a chosen origin to a point in space, and let $\mathbf{r}(t)$ depend upon the variable t in the interval $a \leq t \leq b$. Then as t varies the points $\mathbf{r}(t)$ trace out a curve in space. The curve is said to be continuous if for every value t_0 of t on the interval $a \leq t \leq b$ and for every positive number ϵ there exists a corresponding positive number $\delta(\epsilon, t_0)$ such that whenever

$$|t - t_0| < \delta(\epsilon, t_0)$$

then

$$|\mathbf{r}(t) - \mathbf{r}(t_0)| < \epsilon$$

28

The curve is said to be simple if it does not cross itself for $a < t < b$. It is said to be closed if $\mathbf{r}(a) = \mathbf{r}(b)$.

A set of points is said to be connected if every pair of points in the set can be joined by a continuous curve consisting entirely of points of the set.

A *region*, or *open region*, is an open, connected point set. A *closed region* is a region plus all of its boundary points. A region is said to be *simply connected* if every simple closed curve which can be drawn in the region can be shrunk down continuously to a point of the region without ever crossing a boundary point of the region.

A neighborhood of a point is an open region containing the point.

EXERCISES

1. Repeat the discussion of Sec. 2-1 for point sets in the plane.

2. Repeat the discussion of Sec. 2-1 for point sets on a line.

3. Show how to extend the discussion of Sec. 2-1 to point sets on any surface in space, or on any curve in space.

4. Define what is meant by point, distance between points, and continuous curve in n-dimensional space. Then extend the discussion of Sec. 2-1 to n space.

For the following sets of points tell whether the set is a region, a closed region, or neither. Describe the set, telling which are the interior points and which are the boundary points.

5. In space: $\quad 3 < \sqrt{x^2 + y^2 + z^2} < 6$

6. In space: $\quad x^2 + 2y^2 + 3z^2 < 6$

7. In space: $\quad 2 \geq y^2 - 4x > 1$

8. In space: $\quad x^2 + y^2 < 5 \qquad z \equiv 0$

9. In space: $\quad \left(\cos \dfrac{n\pi}{6}\right)\mathbf{i} + \left(\sin \dfrac{n\pi}{6}\right)\mathbf{j} + n\mathbf{k}; \ n = 0, 1, 2, \ldots$

10. In the plane: $2y + x + 1 > 0$

11. In the plane: $x^2 + y^2 < 5$

12. In the plane: $x^2 + y^2 < 4 \qquad x^2 - y^2 > 1$

13. In the plane: $\left[\dfrac{1}{n} \cos \dfrac{n\pi}{8}\right]\mathbf{i} + \left[\dfrac{1}{n} \sin \dfrac{n\pi}{8}\right]\mathbf{j}; \ n = 0, 1, 2, \ldots$

14. In the plane: $x\mathbf{i} \qquad 0 < x < 1$

15. On a line: $\quad 0 < x < 1$

16. Which of the following are simply connected: a sphere; the region between two concentric spheres; a doughnut-shaped region; a circle in the plane; an annulus in the plane.

2-2. Limit

Let $f(P)$ be a function of the point P defined throughout a region R. Let P_0 be a point of R. Then $f(P)$ approaches the limit F as P approaches P_0, written

$$\lim_{P \to P_0} f(P) = F$$

or

$$f(P) \xrightarrow[P \to P_0]{} F$$

if for every positive ϵ there is a positive $\delta(\epsilon)$ such that for all points P satisfying the inequality

$$0 < |P - P_0| < \delta(\epsilon) \tag{2-1}$$

the function $f(P)$ satisfies the inequality

$$|f(P) - F| < \epsilon$$

The expression $|P - P_0|$ is taken to mean the distance between P and P_0.

Since ϵ may be chosen as small as one pleases, the definition states that by taking P sufficiently close to P_0, $f(P)$ can be brought as close to F as may be prescribed. Note that (2-1) excludes P_0 from the points under consideration. The value $f(P_0)$ has no part in the definition of the limit.

The definition is equally valid for the cases in which P is a point of a line, of a plane, of space, or even of n-dimensional space. In the first case (2-1) represents an interval about P_0; in the second, a circle; in the third, a sphere; and in the last, an n-dimensional sphere.

It is a simple matter to phrase an equivalent definition in terms of any convenient set of coordinates for the points P. Thus, for a function $f(x,y,z)$ of cartesian coordinates in space

$$\lim_{P \to P_0} f(x,y,z) = F$$

if there is a function $\delta(\epsilon)$ defined for all positive ϵ such that whenever

$$\begin{aligned} 0 < |x - x_0| < \delta(\epsilon) \\ 0 < |y - y_0| < \delta(\epsilon) \\ 0 < |z - z_0| < \delta(\epsilon) \end{aligned} \tag{2-2}$$

$f(x,y,z)$ satisfies

$$|f(x,y,z) - F| < \epsilon$$

Note that in this case (2-2) defines a rectangular parallelepiped minus its center, instead of the sphere defined by (2-1). Plainly this is a non-essential difference.

Suppose, now, that

$$\lim_{P \to P_0} f(P) = F$$

$$\lim_{P \to P_0} g(P) = G$$

Then

$$\lim_{P \to P_0} (f(P) \pm g(P)) = F \pm G \qquad (2\text{-}3)$$

$$\lim_{P \to P_0} (f(P)g(P)) = FG \qquad (2\text{-}4)$$

and if $G \neq 0$,

$$\lim_{P \to P_0} \frac{f(P)}{g(P)} = \frac{F}{G} \qquad (2\text{-}5)$$

These are proved by going back to the basic definition of limit.   By way of illustration, the proof of (2-4) will be given.

One has given that for every positive ϵ, there is a positive $\delta(\epsilon)$ such that when

$$0 < |P - P_0| < \delta(\epsilon)$$

then

$$|f(P) - F| < \epsilon \qquad |g(P) - G| < \epsilon$$

One must prove that for every positive ϵ there is a positive $\Delta(\epsilon)$ such that when

$$0 < |P - P_0| < \Delta(\epsilon)$$

then

$$|f(P)g(P) - FG| < \epsilon$$

Write

$$|f(P)g(P) - FG| = |fg - Fg + Fg - FG|$$
$$\leq |f - F| \, |g| + |g - G| \, |F|$$

Now prescribe $\epsilon > 0$.   Then, select a positive number M greater than $|F|$ and $|G|$.   Take $\Delta(\epsilon)$ less than the smaller of $\delta(M)$ and $\delta(\epsilon/4M)$.   If, now,

$$0 < |P - P_0| < \Delta(\epsilon)$$

one has

$$|f - F| < \frac{\epsilon}{4M}$$

$$|g - G| < \frac{\epsilon}{2M}$$

$$|g - G| < M$$

From the last,

$$|g| - |G| < M$$
$$|g| < |G| + M < 2M$$

Hence, finally

$$|f(P)g(P) - FG| < \frac{\epsilon}{4M} \cdot 2M + \frac{\epsilon}{2M} \cdot M = \epsilon$$

Hence the chosen $\Delta(\epsilon)$ is suitable, and the theorem is established.

Suppose that for all points P in a region R and all points T in a region Q, the function $f(P,T)$ is defined. The regions R and Q need not be of the same dimensionality, although they may be. Suppose further that for every point of R,

$$\lim_{T \to T_0} f(P,T) = L(P)$$

This means that there is a function $\delta(\epsilon,P)$, depending upon P in general, such that whenever

$$0 < |T - T_0| < \delta(\epsilon,P)$$

then

$$|f(P,T) - L(P)| < \epsilon$$

If the function $\delta(\epsilon)$ can be chosen so as to be independent of P throughout R, then one says that $f(P,T)$ approaches $L(P)$ uniformly in P. The concept of uniform approach to a limit is essential in the handling of many limit problems.

EXERCISES

1. Discuss the geometric meaning of the definition for limit in the case of a function defined throughout a region (a) of space, (b) of the plane, and (c) of a line.

2. Let $f(P)$ be a function of points P on the surface of a sphere. Set up coordinates for the points on the sphere and in terms of them define $\lim_{P \to P_0} f(P)$ for points on the sphere.

3. Prove (2-3).

4. Prove (2-5).

5. One says that $f(P)$ becomes positively infinite as $P \to P_0$, written

$$\lim_{P \to P_0} f(P) = \infty \qquad \text{or} \qquad f(P) \xrightarrow[P \to P_0]{} \infty$$

if for every positive number M there is a positive number $\delta(M)$ such that when

$$0 < |P - P_0| < \delta(M)$$

then

$$f(P) > M$$

Discuss the geometric meaning of the definition.

6. Define what is meant by $\lim\limits_{P \to P_0} f(P) = -\infty$.

7. Define $\lim\limits_{x \to \infty} f(x) = F$; $\lim\limits_{x \to \infty} f(x) = \infty$; $\lim\limits_{x \to \infty} f(x) = -\infty$.

8. Define $\lim\limits_{x \to -\infty} f(x) = F$; $\lim\limits_{x \to -\infty} f(x) = \infty$; $\lim\limits_{x \to -\infty} f(x) = -\infty$.

9. What does (2-5) become when $G = \infty$? Prove it.

10. Let $f(x,y) = x + y$, $0 \leq x \leq 2$, $0 \leq y \leq 2$. What is $\lim\limits_{x \to 1} f(x,y)$?
Is the approach to the limit uniform in y? Prove what you say.

11. Repeat Exercise 10 with $f(x,y) = xy$.

12. Repeat Exercise 10 with $f(x,y) = x/y$.

13. Let

$$f(x,y) = \frac{x}{1 + yx}$$

Show that for each x on the interval $0 \leq x \leq 1$,

$$\lim_{y \to \infty} f(x,y)$$

exists and that the approach to the limit is uniform in x.

14. Let

$$f(x,y) = \frac{1}{1 + yx}$$

Show that for each x on $0 \leq x \leq 1$

$$\lim_{y \to \infty} f(x,y)$$

exists, but that the approach to the limit is not uniform in x.

15. Let $A(P)$ be a vector function of position within a region R of space. Define what is meant by

$$\lim_{P \to P_0} A(P)$$

where P_0 is a point of R. Give three equivalent definitions, one purely in terms of vectors; one in terms of components; and one in terms of magnitudes and angles.

2-3. Continuity

The function $f(P)$ is said to be continuous at the point P_0 if

$$\lim_{P \to P_0} f(P) = f(P_0) \neq \pm \infty$$

That $f(P)$ should be continuous at a point P_0 requires, first, that $f(P)$

be defined and not infinite in some neighborhood of P_0, including the point P_0 itself; second, that the limit of $f(P)$ as $P \to P_0$ exist; and, third, that this limit be $f(P_0)$.

From the corresponding theorems on limits, one can prove that the sum or difference of two continuous functions is continuous. One can likewise show that the product of two continuous functions is continuous and that their quotient is continuous wherever the divisor does not vanish.

A function $f(P)$ is said to be uniformly continuous in a region R if

$$f(P) \xrightarrow[P \to P_0]{} f(P_0)$$

uniformly in P_0 throughout R.

EXERCISES

1. With a graph of $y = f(x)$, explain geometrically the meaning of continuity of $f(x)$.

2. Prove that the sum or difference of two continuous functions is continuous.

3. Prove that the product of two continuous functions is continuous.

4. Prove that the quotient of two continuous functions is continuous at all points where the divisor does not vanish.

5. Let $f(g)$ be a continuous function of g, and let g be a continuous function of P. Prove that $f(g(P))$ is a continuous function of P.

6. Define continuity for a vector function $\mathbf{A}(P)$ of the points P of space.

7. Show that $\dfrac{1}{x}$ is not continuous at $x = 0$.

8. Show that $\sin \dfrac{1}{x}$ is not continuous at $x = 0$.

9. Show that $x \sin \dfrac{1}{x}$ is continuous at $x = 0$.

10. Show that

$$f = \begin{cases} \dfrac{xy}{x^2 + y^2} & (x,y) \neq (0,0) \\ 0 & (x,y) = (0,0) \end{cases}$$

is not continuous at the origin.

11. Show that

$$f = \begin{cases} \dfrac{xy^3}{x^2 + y^6} & (x,y) \neq (0,0) \\ 0 & (x,y) = (0,0) \end{cases}$$

is not continuous at the origin.

12. Give an analytic definition of uniform continuity. Tell just what uniform continuity means geometrically.

13. Show that $\dfrac{1}{x}$ is not uniformly continuous for $0 < x \leq 1$.

14. Show that $\dfrac{1}{x}$ is uniformly continuous on $0 < \delta \leq x \leq 1$ for any positive δ no matter how small.

2-4. Properties of Continuous Functions

THEOREM 2-1. If $f(P)$ is continuous within a closed region R, then $f(P)$ is uniformly continuous within R.

THEOREM 2-2. If $f(P)$ is continuous within a closed region R, then there is a number M such that (a) $f(P) \leq M$ for all points P in R, and (b) $f(P_M) = M$ for some point P_M of R. Likewise, there is a number m such that (a) $f(P) \geq m$ for all P in R, and (b) $f(P_m) = m$ for some point P_m of R.

In other words, a function continuous within a closed region takes on both an absolute maximum and an absolute minimum value within the region. This is not necessarily true for a region which is not closed.

THEOREM 2-3. If $f(P)$ is continuous within a region R, and if, where P_1 and P_2 lie in R, $f(P_1) = \eta_1$ and $f(P_2) = \eta_2$, then within R, $f(P)$ takes on at least once every value η between η_1 and η_2.

In this case it is not necessary that the region be closed.

EXERCISES

1. Prove, or look up a proof of, Theorem 2-1 for an interval on a line, a region in the plane, and a region in space.

2. Repeat Exercise 1 for Theorem 2-2.

3. Give an example of a function continuous in an open region which does not assume an absolute maximum in the region.

4. Repeat Exercise 1 for Theorem 2-3.

2-5. Derivative. Rolle's Theorem. Law of the Mean

The derivative at a point X of a function $f(x)$ of the real variable x is defined as

$$f'(X) = \lim_{x \to X} \frac{f(x) - f(X)}{x - X}$$

provided the limit exists. A function which has a derivative is said to be differentiable.

Consider a differentiable function $f(x)$. When x changes by an amount $\Delta(x)$, $f(x)$ changes by an amount Δf where

$$\Delta f = f(x + \Delta x) - f(x)$$

The quantity Δf is given approximately by df where

$$df = f'(x) \, \Delta x$$

The quantity df is called the differential of f at x. Applying the definition of differential to the function $f(x) = x$, one gets

$$dx = \Delta x$$

Hence, one can write $f'(x)$ as the quotient of two differentials

$$f'(x) = \frac{df}{dx}$$

THEOREM 2-4. Let $f'(X)$ exist. Then $f(x)$ is continuous at the point X.

THEOREM 2-5. Let $f'(X)$ and $g'(X)$ exist. Then at X, $(f \pm g)'$ exists and is given by

$$(f \pm g)' \Big|_X = f'(X) \pm g'(X)$$

THEOREM 2-6. Let $f'(X)$ and $g'(X)$ exist. Then $(fg)'$ exists at X and is given by

$$(fg)' \Big|_X = f(X)g'(X) + g(X)f'(X)$$

THEOREM 2-7. Let $f'(X)$ exist and suppose $f(X) \neq 0$. Then

$$\left(\frac{1}{f}\right)' \Big|_X = -\frac{f'(X)}{f^2(X)}$$

THEOREM 2-8. Let $f(u)$ be differentiable with respect to u, and let u be a differentiable function of x. Then $f(u(x))$ is differentiable with respect to x, and

$$\frac{df}{dx} = \frac{df}{du}\frac{du}{dx}$$

A function $f(P)$ which is defined in a region R is said to have a relative maximum at the point P_0 of R, if there is a neighborhood of P_0 in which P_0 is an absolute maximum point of $f(P)$. A relative minimum is similarly defined.

A function $f(P)$ is said to have an extremum at a point at which it has a maximum or a minimum, either absolute or relative.

THEOREM 2-9. Let $f(x)$ be defined on the interval $a \leq x \leq b$, and let $f'(x)$ exist thereon, where the prime denotes differentiation with respect to x. Then, if $f(x)$ has an extremum at a point X of the interval $a < x < b, f'(X) = 0$.

Suppose $f'(X)$ is positive. Then when h is sufficiently small

$$\frac{f(X + h) - f(X)}{h} > 0$$

from the definitions of derivative and limit. Hence, if h is positive

$$f(X + h) > f(X)$$

while if h is negative

$$f(X + h) < f(X)$$

It follows that $f(X)$ is not an extremum.

Similarly $f'(X)$ cannot be negative. Accordingly, $f'(X)$ vanishes.

THEOREM 2-10. *Rolle's Theorem.* Let $f(x)$ and $f'(x)$ exist on $a \leq x \leq b$. Suppose that $f(a) = f(b) = 0$. Then there is a point X on $a < x < b$ for which $f'(X) = 0$.

The geometric interpretation of Rolle's theorem is simple. If a function passes through zero at one point, then before it can return to zero again its slope must change sign and hence pass through zero.

To give an analytic proof, note first that at each point at which $f'(x)$ exists, $f(x)$ must be continuous. Hence, $f(x)$ is continuous on the closed interval $a \leq x \leq b$. Thus $f(x)$ has both an absolute maximum and an absolute minimum on the interval. If both are zero, then $f(x) \equiv 0$, and for any X on the interval $f'(X) = 0$. If at least one extremum is not zero, the extremum must be at some point X between a and b, and by Theorem 2-9, $f'(X) = 0$.

THEOREM 2-11. *The Law of the Mean.* Let $f(x)$ be defined and differentiable on $a \leq x \leq b$. Then there is a point X on $a < x < b$ such that

$$f'(X) = \frac{f(b) - f(a)}{b - a} \qquad (2\text{-}6)$$

The reader should interpret (2-6) geometrically. It will be apparent from the underlying geometry that Theorem 2-11 is simply a generalization of Rolle's theorem.

The proof is simple. Note that the function

$$\phi(x) = f(x) - f(a) - \frac{f(b) - f(a)}{b - a} (x - a)$$

satisfies the conditions of Rolle's Theorem on the interval $a \leq x \leq b$. Hence there is an X between a and b for which $\phi'(X) = 0$. But this reduces immediately to (2-6).

EXERCISES

1. Discuss the geometric meaning of the differential df of a function $f(x)$.

2. Prove Theorem 2-4.

3. Prove Theorem 2-5.

4. Prove Theorem 2-6.

5. Prove Theorem 2-7.

6. Obtain a formula for the derivative of the quotient of two differentiable functions.

7. Prove Theorem 2-8.

8. What is the geometric basis for the proof given for Theorem 2-9?

9. Give a geometric interpretation of the law of the mean.

10. Give a geometric interpretation of the function $\phi(x)$ used in proving the law of the mean.

11. Define what is meant by second-, third-, and higher-order derivatives of $f(x)$.

2-6. Partial Differentiation

Let $f(x,y,z, \ldots)$ be a function of a number of variables x, y, z, $\ldots$, as indicated. For the moment hold fixed all the variables y, z, $\ldots$ other than x. Then if f is differentiable with respect to x, the other variables y, z, $\ldots$, remaining fixed, one says that f is partially differentiable with respect to x. The derivative is denoted by $\partial f/\partial x$ and is called the partial derivative with respect to x. Partial derivatives with respect to the other variables are similarly defined.

Higher-order partial derivatives are defined as in the case of a single variable

$$\frac{\partial^2 f}{\partial x^2} = \frac{\partial}{\partial x}\left(\frac{\partial f}{\partial x}\right)$$

$$\frac{\partial^4 f}{\partial z^4} = \frac{\partial}{\partial z}\left(\frac{\partial^3 f}{\partial z^3}\right)$$

and so on. In this case, however, cross derivatives are also possible

$$\frac{\partial^2 f}{\partial y\, \partial x} = \frac{\partial}{\partial y}\left(\frac{\partial f}{\partial x}\right)$$

and so forth.

Let $f(x,y,z, \ldots)$ be a function of the variables x, y, z, $\ldots$. Corresponding to changes Δx, Δy, Δz, $\ldots$ in x, y, z, $\ldots$ there is a change Δf in f, given by

$$\Delta f = f(x + \Delta x, y + \Delta y, z + \Delta z, \ldots) - f(x,y,z, \ldots)$$

THEOREM 2-12.   If f is differentiable in a region R, then throughout R

$$\Delta f = \left(\frac{\partial f}{\partial x}\,\Delta x + \frac{\partial f}{\partial y}\,\Delta y + \frac{\partial f}{\partial z}\,\Delta z + \;\cdots\;\right)$$
$$+ \text{ terms of higher order in } \Delta x, \Delta y, \Delta z, \ldots$$

The differential df of f is defined as

$$df = \frac{\partial f}{\partial x}\,\Delta x + \frac{\partial f}{\partial y}\,\Delta y + \frac{\partial f}{\partial z}\,\Delta z + \;\cdots$$

or, replacing $\Delta x, \Delta y, \Delta z, \ldots$ by $dx, dy, dz, \ldots$:

$$df = \frac{\partial f}{\partial x}\,dx + \frac{\partial f}{\partial y}\,dy + \frac{\partial f}{\partial z}\,dz + \;\cdots$$

THEOREM 2-13.   If $f(x,y,z, \ldots)$ is differentiable in a region R, and $x, y, z, \ldots$ are all differentiable functions of some other variable t, then

$$\frac{df}{dt} = \frac{\partial f}{\partial x}\frac{dx}{dt} + \frac{\partial f}{\partial y}\frac{dy}{dt} + \frac{\partial f}{\partial z}\frac{dz}{dt} + \;\cdots$$

EXERCISES

1. Let
$$f = f(x,y)$$
be a differentiable function of the variables x and y.   Show geometrically the meanings of $\partial f/\partial x$ and $\partial f/\partial y$.

2. Prove Theorem 2-12.

3. Prove Theorem 2-13.

4. Let $f(x,y,z, \ldots)$ be a differentiable function of the variables $x, y, z, \ldots$ Suppose that $x, y, z, \ldots$ are all differentiable functions of other variables $\theta, \phi, \ldots$ Prove that

$$\frac{\partial f}{\partial \theta} = \frac{\partial f}{\partial x}\frac{\partial x}{\partial \theta} + \frac{\partial f}{\partial y}\frac{\partial y}{\partial \theta} + \frac{\partial f}{\partial z}\frac{\partial z}{\partial \theta} + \;\cdots$$
$$\frac{\partial f}{\partial \phi} = \frac{\partial f}{\partial x}\frac{\partial x}{\partial \phi} + \frac{\partial f}{\partial y}\frac{\partial y}{\partial \phi} + \frac{\partial f}{\partial z}\frac{\partial z}{\partial \phi} + \;\cdots$$
$$\vdots$$

2-7. Series

THEOREM 2-14.   TAYLOR'S THEOREM.   Let $f(x)$ possess derivatives of the first n orders throughout some neighborhood of the point $x = a$.

Then throughout that neighborhood

$$f(x) = f(a) + f'(a)(x - a) + \frac{f''(a)}{2!}(x - a)^2 + \cdots$$
$$+ \frac{f^{(n-1)}(a)}{(n - 1)!}(x - a)^{n-1} + \frac{f^{(n)}(X)}{n!}(x - a)^n \quad (2\text{-}7)$$

where $f^{(r)}(x)$ denotes the rth derivative of $f(x)$ and where $a < X < x$.

To prove the theorem, form the function

$$\Phi(u) = F_n(u) - \left(\frac{x - u}{x - a}\right)^n F_n(a)$$

where

$$F_n(u) = f(x) - f(u) - f'(u)(x - u) - \frac{f''(u)}{2!}(x - u)^2 - \cdots$$
$$- \frac{f^{(n-1)}(u)}{(n - 1)!}(x - u)^{n-1}$$

The function Φ is differentiable with respect to u on the interval $a \leq u \leq x$. Also $\Phi(a) = \Phi(x) = 0$. Hence, $\Phi(u)$ satisfies the conditions of Rolle's theorem, and

$$\Phi'(X) = 0$$

for some X such that $a < X < x$. But this leads immediately to (2-7).

THEOREM 2-15. TAYLOR'S SERIES. Let $f(x)$ possess derivatives of all orders throughout some neighborhood of the point $x = a$. Then if the last term on the right of (2-7) vanishes as $n \to \infty$, $f(x)$ is given by the convergent infinite series

$$f(x) = f(a) + f'(a)(x - a) + \frac{f''(a)}{2!}(x - a)^2 + \cdots$$
$$+ \frac{f^{(n)}(a)}{n!}(x - a)^n + \cdots$$

EXERCISES

1. Fill in the details of the proof of Theorem 2-14.
2. Prove Theorem 2-15.
3. To what does Taylor's theorem reduce when $n = 1$?
4. Extend Theorem 2-14 to functions of more than one variable.
5. Extend Theorem 2-15 to functions of more than one variable.

2-8. Fundamental Meshes

In the formation of integrals it becomes necessary to divide a region into elemental subregions. Such a subdivision often can be accomplished conveniently by use of what will be referred to as fundamental meshes. The definition of a mesh will be given first for ordinary space.

Select a convenient set of cartesian coordinates (x,y,z). Then imagine the entire space as divided into elemental cubes by the planes $x = A/2^n$, $y = A/2^n$, $z = A/2^n$, where n is a fixed integer and where A runs through all the integers from $-\infty$ to $+\infty$. The mesh formed by these planes is called the nth fundamental mesh. Each elemental cube has a volume of $1/2^{3n}$. The $(n+1)$th mesh retains all the planes of the nth mesh, simply inserting new planes midway between all adjacent planes of the nth mesh.

Although the example is given for ordinary space, the method of subdivision can be applied to spaces of one, two, three, or any number of dimensions. The concept of a fundamental mesh can also be applied to other than cartesian coordinates, but in the general cases the elemental volumes are not cubes and often are not uniform in size.

2-9. Meaning of Volume, Area, and Arc Length

Let R be a region of space. Using cartesian coordinates, subdivide the region R into elemental volumes by means of fundamental meshes. For the nth mesh let s_n be the sum of the volumes of all elemental cubes lying entirely in R, and let S_n be the sum of the volumes of all cubes which contain at least one point of R. Clearly, as n increases, s_n is nondecreasing, while S_n is nonincreasing. Also any S_n is greater than or equal to every s_m. Hence, as n becomes infinite, S_n and s_n both approach limits, S and s, say, where $S \geq s$. If the equality sign holds, the common limit is called the volume of the region R. In this manner a unique arithmetic meaning is given to the volume of a general region of space, based upon the concept of volume of a cube.

It should now be clear how to define the measure of area for a general region of the plane and the measure of volume for a general region of n space.

To assign a unique number as the measure of area for a warped surface in space is a little more difficult. Once again consider the nth fundamental mesh. Some of the elemental cubes cut out sections of the surface. Consider one such section. Project the section normally onto the coordinate planes. If these projections have areas as defined above, call them ΔS_1, ΔS_2, ΔS_3, and form the vector

$$\Delta \mathbf{S} = \mathbf{i}\,\Delta S_1 + \mathbf{j}\,\Delta S_2 + \mathbf{k}\,\Delta S_3$$

where $\mathbf{i}$, $\mathbf{j}$, and $\mathbf{k}$ are the fundamental vectors of the rectangular coordinate system being used. Over the entire surface take the sum $\Sigma\,|\Delta \mathbf{S}|$.

If this sum approaches a limit S as n becomes infinite, that limit is called the area of the surface.

A similar procedure can be followed to define the length of a curved line in the plane or in space.

Henceforth, the paths, surfaces, and regions dealt with will be assumed to have length, area, or volume in the sense given above.

EXERCISES

1. Prove that if S_n, where n is a positive integer, is bounded above for all n and is nondecreasing as n increases, then S_n approaches a limit as n becomes infinite.

2. Define measure of area for a region in the plane.

3. Define length of a curve in space.

2-10. Integration

Let $f(P)$ be continuous throughout the closed region R. Subdivide R into n elemental subregions $\Delta_\nu R$, and let $\Delta_\nu R$ stand both for the region itself and for its area, volume, or n-dimensional volume as the case may be. Choose a point P_ν in each $\Delta_\nu R$ and form the sum

$$\sum_\nu^n f(P_\nu)\, \Delta_\nu R$$

Let the number of elemental subdivisions increase without limit while the various dimensions of the $\Delta_\nu R$ decrease to zero uniformly. Then, as can be proved, the limit of the sum exists. It is called the integral of $f(P)$ over R, written

$$\lim_{\substack{n \to \infty \\ \Delta_\nu R \to 0}} \sum_\nu^n f(P_\nu)\, \Delta_\nu R = \int_R f(P)\, dR \qquad (2\text{-}8)$$

It is assumed that the reader is acquainted with these facts and that he is familiar with simple and multiple integrals, with line and surface integrals, and with the various means of evaluating them by simple or iterated integration in terms of a convenient coordinate system.

It should be observed that in setting up the integral as in the first paragraph of this section, it is no longer necessary to use fundamental meshes to form the $\Delta_\nu R$. The elemental pieces $\Delta_\nu R$ may have any form as long as their lengths, areas, or volumes, as the case may be, are defined as in Sec. 2-9.

The reader can now show that the volume of a region is given by

$$V = \int_V dV$$

the area of a two-dimensional region by

$$S = \int_S dS$$

or by

$$S = \int_S \mathbf{n} \cdot d\mathbf{S} \tag{2-9}$$

where $d\mathbf{S} = \mathbf{n} \, dS$, $\mathbf{n}$ being the unit normal to the surface; and the length of a path by

$$l = \int_A^B |d\mathbf{r}|$$

where A and B are end points of the path, and $d\mathbf{r}$ is the elemental vector between neighboring points on the path.

EXERCISES

1. Prove, or look up a proof of, the fact that the integral of a continuous function exists.

2. Let R and R' be two nonoverlapping regions. Prove that

$$\int_{R+R'} f(P) \, dR = \int_R f(P) \, dR + \int_{R'} f(P) \, dR$$

3. Let $f(x)$ be a continuous function of the real variable x on the interval $a \leq x \leq b$. Reword the discussion leading to (2-8) so as to apply to

$$\int_a^b f(x) \, dx$$

What does the result of Exercise 2 mean in this case?

4. Let $f(x)$ be continuous for $a \leq x \leq b$. A primitive of $f(x)$ is a function $F(x)$ for which

$$F'(x) = f(x)$$

Prove that

$$\int_a^x f(s) \, ds$$

is a primitive of $f(x)$ on the interval $a \leq x \leq b$.

5. Let $f(x)$ be continuous for $a \leq x \leq b$. Let $F(x)$ be any primitive of $f(x)$. Prove that

$$\int_a^x f(s) \, ds = F(x) - F(a)$$

6. Reword the discussion of (2-8) so as to apply directly to a continuous function $f(x,y)$ of the variables x and y throughout a closed region S of the xy plane. The right member of (2-8) becomes the double integral

$$\iint\limits_{S} f(x,y)\ dS \tag{2-10}$$

What is the difference between (2-10) and the iterated integral

$$\int[\int f(x,y)\ dy]\ dx$$

Prove that (2-10) can be evaluated by a suitable iterated integral.

7. Rework Exercise 6 for the case in which R is a region of space.

8. Discuss (2-8) for the case in which R is a curve in space.

9. Discuss the definition of integral when $f(P)$ in (2-8) is replaced by a vector function $\mathbf{A}(P)$.

10. Establish (2-9).

11. Let S be a surface in space, and let f and $\mathbf{A}$ be continuous functions defined over the surface S. Let $\mathbf{n}(P)$ be the unit normal vector to S at the point P on S. Define what is meant by

$$\int_{S} f\mathbf{n}\ dS \quad \text{or equivalently} \quad \int_{S} f\ d\mathbf{S}$$

$$\int_{S} \mathbf{A} \cdot \mathbf{n}\ dS \quad \text{or equivalently} \quad \int_{S} \mathbf{A} \cdot d\mathbf{S}$$

$$\int_{S} \mathbf{A} \times \mathbf{n}\ dS \quad \text{or equivalently} \quad \int_{S} \mathbf{A} \times d\mathbf{S}$$

12. Let Γ be a curve in space, and let $d\mathbf{r}$ be the vector $\boldsymbol{\tau}\ ds$ where $\boldsymbol{\tau}$ is the unit vector tangent to Γ and ds is the element of arc length on Γ. Let f and $\mathbf{A}$ be continuous on Γ. Define what is meant by

$$\int_{\Gamma} f\ d\mathbf{r}$$

$$\int_{\Gamma} \mathbf{A} \cdot d\mathbf{r}$$

and

$$\int_{\Gamma} \mathbf{A} \times d\mathbf{r}$$

2-11. Law of the Mean for Integrals

Consider the integral

$$\int_{R} f(P)\ dR$$

of a continuous function $f(P)$ defined throughout the closed region R.

Let R also denote the length, area, or volume of the region as the case may be. Then there is a point P' of R such that

$$\int_R f(P) \, dR = f(P')R \tag{2-11}$$

Since $f(P)$ is continuous in R, it has a maximum M and a minimum m in R. Clearly,

$$mR \leq \int_R f(P) \, dR \leq MR$$

Hence

$$\int_R f(P) \, dR = \eta R$$

where η is a number between m and M. But there is a point P' of R for which $f(P') = \eta$. The truth of (2-11) follows.

EXERCISES

1. State (2-11) explicitly for $\int_a^b f(x) \, dx$.

2. State (2-11) explicitly for $\int_S f(x,y) \, dS$.

3. State (2-11) explicitly for $\int_V f(x,y,z) \, dV$.

2-12. An Important Theorem

Let $\mathbf{A}$ be a continuous vector in a region R. Let S be a closed surface within R. From the nth fundamental mesh take the region R' which consists of all the elemental cubes lying entirely within the region bounded by S. Let S' be the surface of R'. Then

$$\lim_{n \to \infty} \int_{S'} \mathbf{A} \cdot d\mathbf{S} = \int_S \mathbf{A} \cdot d\mathbf{S} \tag{2-12}$$

This theorem will be used in the discussion of divergence and Gauss' theorem. The proof is left to the reader. Note carefully that the theorem is not true for integrals of the form $\int_{S'} A \, dS$ and $\int_S A \, dS$; in general,

$$\lim_{n \to \infty} \int_{S'} A \, dS \neq \int_S A \, dS$$

EXERCISE

Prove the theorem stated in Sec. 2-12.

REFERENCES

Courant, R.: "Differential and Integral Calculus," translated by E. J. McShane, Interscience Publishers, Inc., New York, 1937.

Hardy, G. H.: "A Course of Pure Mathematics," Cambridge University Press, New York, 1933.

Osgood, W. F.: "Advanced Calculus," The Macmillan Company, New York, 1933.

Wilson, E. B.: "Advanced Calculus," Ginn & Company, Boston, 1912.

CHAPTER 3

DIFFERENTIATION OF VECTORS

3-1. Limit and Continuity of Vectors

Let the vector **A** be a function of some scalar quantity u. Then as u varies, so does $\mathbf{A}(u)$ in accordance with the functional relationship, whatever it is. For example, let

$$\mathbf{A}(u) = \mathbf{i} \cos u + \mathbf{j} \sin u + \mathbf{k}u$$

and imagine the tail of **A** as always fixed at the origin of coordinates. Then as u varies, the tip of $\mathbf{A}(u)$ traces out a circular helix, the axis of which lies along the **k** axis.

As a second example, suppose that u denotes time, and let $\mathbf{A}(u)$ be the positional vector of a moving particle, that is, the vector from the origin of coordinates to the particle. As the particle moves, $\mathbf{A}(u)$ changes, thus varying with time. If the particle moves in a uniform gravitational field of acceleration g in the negative **k** direction, the explicit form of **A** is easily obtained as

$$\mathbf{A}(u) = \mathbf{r}_0 + \mathbf{v}_0 u - \tfrac{1}{2}(gu^2\mathbf{k}) \tag{3-1}$$

where $\mathbf{r}_0$ and $\mathbf{v}_0$ are the position and velocity of the particle at time $u = 0$.

More generally, **A** may be a function of many variables. A case in point is the velocity of flow of a moving fluid. In such a case the velocity may depend upon the coordinates of position in space and upon time t. If cartesian coordinates (x,y,z) are used, then

$$\mathbf{A} = \mathbf{A}(x,y,z;t)$$

Consider now a vector function $\mathbf{A}(u)$ of the single variable u. The vector $\mathbf{A}(u)$ is said to approach the limit **L** as u approaches u_0, if

$$\lim_{u \to u_0} |\mathbf{A}(u) - \mathbf{L}| = 0 \tag{3-2}$$

In cartesian coordinates, (3-2) implies that

$$\lim_{u \to u_0} \sqrt{(A_1 - L_1)^2 + (A_2 - L_2)^2 + (A_3 - L_3)^2} = 0$$

This can happen if and only if the individual terms under the square root sign vanish as u approaches u_0. Thus $\mathbf{A}$ has the limit $\mathbf{L}$ if and only if A_1, A_2, A_3 individually have the limits L_1, L_2, L_3, respectively.

The familiar limit theorems hold for vectors as they do for scalars. Thus, if

$$\lim_{u \to u_0} \mathbf{A} = \mathbf{L} \qquad \lim_{u \to u_0} \mathbf{B} = \mathbf{M}$$

one has

$$\lim_{u \to u_0} (\mathbf{A} - \mathbf{L}) = 0 \tag{3-3}$$

$$\lim_{u \to u_0} (\mathbf{A} \pm \mathbf{B}) = \mathbf{L} \pm \mathbf{M} \tag{3-4}$$

$$\lim_{u \to u_0} (\mathbf{A} \cdot \mathbf{B}) = \mathbf{L} \cdot \mathbf{M} \tag{3-5}$$

and

$$\lim_{u \to u_0} (\mathbf{A} \times \mathbf{B}) = \mathbf{L} \times \mathbf{M} \tag{3-6}$$

In (3-2) the definition of limit for a vector function was based on a previous concept of limit for scalar quantities. Similarly, the proofs of (3-3) to (3-6) may be based on the corresponding rules for scalar functions. By the way of illustration, the proof of (3-5) may be given. One has

$$
\begin{aligned}
\lim_{u \to u_0} (\mathbf{A} \cdot \mathbf{B}) &= \lim_{u \to u_0} (A_1 B_1 + A_2 B_2 + A_3 B_3) \\
&= \lim_{u \to u_0} A_1 \lim_{u \to u_0} B_1 + \lim_{u \to u_0} A_2 \lim_{u \to u_0} B_2 + \lim_{u \to u_0} A_3 \lim_{u \to u_0} B_3 \\
&= L_1 M_1 + L_2 M_2 + L_3 M_3 \\
&= \mathbf{L} \cdot \mathbf{M}
\end{aligned}
$$

Let $\mathbf{A}(u)$ be defined for all values of u in some neighborhood of u_0. Then $\mathbf{A}(u)$ is said to be continuous at u_0 if and only if

$$\lim_{u \to u_0} \mathbf{A}(u) = \mathbf{A}(u_0)$$

The concepts of limit and continuity are readily extended to vector functions of more than one variable. For example, $\mathbf{A}(x,y,z)$ has the limit $\mathbf{L}$ as x, y, and z approach x_0, y_0, and z_0, if

$$\lim |\mathbf{A}(x,y,z) - \mathbf{L}| = 0 \tag{3-7}$$

as $x \to x_0$, $y \to y_0$, $z \to z_0$ simultaneously. If, in (3-7), $\mathbf{L}$ is $\mathbf{A}(x_0,y_0,z_0)$, then $\mathbf{A}$ is continuous at (x_0,y_0,z_0).

EXERCISES

1. Derive Eq. (3-1) for the motion of a particle in a uniform gravitational field.

2. Prove relation (3-3).

3. Prove relation (3-4).

4. Prove relation (3-6).

5. Prove that the sum or difference of two continuous vectors is a continuous vector.

6. Prove that the scalar product of two continuous vectors is continuous.

7. Prove that the vector product of two continuous vectors is a continuous vector.

8. Discuss the geometric meaning of the definition of limit for a vector.

3-2. Differentiation of a Vector with Respect to a Scalar

Consider a vector function $\mathbf{A}$ of the scalar u. In general, to a change Δu in u corresponds a change $\Delta \mathbf{A}$ in $\mathbf{A}$ given by

$$\Delta \mathbf{A} = \mathbf{A}(u + \Delta u) - \mathbf{A}(u)$$

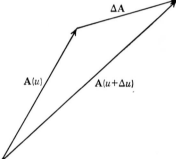

The quantity $\Delta \mathbf{A}$, being the difference of two vectors, is itself a vector. Geometrically, $\mathbf{A}(u)$, $\mathbf{A}(u + \Delta u)$, and $\Delta \mathbf{A}$ are related as shown in Fig. 3-1. Now divide $\Delta \mathbf{A}$ by Δu, obtaining a new vector

$$\frac{\Delta \mathbf{A}}{\Delta u}$$

Fig. 3-1.

If this vector approaches a limit as Δu vanishes, this limit is called the derivative of $\mathbf{A}$ with respect to u, written:

$$\frac{d\mathbf{A}}{du} = \lim_{\Delta u \to 0} \frac{\Delta \mathbf{A}}{\Delta u}$$

In cartesian coordinate form, if the axes are fixed, one has

$$\frac{\Delta \mathbf{A}}{\Delta u} = \frac{\Delta A_1}{\Delta u}\mathbf{i} + \frac{\Delta A_2}{\Delta u}\mathbf{j} + \frac{\Delta A_3}{\Delta u}\mathbf{k}$$

whence,

$$\frac{d\mathbf{A}}{du} = \frac{dA_1}{du}\mathbf{i} + \frac{dA_2}{du}\mathbf{j} + \frac{dA_3}{du}\mathbf{k}$$

The notation $\mathbf{A}'$ is often used to signify the derivative when the variable of differentiation is clear from the context. It is also common to place a dot above the vector to indicate total differentiation with respect to time t; thus:

$$\dot{\mathbf{B}} = \frac{d\mathbf{B}}{dt}$$

Formally, the definition of the derivative of a vector is identical with that for the derivative of a scalar function. In fact, the ordinary rules of the differential calculus follow from the definition, precisely as they do for the derivatives of scalars. Specifically, if $\mathbf{A}'$ and $\mathbf{B}'$ exist, one has

$$(\mathbf{A} \pm \mathbf{B})' = \mathbf{A}' \pm \mathbf{B}' \tag{3-8}$$
$$(\mathbf{A} \cdot \mathbf{B})' = \mathbf{A}' \cdot \mathbf{B} + \mathbf{A} \cdot \mathbf{B}' \tag{3-9}$$
$$(\mathbf{A} \times \mathbf{B})' = \mathbf{A}' \times \mathbf{B} + \mathbf{A} \times \mathbf{B}' \tag{3-10}$$

To prove (3-9), for example, assume that $\mathbf{A}'$ and $\mathbf{B}'$ exist. Let $\Delta(\mathbf{A} \cdot \mathbf{B})$, $\Delta\mathbf{A}$, and $\Delta\mathbf{B}$ be the changes in $\mathbf{A} \cdot \mathbf{B}$, $\mathbf{A}$, and $\mathbf{B}$ corresponding to an increment Δu in u. Since $\mathbf{A}'$ and $\mathbf{B}'$ exist, $\mathbf{A}$ and $\mathbf{B}$ are continuous, and $\Delta\mathbf{A}$ and $\Delta\mathbf{B}$ vanish as Δu does. One has

$$\Delta(\mathbf{A} \cdot \mathbf{B}) = (\mathbf{A} + \Delta\mathbf{A}) \cdot (\mathbf{B} + \Delta\mathbf{B}) - \mathbf{A} \cdot \mathbf{B}$$
$$= \Delta\mathbf{A} \cdot \mathbf{B} + \mathbf{A} \cdot \Delta\mathbf{B} + \Delta\mathbf{A} \cdot \Delta\mathbf{B}$$
$$\frac{\Delta(\mathbf{A} \cdot \mathbf{B})}{\Delta u} = \frac{\Delta\mathbf{A}}{\Delta u} \cdot \mathbf{B} + \mathbf{A} \cdot \frac{\Delta\mathbf{B}}{\Delta u} + \Delta\mathbf{A} \cdot \frac{\Delta\mathbf{B}}{\Delta u}$$

Let $\Delta u \to 0$. The last term on the right vanishes, since $\dfrac{\Delta\mathbf{B}}{\Delta u} \to \mathbf{B}'$ and $\Delta\mathbf{A} \to 0$. From the remaining terms, one gets

$$(\mathbf{A} \cdot \mathbf{B})' = \mathbf{A}' \cdot \mathbf{B} + \mathbf{A} \cdot \mathbf{B}'$$

as was to be proved.

Perhaps a word of caution should be inserted in connection with (3-10). Inasmuch as vector products are involved, the original order of the factors $\mathbf{A}$ and $\mathbf{B}$ must be maintained throughout the equation, since commuting the order of factors changes the sign of a vector product.

If the vector $\mathbf{A}$ is a differentiable function of u, which is in turn a differentiable function of t, then

$$\frac{d\mathbf{A}}{dt} = \frac{d\mathbf{A}}{du}\frac{du}{dt} \tag{3-11}$$

To prove this, observe that the existence of $\dfrac{d\mathbf{A}}{du}$ implies that

$$\Delta\mathbf{A} = \left(\frac{d\mathbf{A}}{du} + \zeta\right)\Delta u$$

where ζ vanishes with Δu. Similarly

$$\Delta u = \left(\frac{du}{dt} + \eta\right)\Delta t$$

where η vanishes with Δt. Thus

$$\Delta\mathbf{A} = \left(\frac{d\mathbf{A}}{du} + \zeta\right)\left(\frac{du}{dt} + \eta\right)\Delta t$$

$$\frac{\Delta\mathbf{A}}{\Delta t} = \frac{d\mathbf{A}}{du}\frac{du}{dt} + \eta\frac{d\mathbf{A}}{du} + \zeta\frac{du}{dt} + \zeta\eta$$

Let $\Delta t \to 0$. Then $\Delta u \to 0$ also, and one gets (3-11).

Suppose that $\mathbf{A}$ is a function of several scalar variables $(x,y,z, \ldots)$. Then the partial derivative of $\mathbf{A}$ with respect to x is defined as

$$\frac{\partial\mathbf{A}}{\partial x} = \lim_{\Delta x \to 0} \frac{\Delta_x\mathbf{A}}{\Delta x}$$

where $\Delta_x\mathbf{A}$ denotes the increment in $\mathbf{A}$ due to a change Δx in x, all of the other variables remaining fixed. Similar definitions apply for the partial derivatives of $\mathbf{A}$ with respect to the other variables y, z, ... Here again, because the definition of partial differentiation of vectors is identical with that for partial differentiation of scalar functions, the familiar rules apply.

EXERCISES

1. Prove that the existence of $\dfrac{d\mathbf{A}}{du}$ implies that $\mathbf{A}$ is continuous.

2. Give definitions for second derivative, third derivative, etc., of a vector. Also give definitions of the various higher-order partial derivatives.

3. Differentiate with respect to x: $\mathbf{A} = x\mathbf{i} + \sin x\mathbf{j} + \cos x\mathbf{k}$.

4. Obtain the second derivative with respect to t:

$$\mathbf{r} = (5 + 3t)\mathbf{i} + (3 - 2t)\mathbf{j} + (4 + t - 16t^2)\mathbf{k}$$

5. Prove (3-8).

6. Prove (3-10).

7. Let $\mathbf{A}(t)$ be a unit differentiable vector, where t denotes time. Show that $\dfrac{d\mathbf{A}}{dt}$ is perpendicular to $\mathbf{A}(t)$ and that $\left|\dfrac{d\mathbf{A}}{dt}\right|$ is equal to the rate of turning of $\mathbf{A}(t)$. (A unit vector is a vector of unit magnitude.)

8. By analogy with the scalar calculus, define the differential vector $d\mathbf{A}$.

9. Explain the difference between $\left|\dfrac{d\mathbf{A}}{dt}\right|$ and $\dfrac{dA}{dt}$.

10. Prove that $\mathbf{A} \cdot \dfrac{d\mathbf{A}}{du} = A \cdot \dfrac{dA}{du}$.

11. Let s be arc length along a curve in space measured from a suitable initial point on the curve. Let the vector $\mathbf{P}(s)$, which traces out the curve as s varies, be differentiable. Show that $\dfrac{d\mathbf{P}}{ds}$ is the unit vector tangent to the curve in the direction of increasing s.

12. Let $\mathbf{P}(s)$ be the vector function of Exercise 11. Prove that $\dfrac{d^2\mathbf{P}}{ds^2}$ is normal to the curve, and that its magnitude is equal to the curvature of the curve.

13. Let $\mathbf{r}(t)$ be the vector from a fixed origin to a moving point, t being time. Show that $\mathbf{r} \times \dot{\mathbf{r}}/2$ is the rate at which the vector $\mathbf{r}$ sweeps out area, where $\dot{\mathbf{r}} = \dfrac{d\mathbf{r}}{dt}$.

3-3. The Gradient of a Scalar Function of Position

Suppose that ϕ is a scalar function of position throughout some region of space. As an example, ϕ might be the temperature at each point of the region in question. Choose a set of rectangular coordinate axes, denote coordinates relative to these axes by x, y, and z, and let the fundamental unit vectors along the x, y, and z axes be $\mathbf{i}$, $\mathbf{j}$, and $\mathbf{k}$, respectively. Form the vector

$$\mathbf{i}\frac{\partial \phi}{\partial x} + \mathbf{j}\frac{\partial \phi}{\partial y} + \mathbf{k}\frac{\partial \phi}{\partial z} \tag{3-12}$$

it being assumed that the derivatives exist.

The vector (3-12) is known as the gradient of ϕ and is denoted by grad ϕ. There is such a vector grad ϕ corresponding to each point of any region in which ϕ is defined and differentiable.

Fix attention upon a point $\mathbf{r} = x\mathbf{i} + y\mathbf{j} + z\mathbf{k}$. Imagine a small displacement

$$d\mathbf{r} = dx\,\mathbf{i} + dy\,\mathbf{j} + dz\,\mathbf{k}$$

from $\mathbf{r}$. In such a displacement the value of ϕ changes by an amount $d\phi$ where

$$d\phi = \frac{\partial \phi}{\partial x}\,dx + \frac{\partial \phi}{\partial y}\,dy + \frac{\partial \phi}{\partial z}\,dz$$

which is clearly the same as

$$d\phi = d\mathbf{r} \cdot \text{grad } \phi \tag{3-13}$$

If ds is the magnitude of $d\mathbf{r}$, one also has

$$\frac{d\phi}{ds} = \frac{d\mathbf{r}}{ds} \cdot \text{grad } \phi \tag{3-14}$$

But $d\phi/ds$ is the derivative of ϕ in the direction of $d\mathbf{r}$. Also $d\mathbf{r}/ds$ is the unit vector in the same direction; whence $d\mathbf{r}/ds \cdot \text{grad } \phi$ is simply the projection of grad ϕ upon $d\mathbf{r}/ds$. It follows from (3-14) therefore, that the component of grad ϕ in any direction is the rate of change of ϕ with distance from $\mathbf{r}$ in that direction. Since $d\mathbf{r}/ds \cdot \text{grad } \phi$ is algebraically greatest when the direction of $d\mathbf{r}/ds$ is the same as that of grad ϕ, it follows further that the magnitude and direction of grad ϕ are those of the algebraically maximum directional derivative of ϕ.

This latter property serves to specify grad ϕ completely and, what is more important, does so independently of any coordinate system. For this reason, the following, rather than (3-12), is taken as the definition of grad ϕ.

Let ϕ be a scalar function of position within a region of space, and suppose that at each point the directional derivatives of ϕ in all directions exist. Associate with each point of the region that vector which has the magnitude and direction of the algebraically maximum directional derivative of ϕ. This vector is called the gradient of ϕ at the point with which it is associated, and is denoted by grad ϕ.

The expression (3-12) now becomes, not the definition of grad ϕ, but its analytic representation in terms of rectangular coordinates.

Since the meanings of $d\phi$, $d\mathbf{r}$, and grad ϕ are all independent of any coordinate system, relations (3-13) and (3-14) are likewise independent of the frame of reference employed.

EXERCISES

1. Let ϕ be a differentiable function of u, which in turn is a differentiable function of x, y, and z. Show that

$$\text{grad } \phi = \frac{d\phi}{du} \text{ grad } u$$

2. Let $\mathbf{r}$ be the vector $x\mathbf{i} + y\mathbf{j} + z\mathbf{k}$, where x, y, z, are rectangular coordinates. Express grad r in terms of $\mathbf{r}$ and r.

3. Using the notation of Exercise 2, express grad r^n in terms of $\mathbf{r}$ and r, where n is an integer.

4. Write the answers to Exercises 2 and 3 in terms of x, y, z, $\mathbf{i}$, $\mathbf{j}$, and $\mathbf{k}$.

5. If $\mathbf{A}$ is a constant vector, prove that

$$\text{grad } (\mathbf{A} \cdot \mathbf{r}) = \mathbf{A}$$

6. Show that a necessary condition that a differentiable function $\phi(x,y,z)$ have an extremum at a point P is that at P

$$\text{grad } \phi = 0$$

7. Let $\phi(x,y,z)$ be a differentiable function of x, y, and z. Show that at point P, grad ϕ is normal to the surface

$$\phi(x,y,z) = \phi(P)$$

8. Find a unit vector normal to the surface

$$x^2 - y^2 + yz = 2$$

at the point $(2,1,-1)$.

9. Describe a method for obtaining a unit vector tangent at a specified point to the curve of intersection of two intersecting surfaces in space. Assume that the surfaces can be expressed in terms of differentiable functions.

10. Find a unit vector tangent to the intersection of

$$x^2 + y^2 + z^2 = 24$$
$$x - y = 0$$

at the point in the first octant where these two surfaces intersect with the third surface

$$2y - z = 0$$

REFERENCES

Graustein, W. C.: "Differential Geometry," The Macmillan Company, New York, 1935.

Phillips, H. B.: "Vector Analysis," John Wiley & Sons, Inc., New York, 1933.

CHAPTER 4

DIVERGENCE AND CURL

4-1. Divergence of a Vector

Let **A** be a continuous vector function of position within some region R of space. Fix attention upon a point P_0 of R, and let ΔV be a rectangular parallelepiped lying in R and containing P_0 in its interior. Form the integral†

$$\oint_S \mathbf{A} \cdot d\mathbf{S} \tag{4-1}$$

where S is the boundary of ΔV and $d\mathbf{S}$ is the vector $\mathbf{n}\,dS$, $\mathbf{n}$ being the unit outer normal to S at some point within the element of area dS. By outer normal is meant the normal pointing away from the interior of ΔV.

The quantity $\mathbf{A} \cdot d\mathbf{S}$ is simply the area dS times the projection of $\mathbf{A}$ onto the normal to dS; hence $\mathbf{A} \cdot d\mathbf{S}$ is the flux of the vector $\mathbf{A}$ through dS. Thus, if $\mathbf{A}$ is the velocity of a fluid, $\mathbf{A} \cdot d\mathbf{S}$ measures the rate of flow of fluid through the surface element dS. It is plain, then, that (4-1) gives the total flux of $\mathbf{A}$ from within V outward through the surface S. If the integral vanishes there is no net outward flux. In this case any outward flux of $\mathbf{A}$ over part of S is balanced by an equal inward flux over the rest of S. If the integral is positive, the flux out of ΔV exceeds that into ΔV, and one says that there are "sources" of $\mathbf{A}$ within the volume. A negative value of the integral indicates the existence within ΔV of "sinks," or points at which $\mathbf{A}$ is being destroyed. If there are both sources and sinks within ΔV, (4-1) gives a measure of their algebraically combined strength.

One can obtain a normalized measure of the total strength of sources and sinks within ΔV by dividing (4-1) by ΔV. If, then, the volume ΔV be made to approach zero in such a manner that the longest diagonal of ΔV vanishes, while at the same time point P_0 remains interior to ΔV, the

---

† Here and henceforth the little circle through the integral sign will be used to indicate that the integration is carried out over a closed surface or around a closed curve, as the case may be.

limit

$$\lim_{\Delta V \to 0} \frac{1}{\Delta V} \oint_S \mathbf{A} \cdot d\mathbf{S}$$

if it exists, is a measure of the source strength of the point P_0. It is called the divergence of $\mathbf{A}$ at P_0, written

$$\text{div } \mathbf{A} = \lim_{\Delta V \to 0} \frac{1}{\Delta V} \oint_{\substack{\text{bdy} \\ \text{of } \Delta V}} \mathbf{A} \cdot d\mathbf{S} \qquad (4\text{-}2)$$

EXERCISES

1. A fluid of density ρ per unit volume is flowing with a velocity of $2\mathbf{i} - \mathbf{j} - \mathbf{k}$ units per second. Compute the mass per second flowing through a unit area normal to (a) each axis, (b) $\mathbf{i} - 2\mathbf{j}$, (c) $\mathbf{i} + \mathbf{j} + \mathbf{k}$.

2. Using the definition (4-2), compute div $\mathbf{r}$, where $\mathbf{r} = x\mathbf{i} + y\mathbf{j} + z\mathbf{k}$.

3. The electric flux density vector $\mathbf{D}$ satisfies a relation of the form

$$\oint_S \mathbf{D} \cdot d\mathbf{S} = \beta q$$

where S is a closed surface bounding a volume V, q is the total charge within V, and β is a constant. Suppose that q is distributed throughout V with a continuous, but not necessarily uniform, density ρ. Using (4-2), compute div $\mathbf{D}$ at a given point P within V.

4-2. The Expression of div A in Rectangular Coordinates

Suppose that $\mathbf{A}$ has continuous first derivatives in the neighborhood of the point $\mathbf{r}_0$. Select a convenient set of rectangular coordinates, and imagine a rectangular parallelepiped with center at $\mathbf{r}_0$ and with edges Δx, Δy, Δz, parallel to the coordinate axes. The divergence of $\mathbf{A}$ can be computed by forming the integral of $\mathbf{A} \cdot d\mathbf{S}$ over the surface of the parallelepiped, dividing by the volume $\Delta x \, \Delta y \, \Delta z$, and taking the limit as the volume is made to vanish.

The contribution of the faces perpendicular to the x direction is approximately

$$\left[A_1\left(\mathbf{r}_0 + \mathbf{i}\,\frac{\Delta x}{2}\right) - A_1\left(\mathbf{r}_0 - \mathbf{i}\,\frac{\Delta x}{2}\right) \right] \Delta y \, \Delta z \qquad (4\text{-}3)$$

If $\mathbf{r}_0 = x_0\mathbf{i} + y_0\mathbf{j} + z_0\mathbf{k}$, then $A_1\left(\mathbf{r}_0 + \mathbf{i}\,\frac{\Delta x}{2}\right)$, for example, could also have been written as $A_1\left(x_0 + \frac{\Delta x}{2}, y_0, z_0\right)$. The two notations are equivalent. The negative sign of the second term in the brackets is due to the fact that the outer normal to the back face of the parallelepiped is $-\mathbf{i}$. By the law of the mean the expression in brackets can be replaced by

$$\frac{\partial A_1(\mathbf{r}_0 + \mathbf{i}\theta_1 \Delta x/2)}{\partial x} \Delta x$$

where $-1 < \theta_1 < 1$. Hence the contribution of the faces normal to the x direction is

$$\frac{\partial A_1(\mathbf{r}_0 + \mathbf{i}\theta_1 \Delta x/2)}{\partial x} \Delta x \, \Delta y \, \Delta z$$

Similarly, the contributions of the faces perpendicular to the y and z directions are

$$\frac{\partial A_2(\mathbf{r}_0 + \mathbf{j}\theta_2 \Delta y/2)}{\partial y} \Delta x \, \Delta y \, \Delta z$$

and

$$\frac{\partial A_3(\mathbf{r}_0 + \mathbf{k}\theta_3 \Delta z/2)}{\partial z} \Delta x \, \Delta y \, \Delta z$$

respectively, where $-1 < \theta_2, \theta_3 < 1$.† Adding, and dividing by $\Delta x \, \Delta y \, \Delta z = \Delta V$,

$$\frac{1}{\Delta V} \oint_S \mathbf{A} \cdot d\mathbf{S} = \frac{\partial A_1(\mathbf{r}_0 + \mathbf{i}\theta_1 \Delta x/2)}{\partial x} + \frac{\partial A_2(\mathbf{r}_0 + \mathbf{j}\theta_2 \Delta y/2)}{\partial y}$$
$$+ \frac{\partial A_3(\mathbf{r}_0 + \mathbf{k}\theta_3 \Delta z/2)}{\partial z} \quad (4\text{-}4)$$

Letting $\Delta V \to 0$, the points $\mathbf{r}_0 + \mathbf{i}\theta_1 \Delta x/2$, $\mathbf{r}_0 + \mathbf{j}\theta_2 \Delta y/2$, and $\mathbf{r}_0 + \mathbf{k}\theta_3 \Delta z/2$, all approach $\mathbf{r}_0$. Since the derivatives of $\mathbf{A}$ have been assumed continuous, the expression on the right approaches

$$\frac{\partial A_1(\mathbf{r}_0)}{\partial x} + \frac{\partial A_2(\mathbf{r}_0)}{\partial y} + \frac{\partial A_3(\mathbf{r}_0)}{\partial z}$$

as ΔV vanishes. Hence div $\mathbf{A}(\mathbf{r}_0)$ exists and is given by

$$\text{div } \mathbf{A}(\mathbf{r}_0) = \lim_{\Delta V \to 0} \frac{1}{\Delta V} \oint_S \mathbf{A} \cdot d\mathbf{S} = \frac{\partial A_1(\mathbf{r}_0)}{\partial x} + \frac{\partial A_2(\mathbf{r}_0)}{\partial y} + \frac{\partial A_3(\mathbf{r}_0)}{\partial z} \quad (4\text{-}5)$$

If the vector $\mathbf{A}$ has continuous first derivatives throughout a given open region, then from the above discussion one concludes that div $\mathbf{A}$ exists at every point of the region and is given by an expression of the

† This expression is used to mean: " $-1 < \theta_2 < 1$ and $-1 < \theta_3 < 1$".

form (4-5). Moreover, if R is any closed region contained within the given open region, then (4-4) can be used to show that throughout R

$$\frac{1}{\Delta V} \oint_S \mathbf{A} \cdot d\mathbf{S} \xrightarrow[\Delta V \to 0]{} \text{div } \mathbf{A}(\mathbf{r}_0)$$

uniformly in $\mathbf{r}_0$. By the latter is meant the following: Let $\mathbf{r}_0$ be any point of R, and let ΔV be a rectangular parallelepiped containing $\mathbf{r}_0$. Then there is a function $\delta(\epsilon)$, the same function for every $\mathbf{r}_0$ in R, defined for all $\epsilon > 0$, such that whenever

$$0 < \Delta V < \delta(\epsilon)$$

then

$$\left| \frac{1}{\Delta V} \oint_S \mathbf{A} \cdot d\mathbf{S} - \text{div } A(\mathbf{r}_0) \right| < \epsilon$$

It is the fact that $\delta(\epsilon)$ is independent of $\mathbf{r}_0$ that makes the approach to the limit uniform.

Critique. The discussion of divergence and that of Gauss' theorem immediately to follow are intentionally detailed in order to show how the subject may be handled with mathematical rigor. A more intuitive approach is customary in the usual applications of the vector calculus, and such an intuitive approach will be taken in the remainder of this text. The basis of an accurate intuition, however, is to be found in a genuine understanding of fundamentals, whether they be physical or mathematical. In this connection the student can gain much by giving careful attention to the present rigorous treatment. He should seek out the reasons for each step and examine carefully the validity of each assertion.

As an example, consider the quantity (4-3). The sort of approximation contained therein is commonly used. The reader will find it intuitively obvious and readily acceptable—unless he thinks about it. It is recommended that he think about (4-3) and that he attempt to establish rigorously the validity of the approximation as it is used.

The student should also be clear about what has and what has not been proved so far. At this stage one knows that if the vector $\mathbf{A}$ has continuous first derivatives in the neighborhood of a point $\mathbf{r}_0$, that if a rectangular coordinate system with base vectors $\mathbf{i}, \mathbf{j}, \mathbf{k}$, be chosen in which

$$\mathbf{r}_0 = x_0\mathbf{i} + y_0\mathbf{j} + z_0\mathbf{k}$$
$$\mathbf{A} = A_1\mathbf{i} + A_2\mathbf{j} + A_3\mathbf{k}$$

and if rectangular parallelepipeds with edges parallel to $\mathbf{i}, \mathbf{j}$, and $\mathbf{k}$ be used in (4-2), then one can show that div $\mathbf{A}$ exists at $\mathbf{r}_0$ and is given by

(4-5). It is also clear that if a second rectangular coordinate system be chosen, designated by primes, in which

$$\mathbf{r}_0 = x_0'\mathbf{i}' + y_0'\mathbf{j}' + z_0'\mathbf{k}'$$
$$\mathbf{A} = A_1'\mathbf{i}' + A_2'\mathbf{j}' + A_3'\mathbf{k}'$$

then using in (4-2) rectangular parallelepipeds with edges parallel to $\mathbf{i}'$, $\mathbf{j}'$, and $\mathbf{k}'$, one gets

$$\operatorname{div} \mathbf{A}(\mathbf{r}_0) = \frac{\partial A_1'}{\partial x'} + \frac{\partial A_2'}{\partial y'} + \frac{\partial A_3'}{\partial z'} \tag{4-6}$$

Without further examination, however, it is not clear that (4-5) and (4-6) give the same value for div $\mathbf{A}$. It is left to the reader to prove that the right members of (4-5) and (4-6) are actually equal.

In the next section the facts just established will be used to prove Gauss' theorem. In turn, Gauss' theorem will then be used to remove the restriction that the volumes ΔV in (4-2) must be rectangular parallelepipeds.

EXERCISES

1. Evaluate div $\mathbf{r}$, where $\mathbf{r} = x\mathbf{i} + y\mathbf{j} + z\mathbf{k}$.

2. Evaluate div grad ϕ where $\phi = x^2 + 2y^2 + 3z^2$.

3. Evaluate div (grad $\phi \times$ grad ψ) where ϕ and ψ are scalar functions of position with continuous second derivatives.

4. Show that the approximation used in (4-3) is a valid one. [*Hint:* The contribution of the faces perpendicular to the x direction can be put in the form

$$\int_S F(y,z) \, dy \, dz$$

where

$$F(y,z) = A_1\left(x_0 + \frac{\Delta x}{2}, y, z\right) - A_1\left(x_0 - \frac{\Delta x}{2}, y, z\right)$$

Apply the law of the mean for integrals. Then apply the first law of the mean of the differential calculus. The expression so obtained gives exactly the contribution of the faces perpendicular to the x direction. Show that the expression differs from (4-3) by only higher-order terms.]

5. Let $\mathbf{i}$, $\mathbf{j}$, $\mathbf{k}$ and $\mathbf{i}'$, $\mathbf{j}'$, $\mathbf{k}'$ be base vectors for two rectangular coordinate systems. Let $\mathbf{A}$ be a differentiable vector function of position

$$\mathbf{A} = A_1\mathbf{i} + A_2\mathbf{j} + A_3\mathbf{k} = A_1'\mathbf{i}' + A_2'\mathbf{j}' + A_3'\mathbf{k}'$$

Show that

$$\frac{\partial A_1}{\partial x} + \frac{\partial A_2}{\partial y} + \frac{\partial A_3}{\partial z} = \frac{\partial A_1'}{\partial x'} + \frac{\partial A_2'}{\partial y'} + \frac{\partial A_3'}{\partial z'}$$

(*Hint:* The theorem is obvious if the two coordinate systems are related by a simple translation.   Consider, then, the case of a rotation of coordinates.   The primed and unprimed coordinates are related by a homogeneous linear transformation the coefficients of which are the cosines of the angles between the **i**, **j**, **k** vectors and the **i′**, **j′**, **k′** vectors.   The quantities A_1', A_2', A_3' are related to A_1, A_2, A_3 by exactly the same transformation.   Use these facts and the rules for partial differentiation.)

6. Let **A** have continuous first derivatives in a region containing the closed region R.   From (4-4) show that

$$\frac{1}{\Delta V} \oint_S \mathbf{A} \cdot d\mathbf{S} \xrightarrow[\Delta V \to 0]{} \operatorname{div} \mathbf{A}(\mathbf{r}_0)$$

uniformly in $\mathbf{r}_0$ throughout R.

4-3. Gauss' Theorem

Let **A** have continuous first derivatives within a region R.   Then for every closed subregion R' of R, the integral

$$\int_{R'} \operatorname{div} \mathbf{A} \, dV$$

exists; and furthermore

$$\int_{R'} \operatorname{div} \mathbf{A} \, dV = \oint_{S'} \mathbf{A} \cdot d\mathbf{S} \tag{4-7}$$

where S' is the boundary of R'.   The relation (4-7) is commonly referred to as Gauss' theorem.

Under the conditions stated, div **A** exists and is continuous throughout R, as follows from the discussion of Sec. 4-2.   Hence, if R' is a closed subregion of R, $\int_{R'} \operatorname{div} \mathbf{A} \, dV$ exists.

Now consider the nth fundamental mesh, dividing R' into elemental parallelepipeds $\Delta_\nu V$.   Let R'' be the volume made up of all the $\Delta_\nu V$ lying entirely in R'.

For each $\Delta_\nu V$ in R',

$$\frac{1}{\Delta_\nu V} \oint_{\Delta_\nu S} \mathbf{A} \cdot d\mathbf{S} = \operatorname{div} \mathbf{A}(P_\nu) + \zeta_\nu \tag{4-8}$$

where $\Delta_\nu S$ is the boundary of $\Delta_\nu V$, P_ν is any point interior to $\Delta_\nu V$, and where uniformly throughout R'

$$\zeta_\nu \xrightarrow[\Delta_\nu V \to 0]{} 0$$

The last fact was pointed out at the end of Sec. 4-2.   In the present case it can be taken to mean that for all n sufficiently large (thereby making all $\Delta_\nu V$ sufficiently small),

$$|\zeta_\nu| < \frac{\epsilon}{V''}$$

where ϵ is an arbitrary positive number and V'' is the volume of R''.

One can rewrite (4-8) as

$$\oint_{\Delta_\nu S} \mathbf{A} \cdot d\mathbf{S} - \operatorname{div} \mathbf{A}(P_\nu) \, \Delta_\nu V = \zeta_\nu \, \Delta_\nu V$$

Summing over the region R'',

$$\sum_{R''} \oint_{\Delta_\nu S} \mathbf{A} \cdot d\mathbf{S} - \sum_{R''} \operatorname{div} \mathbf{A}(P_\nu) \, \Delta_\nu V = \sum_{R''} \zeta_\nu \, \Delta_\nu V \qquad (4\text{-}9)$$

The first sum on the left of (4-9) reduces to

$$\oint_{S''} \mathbf{A} \cdot d\mathbf{S}$$

where S'' is the boundary of R''. This is due to the fact that the integration over any part of a $\Delta_\nu S$ lying within R'' is canceled by integration over the same surface regarded as bounding elemental volumes adjacent to $\Delta_\nu V$. For the latter integrations the elements of area $d\mathbf{S}$ are directed into $\Delta_\nu V$ instead of outward from it.

Hence, for all n sufficiently large

$$\left| \oint_{S''} \mathbf{A} \cdot d\mathbf{S} - \sum_{R''} \operatorname{div} \mathbf{A}(P_\nu) \, \Delta_\nu V \right| \le \left| \sum_{R''} \zeta_\nu \, \Delta_\nu V \right| < \frac{\epsilon}{V''} \sum_{R''} \Delta_\nu V = \epsilon$$

Now let n become infinite. Using the theorem of Sec. 2-12, it is seen that

$$\oint_{S''} \mathbf{A} \cdot d\mathbf{S} \xrightarrow[n \to \infty]{} \oint_{S'} \mathbf{A} \cdot d\mathbf{S}$$

It is also plain that

$$\sum_{R''} \operatorname{div} \mathbf{A}(P_\nu) \, \Delta_\nu V \xrightarrow[n \to \infty]{} \int_R \operatorname{div} \mathbf{A} \, dV$$

Thus

$$\left| \oint_{S'} \mathbf{A} \cdot d\mathbf{S} - \int_{R'} \operatorname{div} \mathbf{A} \, dV \right| < \epsilon$$

But ϵ was arbitrary. Hence (4-7) must hold.

An immediate consequence of Gauss' theorem is that the volume ΔV of (4-2) no longer need be a rectangular parallelepiped. Assume $\operatorname{div} \mathbf{A}$ continuous throughout a region R. Let ΔV be any closed region in R

containing the point P_0. Then by Gauss' theorem

$$\oint_{\substack{\text{bdy} \\ \text{of } \Delta V}} \mathbf{A} \cdot d\mathbf{S} = \int_{\Delta V} \text{div } \mathbf{A} \, dV$$

By the law of the mean,

$$\oint_{\substack{\text{bdy} \\ \text{of } \Delta V}} \mathbf{A} \cdot d\mathbf{S} = \text{div } \mathbf{A}(P) \, \Delta V$$

where P is some point of ΔV. Hence, if div $\mathbf{A}$ is continuous at P_0,

$$\lim_{\Delta V \to 0} \frac{1}{\Delta V} \oint_{\substack{\text{bdy} \\ \text{of } \Delta V}} \mathbf{A} \cdot d\mathbf{S} = \text{div } \mathbf{A}(P_0)$$

whatever the shape of ΔV.

EXERCISES

1. Evaluate

$$\oint_S \text{grad } \phi \cdot d\mathbf{S}$$

where

$$\phi = x^2 + y^3 + z^4$$

and S is the surface of the cube bounded by the planes

$$x = \pm 1$$
$$y = \pm 1$$
$$z = \pm 1$$

2. Using Gauss' theorem, obtain the area of the surface of a sphere in terms of the radius of the sphere, assuming the volume of the sphere as known. (*Hint:* Take the sphere with center at the origin of coordinates, and use the fact that $\mathbf{r} = \mathbf{n}r$ where $\mathbf{n}$ is the unit normal to the surface of the sphere.)

3. A fluid of density ρ flows with a velocity $\mathbf{v}$, where ρ and $\mathbf{v}$ are functions of position in space. Assume that ρ and $\mathbf{v}$ have continuous first derivatives.

a. Show that the net mass flow through a simple closed surface S is given by

$$\int_V \text{div } (\rho \mathbf{v}) \, dV$$

where V is the volume bounded by S.

b. Show that the net rate of loss of mass from the volume V is given by

$$- \frac{\partial}{\partial t} \int_V \rho \, dV$$

c. Assume that mass is neither created nor destroyed. Show that at every point

$$\text{div} \, (\rho \mathbf{v}) + \frac{\partial \rho}{\partial t} = 0 \tag{4-10}$$

Relation (4-10) is called the *equation of continuity* for fluid flow.

4-4. Circulation

Let the vector $\mathbf{A}$ be defined and continuous within a region R. Let C be a simple closed curve within R. Then the circulation of $\mathbf{A}$ about the curve C is defined by the relation†

$$\text{Circulation of } \mathbf{A} \text{ about } C = \oint_C \mathbf{A} \cdot d\mathbf{r}$$

Since $\mathbf{A} \cdot d\mathbf{r}$ is the projection of $\mathbf{A}$ upon $d\mathbf{r}$, multiplied by $|d\mathbf{r}|$, the integral furnishes a measure of the tendency of $\mathbf{A}$ to flow along the curve C.

Using the notation indicated in Fig. 4-1 write

$$\oint_C \mathbf{A} \cdot d\mathbf{r} = \int_{\substack{P_1 P_2 \\ \text{lower}}} \mathbf{A} \cdot d\mathbf{r} + \int_{\substack{P_2 P_1 \\ \text{upper}}} \mathbf{A} \cdot d\mathbf{r}$$

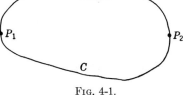

Fig. 4-1.

Suppose the circulation positive. Then if both integrals on the right are positive the rotational character of the vector field $\mathbf{A}$ is apparent. On the other hand, if one of the integrals on the right, say the second, is negative, rewrite the equation as follows:

$$\int_C \mathbf{A} \cdot d\mathbf{r} = \int_{\substack{P_1 P_2 \\ \text{lower}}} \mathbf{A} \cdot d\mathbf{r} - \int_{\substack{P_1 P_2 \\ \text{upper}}} \mathbf{A} \cdot d\mathbf{r}$$

where now the second integral on the right is positive. In this case it is plain that the lower arc $P_1 P_2$ furnishes a greater contribution to the circulation integral. One might say that the vector $\mathbf{A}$ has a greater flow along the lower arc, and this suggests that the vector field has a rotational character.

† See footnote, page 55.

EXERCISES

1. Let ϕ be a differentiable scalar function of position within a region R of space. Evaluate the circulation of grad ϕ about any simple closed path in R.

2. Let $\mathbf{A} = x\mathbf{j}$. Calculate the circulation of $\mathbf{A}$ about the rectangle of sides $x = \pm a$, $y = \pm b$ in the xy plane.

3. Let $\mathbf{A}$ be a vector function of position (x,y) within the xy plane. Let $\mathbf{r}$ be the vector $x\mathbf{i} + y\mathbf{j}$. Suppose that for all points other than the origin

$$A = \frac{M}{r}$$

$$\mathbf{A} \cdot \mathbf{r} = 0$$

$$\mathbf{k} \cdot \mathbf{A} \times \mathbf{r} > 0 \qquad \mathbf{k} = \mathbf{i} \times \mathbf{j}$$

Evaluate the circulation of $\mathbf{A}$ about any simple closed path encircling the origin. [*Hint:* Let (r,θ) be polar coordinates of the point (x,y). Show that $\mathbf{A} \cdot d\mathbf{r} = \pm Ar\, d\theta$. Also use the last of the given relations to determine the algebraic sign of your answer.]

4-5. Curl of a Vector

Again let $\mathbf{A}$ be defined and continuous within a closed region R. Therein let ΔS be a small surface bounded by a simple closed curve C. By $\Delta \mathbf{S}$ denote the vector $\mathbf{n}\,\Delta S$, where $\mathbf{n}$ is the normal to ΔS at some point P of ΔS. Define L_n by the relation

$$L_n = \lim_{\Delta S \to 0} \frac{1}{\Delta S} \oint_C \mathbf{A} \cdot d\mathbf{r} \tag{4-11}$$

where ΔS is made to vanish in such a way that (1) P remains interior to ΔS, (2) the direction $\mathbf{n}$ remains fixed, (3) all the linear dimensions of ΔS vanish with ΔS, and (4) the boundary C of ΔS is always a simple closed curve. Here, and henceforth, the direction of integration is such as to be counterclockwise when viewed from the tip of $\mathbf{n}$.

The integral on the right of (4-11) is the circulation of $\mathbf{A}$ around C. Dividing by ΔS yields a circulation per unit area for the bounded surface, which is in the nature of an intensity of circulation. By taking the limit as indicated, an intensity of circulation at the point P, normal to the direction $\mathbf{n}$, is obtained, provided, of course, that the limit exists.

Now select a right-handed set of mutually orthogonal vectors $\mathbf{i}$, $\mathbf{j}$, $\mathbf{k}$. Consider the small tetrahedron shown in Fig. 4-2, with edges a, b, c, x, y, and z. Let $\mathbf{n}$ be the unit vector normal to the face abc, of area ΔS. Let

L_n be the circulation intensity normal to **n** at P. Then

$$L_n \, \Delta S \cong \oint_{abc} \mathbf{A} \cdot d\mathbf{r}$$

Similarly, if L_x, L_y, L_z, are the circulation intensities at P normal to **i**, **j**, and **k** respectively, then

$$L_x \mathbf{i} \cdot \mathbf{n} \, \Delta S \cong \oint_{azy} \mathbf{A} \cdot d\mathbf{r}$$

$$L_y \mathbf{j} \cdot \mathbf{n} \, \Delta S \cong \oint_{bxz} \mathbf{A} \cdot d\mathbf{r}$$

$$L_z \mathbf{k} \cdot \mathbf{n} \, \Delta S \cong \oint_{cyx} \mathbf{A} \cdot d\mathbf{r}$$

Adding,

$$(L_x \mathbf{i} + L_y \mathbf{j} + L_z \mathbf{k}) \cdot \mathbf{n} \, \Delta S \cong \oint_{abc} \mathbf{A} \cdot d\mathbf{r}$$

since integrations over the paths x, y, and z are carried out once in one direction and once in the opposite, thus canceling and leaving only the

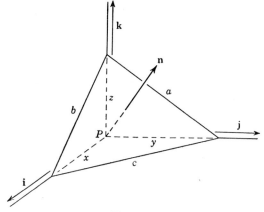

Fig. 4-2.

integrations over a, b, and c. Dividing by ΔS and letting the tetrahedron diminish with **n** constant,

$$(L_x \mathbf{i} + L_y \mathbf{j} + L_z \mathbf{k}) \cdot \mathbf{n} = L_n \qquad (4\text{-}12)$$

The quantity $L_x \mathbf{i} + L_y \mathbf{j} + L_z \mathbf{k}$ is a vector with the property that its scalar product with any unit directional vector **n** gives the circulation intensity normal to **n**. The vector is called the curl of **A**, written

$$\operatorname{curl} \mathbf{A} = L_x \mathbf{i} + L_y \mathbf{j} + L_z \mathbf{k} \qquad (4\text{-}13)$$

As given in (4-13) curl **A** appears to depend upon the coordinate system used; that is, upon the choice of vectors **i**, **j**, and **k**. On the other hand, note from (4-12) that, at a specified point, $|L_n|$ is always less than or equal to $|\text{curl } \mathbf{A}|$. Also, when $\mathbf{n}$ has the direction of curl $\mathbf{A}$, then

$$|L_n| = |\text{curl } \mathbf{A}|$$

Hence, at a point P, curl $\mathbf{A}$ is that vector the direction of which is normal to the plane of the algebraically maximum circulation intensity at P and the magnitude of which is the maximum circulation intensity. These properties define curl $\mathbf{A}$ independently of any coordinate system.

EXERCISE

Let $\mathbf{A}$ be the vector

$$\mathbf{A} = y\mathbf{i} + z\mathbf{j} + x\mathbf{k}$$

By evaluating the quantities L_x, L_y, L_z in (4-13), obtain curl $\mathbf{A}$.

4-6. Stokes' Theorem

Let C be a simple closed curve within a region R in which the vector curl $\mathbf{A}$ is continuous. Let S be a simple surface spanning C. Then

$$\int_S \text{curl } \mathbf{A} \cdot d\mathbf{S} = \oint_C \mathbf{A} \cdot d\mathbf{r}$$

This is Stokes' theorem. It follows directly from the definition of the curl.

At any point of S

$$\text{curl } \mathbf{A} \cdot \mathbf{n} = \lim_{\Delta S \to 0} \frac{1}{\Delta S} \oint_{\substack{\text{bdy} \\ \text{of } \Delta S}} \mathbf{A} \cdot d\mathbf{r}$$

or

$$\text{curl } \mathbf{A} \cdot \mathbf{n} \, \Delta S \cong \oint_{\substack{\text{bdy} \\ \text{of } \Delta S}} \mathbf{A} \cdot d\mathbf{r} \tag{4-14}$$

Divide the area S into m elemental areas $\Delta_\nu S$. For each of these a relation like (4-14) holds. Sum over ν:

$$\sum_\nu^m \text{curl } \mathbf{A}_\nu \cdot \mathbf{n}_\nu \, \Delta_\nu S \cong \sum_\nu^m \oint_{\substack{\text{bdy} \\ \text{of } \Delta_\nu S}} \mathbf{A} \cdot d\mathbf{r} = \oint_C \mathbf{A} \cdot d\mathbf{r}$$

The equality on the right holds, since in the sum of the integrals over the boundaries of the $\Delta_\nu S$, all integrations cancel except for those portions which are taken along the boundary C of S. Letting $m \to \infty$ and the $\Delta_\nu S \to 0$,

$$\int_S \text{curl } \mathbf{A} \cdot d\mathbf{S} = \oint_C \mathbf{A} \cdot d\mathbf{r}$$

EXERCISES

1. Let ϕ be a scalar function of position in space with continuous second derivatives. Use Stokes' theorem to prove that

$$\text{curl (grad } \phi) \equiv 0$$

2. Let **A** be a vector function of position in space, with continuous second derivatives. Use Gauss' theorem and Stokes' theorem in combination to prove that

$$\text{div (curl } \mathbf{A}) \equiv 0$$

3. Review the discussion of Secs. 4-5 and 4-6 listing the things which must be done to make the treatment rigorous.

4-7. Representation of curl A in Rectangular Coordinates

It has already been shown that in rectangular coordinates

$$\text{curl } \mathbf{A} = L_x\mathbf{i} + L_y\mathbf{j} + L_z\mathbf{k}$$

where, for example, L_x is the circulation intensity normal to the direction of **i**. The value of L_x at a point $P:(x_p, y_p, z_p)$ is given by

$$L_x = \lim_{\Delta S \to 0} \frac{1}{\Delta S} \oint_C \mathbf{A} \cdot d\mathbf{r}$$

where C can be taken as the perimeter of the rectangle shown in Fig. 4-3,

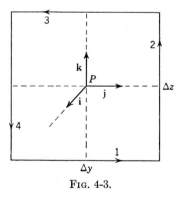

Fig. 4-3.

of area $\Delta S = \Delta y\,\Delta z$. Contributions to the integral are as follows:
First, over sides 1 and 3 one gets

$$\int_1 \mathbf{A} \cdot d\mathbf{r} + \int_3 \mathbf{A} \cdot d\mathbf{r} = \int_1 A_2 \, dy + \int_3 A_2 \, dy$$

$$= \int_{y_p - \Delta y/2}^{y_p + \Delta y/2} \left[A_2\left(x_p, y, z_p - \frac{\Delta z}{2}\right) - A_2\left(x_p, y, z_p + \frac{\Delta z}{2}\right) \right] dy$$

$$= \int_{y_p - \Delta y/2}^{y_p + \Delta y/2} - \frac{\partial A_2(x_p, y, z_p + \theta' \, \Delta z/2)}{\partial z} \, \Delta z \, dy \dagger$$

$$= - \frac{\partial A_2(x_p, y_p + \theta \, \Delta y/2, z_p + \theta' \, \Delta z/2)}{\partial z} \, \Delta y \, \Delta z$$

where $-1 < \theta, \theta' < 1$. Similarly, from sides 2 and 4

$$\int_2 \mathbf{A} \cdot d\mathbf{r} + \int_4 \mathbf{A} \cdot d\mathbf{r} = \frac{\partial A_3(x_p, y_p + \theta'' \, \Delta y/2, z_p + \theta''' \, \Delta z/2)}{\partial y} \, \Delta y \, \Delta z$$

where $-1 < \theta'', \theta''' < 1$. Hence

$$\frac{1}{\Delta S} \oint_C \mathbf{A} \cdot d\mathbf{r} = \frac{\partial A_3(P')}{\partial y} - \frac{\partial A_2(P'')}{\partial z} \tag{4-15}$$

where P' and P'' lie in ΔS. Since the derivatives of $\mathbf{A}$ are continuous, by letting $\Delta S \to 0$ one gets for the value of L_x at P

$$L_x = \frac{\partial A_3(P)}{\partial y} - \frac{\partial A_2(P)}{\partial z}$$

or symbolically,

$$L_x = \begin{vmatrix} \dfrac{\partial}{\partial y} & \dfrac{\partial}{\partial z} \\ A_2 & A_3 \end{vmatrix}$$

Similarly,

$$L_y = \begin{vmatrix} \dfrac{\partial}{\partial z} & \dfrac{\partial}{\partial x} \\ A_3 & A_1 \end{vmatrix}$$

$$L_z = \begin{vmatrix} \dfrac{\partial}{\partial x} & \dfrac{\partial}{\partial y} \\ A_1 & A_2 \end{vmatrix}$$

Finally, symbolically,

$$\text{curl } \mathbf{A} = \begin{vmatrix} \mathbf{i} & \mathbf{j} & \mathbf{k} \\ \dfrac{\partial}{\partial x} & \dfrac{\partial}{\partial y} & \dfrac{\partial}{\partial z} \\ A_1 & A_2 & A_3 \end{vmatrix} \tag{4-16}$$

† Note that θ' is a function of y: $\theta' = \theta'(y)$. Hence, in the next line

$$\theta' = \theta'(y_p + \theta \, \Delta y/2)$$

EXERCISES

1. Use (4-16) to do the Exercise of Sec. 4-5.

2. Calculate curl $\mathbf{A}$, where $\mathbf{A} = xe^y\mathbf{i} + ye^z\mathbf{j} + ze^x\mathbf{k}$.

3. Calculate curl $\mathbf{A}$, where

$$\mathbf{A} = e^x \sin y \cos z\mathbf{i} + e^x \cos y \cos z\mathbf{j} - e^x \sin y \sin z\mathbf{k}$$

4. Let ϕ be a scalar function of position with continuous second derivatives. Using (4-16), show that

$$\text{curl grad } \phi \equiv 0$$

5. Let $\phi = xyz$. By direct calculation, verify that curl grad ϕ vanishes identically.

6. Let $\mathbf{A}$ be a vector function of position with continuous second derivatives. Using (4-16), show that

$$\text{div (curl } \mathbf{A}) \equiv 0$$

7. Let $\mathbf{A} = y\mathbf{i} + z\mathbf{j} + x\mathbf{k}$. Verify directly that div (curl $\mathbf{A}$) vanishes everywhere.

4-8. Critique

The reader will have noted that the discussion of Secs. 4-5 through 4-7, although plausible, was not entirely rigorous. The reasoning required to tie up all the loose ends is somewhat involved but not especially difficult. The following is a sequence of steps which can be used.

First it is assumed that $\mathbf{A}$ has continuous first derivatives in a region R. Hence, both $\mathbf{A}$ and its first derivatives are uniformly continuous in any closed subregion of R.

Second, a discussion similar to that of Sec. 4-7 shows that if ΔS in (4-11) is taken as a rectangle, then (1) the circulation L_n exists at every point of R for every $\mathbf{n}$, and (2) L_n is continuous throughout R. Moreover, from (4-15) it can be shown that in any closed subregion of R, for each $\mathbf{n}$

$$\frac{1}{\Delta S} \oint_C \mathbf{A} \cdot d\mathbf{r} \xrightarrow[\Delta S \to 0]{} L_n$$

uniformly.

It is now a simple matter to establish for any plane area S, of boundary C, both lying in R, that

$$\int_S L_n \, dS = \oint_C \mathbf{A} \cdot d\mathbf{r}$$

where $\mathbf{n}$ is the normal to S. This is simply Stokes' theorem for plane areas and their boundaries. From it one can now conclude that the area ΔS in (4-11) may be any plane area containing the point P.

The above facts are sufficient to show that the discussion of Sec. 4-5 leading to the definition of curl **A** is rigorously sound, even though the point P of Fig. 4-2 is a corner of the tetrahedron.

One can now proceed to a rigorous proof of Stokes' theorem in the general case much along the lines followed in Sec. 4-3 in proving Gauss' theorem. It will be of advantage to use suitable analogs of the theorem stated in Sec. 2-12, both for the surface S in question and for its boundary C.

On the basis of Stokes' theorem, finally, the area ΔS and its boundary in (4-11) no longer need be planar.

EXERCISE

Rewrite the discussion of Secs. 4-5 through 4-7 so as to make it rigorously correct.

REFERENCES

Abraham, M., and R. Becker: "The Classical Theory of Electricity and Magnetism," translated by J. Dougall, Hafner Publishing Company, New York, 1932.

Joos, G.: "Theoretical Physics," translated by I. M. Freeman, G. E. Stechert & Company, New York, 1934.

Phillips, H. B.: "Vector Analysis," John Wiley & Sons, Inc., New York, 1933.

CHAPTER 5

THE OPERATOR ∇

5-1. Definition of ∇

The operator ∇, read "del," or "nabla," is defined by the relation

$$\nabla = \lim_{\Delta V \to 0} \frac{1}{\Delta V} \oint_{\substack{\text{bdy} \\ \text{of } \Delta V}} d\mathbf{S} \tag{5-1}$$

where ΔV is a simply connected volume containing the point P at which the operator is being applied. There are three distinct steps to follow in definite order: (1) formation of the integral, (2) division by the volume ΔV, and (3) passage to the limit as ΔV vanishes.

Each of the steps followed in applying the operator ∇ has a meaning completely independent of any coordinate system. In any actual calculation the coordinates to be used may be selected for their convenience.

In the discussion to follow, it will be assumed that the result of applying ∇ to a scalar ϕ or a vector $\mathbf{A}$ is independent of the choice of ΔV. Then by choosing ΔV suitably, the quantities $\nabla \phi$, $\nabla \cdot \mathbf{A}$, and $\nabla \times \mathbf{A}$ will be identified respectively with grad ϕ, div $\mathbf{A}$, and curl $\mathbf{A}$. Because of the stated assumption, the treatment is incomplete. The reader can, however, remove this incompleteness by expanding the discussion along the lines followed earlier in handling divergence and Gauss' theorem.

5-2. The Quantity ∇φ

Within a region R of space, let ϕ be a scalar function of position with continuous first derivatives. Let P be a point of R, and choose an elemental volume ΔV containing P. Then

$$\nabla \phi = \lim_{\Delta V \to 0} \frac{1}{\Delta V} \oint_{\substack{\text{bdy} \\ \text{of } \Delta V}} d\mathbf{S} \, \phi$$

The quantity $\nabla \phi$ is plainly a vector. By making an appropriate choice of the volume ΔV, the nature of this vector can easily be determined.

Consider the surface

$$\phi = \phi_0 = \phi(P) \tag{5-2}$$

passing through P.   Let ΔV be a cylinder with elements normal to (5-2) and bases lying in surfaces

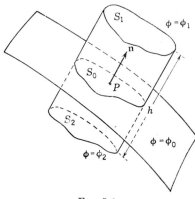

$$\phi = \phi_1$$
$$\phi = \phi_2$$

adjacent to and lying on opposite sides of (5-2), as shown in Fig. 5-1.

In forming the integral it is found that the sides contribute nothing. For every element $d\mathbf{S} \; \phi$, there is a corresponding element $-d\mathbf{S} \; \phi$, on the opposite side of the cylinder, with the same value of ϕ in both cases, and the two together cancel. It remains, then, to estimate the contribution made by the ends of the cylinder.   This is plainly†

FIG. 5-1.

$$(\phi_1 S_1 - \phi_2 S_2)\mathbf{n} \cong (\phi_1 - \phi_2) S_0 \mathbf{n}$$
$$\cong \frac{\partial \phi}{\partial n}\Big|_0 h S_0 \mathbf{n}$$
$$\cong \Delta V \frac{\partial \phi}{\partial n}\Big|_0 \mathbf{n}$$

where $\mathbf{n}$ is used to denote the normal to (5-2) at P.   Dividing by ΔV and taking the limit as ΔV vanishes,

$$\nabla \phi = \frac{\partial \phi}{\partial n} \mathbf{n}$$

But this is the vector in the direction of the maximum rate of change of ϕ with distance and of magnitude equal to that rate of change.   Hence

$$\nabla \phi = \text{grad } \phi \tag{5-3}$$

EXERCISES

1. Using rectangular coordinates, and taking ΔV in (5-1) as a rectangular parallelepiped with faces parallel to the coordinate planes, show that

$$\nabla \phi = \text{grad } \phi$$

† The notation $\partial \phi / \partial n$ is used to denote the derivative of ϕ with respect to arc length in the direction of the unit vector $\mathbf{n}$.

2. Let ϕ have continuous first derivatives in a region containing the volume V. Prove that

$$\int_V \text{grad } \phi \, dV = \oint_{\substack{\text{bdy} \\ \text{of } V}} \phi \, d\mathbf{S} \tag{5-4}$$

3. Prove that for every simple closed surface S

$$\oint_S d\mathbf{S} = 0$$

[*Hint:* Use (5-4).]

4. Let (r,θ,z) be cylindrical polar coordinates of points in space, as shown in Fig. 5-2. At the point (r,θ,z) let $\mathbf{i}_1$, $\mathbf{i}_2$, $\mathbf{i}_3$ be unit vectors in the directions of increasing r, increasing θ, and increasing z, respectively.

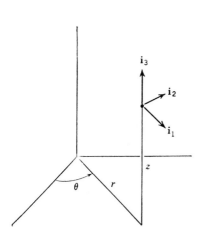

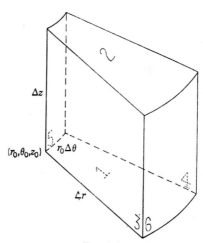

FIG. 5-2. Base vectors for cylindrical polar coordinates.

FIG. 5-3.

These vectors can be used as a basis for representing an arbitrary vector $\mathbf{A}$ in the form

$$\mathbf{A} = A_1\mathbf{i}_1 + A_2\mathbf{i}_2 + A_3\mathbf{i}_3$$

In particular, the vector grad Φ can be so represented. The problem of calculating grad Φ in cylindrical polar coordinates is simply one of determining the $\mathbf{i}_1$, $\mathbf{i}_2$, $\mathbf{i}_3$ components of grad Φ for the general point.

The calculation of grad Φ in cylindrical coordinates can be carried out by using (5-1) and the fact that grad $\Phi = \nabla\Phi$. For the volume ΔV one takes the elemental volume bounded by the planes $\theta = \theta_0$, $\theta = \theta_0 + \Delta\theta$, $z = z_0$, $z = z_0 + \Delta z$, and the cylinders $r = r_0$, $r = r_0 + \Delta r$, as shown in Fig. 5-3. One has

$$\Delta V = r_0 \,\Delta r \,\Delta\theta \,\Delta z + \text{higher-order terms}$$
$$\text{area (1)} = \text{area (2)} = r_0 \,\Delta r \,\Delta\theta + \text{higher-order terms}$$
$$\text{area (3)} = \text{area (4)} = \Delta r \,\Delta z$$
$$\text{area (5)} = r_0 \,\Delta\theta \,\Delta z$$
$$\text{area (6)} = (r_0 + \Delta r) \,\Delta\theta \,\Delta z$$

Calculate the contributions of the different faces of ΔV to the surface integral of (5-1). Sum the contributions and divide by ΔV. Then let ΔV vanish, thereby getting an expression for $\nabla\Phi$ in cylindrical polar coordinates.

By way of caution, note that it is essential to include all the contributions to the surface integral from the different faces. If this is not done, errors may result, as in the following fallacious argument:

The contribution of faces 1 and 2 is

$$[\Phi(r,\theta,\,z_0 + \Delta z) - \Phi(r,\theta,z_0)]r_0 \,\Delta r \,\Delta\theta \mathbf{i}_3 = \frac{\partial\Phi}{\partial z}\, r_0 \,\Delta r \,\Delta\theta \,\Delta z \mathbf{i}_3$$

That of faces 3 and 4 is

$$[\Phi(r,\,\theta_0 + \Delta\theta,\,z) - \Phi(r,\theta_0,z)] \,\Delta r \,\Delta z \mathbf{i}_2 = \frac{\partial\Phi}{\partial\theta} \,\Delta r \,\Delta\theta \,\Delta z \mathbf{i}_2$$

From faces 5 and 6,

$$\Phi(r_0 + \Delta r,\, \theta,z)(r_0 + \Delta r) \,\Delta\theta \,\Delta z - \Phi(r_0,\theta,z)r_0 \,\Delta\theta \,\Delta z]\mathbf{i}_1 = \frac{\partial\Phi}{\partial r}\, r_0 \,\Delta r \,\Delta\theta \,\Delta z \mathbf{i}_1$$
$$+ \Phi(r_0 + \Delta r,\, \theta,z) \,\Delta r \,\Delta\theta \,\Delta z \mathbf{i}_1$$

Hence, summing, dividing by ΔV, and letting $\Delta V \to 0$, one gets:

$$\left(\frac{1}{r_0}\,\Phi + \frac{\partial\Phi}{\partial r}\right)\mathbf{i}_1 + \frac{1}{r_0}\frac{\partial\Phi}{\partial\theta}\,\mathbf{i}_2 + \frac{\partial\Phi}{\partial z}\,\mathbf{i}_3 \tag{5-5}$$

But (5-5) is not the correct expression for grad Φ. Show where the error occurred and correct it.

5. Obtain an expression for grad Φ in spherical polar coordinates (r,θ,ϕ), using for $\mathbf{i}_1$, $\mathbf{i}_2$, $\mathbf{i}_3$ unit vectors in the directions of increasing r, increasing θ, and increasing ϕ, respectively.

5-3. The Quantity $\nabla \cdot \mathbf{A}$

Let $\mathbf{A}$ have continuous first derivatives throughout a region R. By definition, at the point P,

$$\nabla \cdot \mathbf{A} = \lim_{\Delta V \to 0} \frac{1}{\Delta V} \oint_{\substack{\text{bdy} \\ \text{of } \Delta V}} d\mathbf{S} \cdot \mathbf{A}$$

where ΔV contains P. But, also by definition, the quantity on the right is the divergence of $\mathbf{A}$ at point P. Hence

$$\nabla \cdot \mathbf{A} = \operatorname{div} \mathbf{A} \tag{5-6}$$

EXERCISES

1. Using (5-6), obtain an expression for div **A** in cylindrical polar coordinates.

2. Using (5-6), obtain an expression for div **A** in spherical polar coordinates.

5-4. The Quantity $\nabla \times$ A

Again let **A** have continuous first derivatives in a region R. At the point P of R,

$$\nabla \times A = \lim_{\Delta V \to 0} \frac{1}{\Delta V} \oint_{\substack{\text{bdy} \\ \text{of } \Delta V}} dS \times A$$

where ΔV contains P. Choose a set **i**, **j**, **k** of mutually orthogonal reference vectors, and write

$$\oint dS \times A = \oint dS \times iA_1 + \oint dS \times jA_2 + \oint dS \times kA_3 \quad (5\text{-}7)$$

Let ΔV be a rectangular parallelepiped of edges dx, dy, and dz parallel to **i**, **j**, and **k** and with center at P, as in Fig. 5-4.

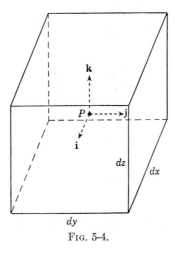

Fig. 5-4.

Consider the first integral on the right of (5-7). For the faces normal to **i**, $dS = \pm i\, dy\, dz$, and $dS \times iA_1$ vanishes. For the faces normal to **j**, $dS = \pm j\, dx\, dz$, and

$$dS \times iA_1 \cong A_1\, dx\, dz\, (\mp k)$$

Hence, using the law of the mean and the continuity of $\dfrac{\partial A_1}{\partial y}$,

$$\int_{\substack{\text{faces} \\ \perp \text{ to } \mathbf{j}}} d\mathbf{S} \times \mathbf{i}A_1 \cong -\left.\frac{\partial A_1}{\partial y}\right|_P dx\, dy\, dz\, \mathbf{k}$$

Similarly,

$$\int_{\substack{\text{faces} \\ \perp \text{ to } \mathbf{k}}} d\mathbf{S} \times \mathbf{i}A_1 \cong \left.\frac{\partial A_1}{\partial z}\right|_P dx\, dy\, dz\, \mathbf{j}$$

Finally,

$$\lim_{\Delta V \to 0} \frac{1}{\Delta V} \oint_{\substack{\text{bdy} \\ \text{of } \Delta V}} d\mathbf{S} \times \mathbf{i}A_1 = \frac{\partial A_1}{\partial z}\mathbf{j} - \frac{\partial A_1}{\partial y}\mathbf{k}$$

In precisely the same fashion, one gets

$$\lim_{\Delta V \to 0} \frac{1}{\Delta V} \oint_{\substack{\text{bdy} \\ \text{of } \Delta V}} d\mathbf{S} \times \mathbf{j}A_2 = \frac{\partial A_2}{\partial x}\mathbf{k} - \frac{\partial A_2}{\partial z}\mathbf{i}$$

$$\lim_{\Delta V \to 0} \frac{1}{\Delta V} \oint_{\substack{\text{bdy} \\ \text{of } \Delta V}} d\mathbf{S} \times \mathbf{k}A_3 = \frac{\partial A_3}{\partial y}\mathbf{i} - \frac{\partial A_3}{\partial x}\mathbf{j}$$

Combining all these results,

$$\nabla \times \mathbf{A} = \left(\frac{\partial A_3}{\partial y} - \frac{\partial A_2}{\partial z}\right)\mathbf{i} + \left(\frac{\partial A_1}{\partial z} - \frac{\partial A_3}{\partial x}\right)\mathbf{j} + \left(\frac{\partial A_2}{\partial x} - \frac{\partial A_1}{\partial y}\right)\mathbf{k}$$

$$= \begin{vmatrix} \mathbf{i} & \mathbf{j} & \mathbf{k} \\ \dfrac{\partial}{\partial x} & \dfrac{\partial}{\partial y} & \dfrac{\partial}{\partial z} \\ A_1 & A_2 & A_3 \end{vmatrix}$$

or

$$\nabla \times \mathbf{A} = \text{curl } \mathbf{A} \tag{5-8}$$

EXERCISES

1. Prove

$$\int_V \text{curl } \mathbf{A}\, dV = \oint_{\substack{\text{bdy} \\ \text{of } V}} d\mathbf{S} \times \mathbf{A}$$

where V is a simply connected volume in a region in which $\mathbf{A}$ has continuous first derivatives.

2. Using (5-8) obtain an expression for curl $\mathbf{A}$ in cylindrical polar coordinates.

3. Using (5-8) obtain an expression for curl $\mathbf{A}$ in spherical polar coordinates.

4. Let C be a simple closed curve spanned by the surface S, and let ϕ be a scalar function with continuous first derivatives. Let **i**, **j**, **k** be base vectors for rectangular coordinates (x,y,z). Prove that

$$\int_S (d\mathbf{S} \times \nabla\phi) \cdot \mathbf{i} = \oint_C \phi \, dx$$

(*Hint:* Apply Stokes' theorem to the vector $\phi\mathbf{i}$.)

5. Let C be a simple closed curve spanned by the surface S. Let ϕ have continuous first derivatives. Prove that

$$\int_S d\mathbf{S} \times \nabla\phi = \oint_C \phi \, d\mathbf{r}$$

5-5. Representation of ∇ in Rectangular Coordinates

The definition of ∇ does not involve any special system of coordinates. The fact that $\nabla\phi$, $\nabla \cdot \mathbf{A}$, and $\nabla \times \mathbf{A}$ are respectively grad ϕ, div $\mathbf{A}$, and curl $\mathbf{A}$ is likewise independent of choice of coordinates. The use of cartesian coordinates to establish the relationship (5-8), for example, was purely a matter of convenience. As an operator defined by (5-1), ∇ turns out to provide a very general means of determining grad ϕ, div $\mathbf{A}$, and curl $\mathbf{A}$. But as defined by (5-1), the operator is cumbersome and inconvenient to use. For rectangular coordinates, it is possible to give the operator a much simpler form.

By virtue of (5-3), (5-6), and (5-8), one has in cartesian coordinate form,

$$\nabla\phi = \mathbf{i} \frac{\partial\phi}{\partial x} + \mathbf{j} \frac{\partial\phi}{\partial y} + \mathbf{k} \frac{\partial\phi}{\partial z}$$

$$\nabla \cdot \mathbf{A} = \frac{\partial A_1}{\partial x} + \frac{\partial A_2}{\partial y} + \frac{\partial A_3}{\partial z}$$

$$\nabla \times \mathbf{A} = \begin{vmatrix} \mathbf{i} & \mathbf{j} & \mathbf{k} \\ \dfrac{\partial}{\partial x} & \dfrac{\partial}{\partial y} & \dfrac{\partial}{\partial z} \\ A_1 & A_2 & A_3 \end{vmatrix}$$

All of these expressions can be obtained immediately by regarding ∇ as a vector of the form

$$\mathbf{i} \frac{\partial}{\partial x} + \mathbf{j} \frac{\partial}{\partial y} + \mathbf{k} \frac{\partial}{\partial z} \tag{5-9}$$

and performing the operations indicated. Note that ∇ always operates from the left, obeying all the laws of vector multiplication; and note also that the differentiating operators, $\dfrac{\partial}{\partial x}, \dfrac{\partial}{\partial y}, \dfrac{\partial}{\partial z}$, must be applied to all functions of x, y, and z in the quantity on which ∇ operates. Plainly (5-9) is simpler to use than (5-1). But it should be reemphasized that (5-9) is valid only for rectangular coordinates.

EXERCISES

1. By actually performing the indicated operations in $\nabla\phi$, $\nabla \cdot \mathbf{A}$, and $\nabla \times \mathbf{A}$, verify that in rectangular coordinates ∇ may be given the form (5-9).

2. For rectangular coordinates prove that

$$\nabla \cdot \mathbf{A} = \mathbf{i} \cdot \frac{\partial \mathbf{A}}{\partial x} + \mathbf{j} \cdot \frac{\partial \mathbf{A}}{\partial y} + \mathbf{k} \cdot \frac{\partial \mathbf{A}}{\partial z}$$

3. For rectangular coordinates prove that

$$\nabla \cdot \mathbf{A} = \mathbf{i} \cdot \nabla A_1 + \mathbf{j} \cdot \nabla A_2 + \mathbf{k} \cdot \nabla A_3$$

4. For rectangular coordinates prove that

$$\nabla \times \mathbf{A} = \mathbf{i} \times \frac{\partial \mathbf{A}}{\partial x} + \mathbf{j} \times \frac{\partial \mathbf{A}}{\partial y} + \mathbf{k} \times \frac{\partial \mathbf{A}}{\partial z}$$

5. For rectangular coordinates prove that

$$\nabla \times \mathbf{A} = -(\mathbf{i} \times \nabla A_1 + \mathbf{j} \times \nabla A_2 + \mathbf{k} \times \nabla A_3)$$

REFERENCE

Joos, G.: "Theoretical Physics," translated by I. M. Freeman, G. E. Stechert & Company, New York, 1934.

CHAPTER 6

RELATIONSHIPS INVOLVING ∇

6-1. Relations Independent of Coordinate System

The following relations are easy to establish using rectangular coordinates:

$$\nabla \cdot (\phi \mathbf{A}) = \phi \nabla \cdot \mathbf{A} + \mathbf{A} \cdot \nabla \phi \qquad (6\text{-}1)$$

$$\nabla \times (\phi \mathbf{A}) = \phi \nabla \times \mathbf{A} + \nabla \phi \times \mathbf{A} \qquad (6\text{-}2)$$

$$\nabla \cdot (\mathbf{A} \times \mathbf{B}) = \mathbf{B} \cdot \nabla \times \mathbf{A} - \mathbf{A} \cdot \nabla \times \mathbf{B} \qquad (6\text{-}3)$$

Since, however, the meaning of each factor and term is independent of the coordinate system used, the relations hold generally.

First,

$$\nabla \cdot (\phi \mathbf{A}) = \frac{\partial}{\partial x} (\phi A_1) + \frac{\partial}{\partial y} (\phi A_2) + \frac{\partial}{\partial z} (\phi A_3)$$

$$= \frac{\partial \phi}{\partial x} A_1 + \frac{\partial \phi}{\partial y} A_2 + \frac{\partial \phi}{\partial z} A_3 + \phi \frac{\partial A_1}{\partial x} + \phi \frac{\partial A_2}{\partial y} + \phi \frac{\partial A_3}{\partial z}$$

$$= \nabla \phi \cdot \mathbf{A} + \phi \nabla \cdot \mathbf{A}$$

Next,

$$\nabla \times (\phi \mathbf{A}) = \begin{vmatrix} \mathbf{i} & \mathbf{j} & \mathbf{k} \\ \dfrac{\partial}{\partial x} & \dfrac{\partial}{\partial y} & \dfrac{\partial}{\partial z} \\ \phi A_1 & \phi A_2 & \phi A_3 \end{vmatrix}$$

$$= \begin{vmatrix} \mathbf{i} & \mathbf{j} & \mathbf{k} \\ \phi \dfrac{\partial}{\partial x} & \phi \dfrac{\partial}{\partial y} & \phi \dfrac{\partial}{\partial z} \\ A_1 & A_2 & A_3 \end{vmatrix} + \begin{vmatrix} \mathbf{i} & \mathbf{j} & \mathbf{k} \\ \dfrac{\partial \phi}{\partial x} & \dfrac{\partial \phi}{\partial y} & \dfrac{\partial \phi}{\partial z} \\ A_1 & A_2 & A_3 \end{vmatrix}$$

$$= \phi \nabla \times \mathbf{A} + \nabla \phi \times \mathbf{A}$$

Finally,

$$\nabla \cdot (\mathbf{A} \times \mathbf{B}) = \frac{\partial}{\partial x}(A_2 B_3 - A_3 B_2) + \frac{\partial}{\partial y}(A_3 B_1 - A_1 B_3)$$

$$+ \frac{\partial}{\partial z}(A_1 B_2 - A_2 B_1)$$

$$= B_1\left(\frac{\partial A_3}{\partial y} - \frac{\partial A_2}{\partial z}\right) + B_2\left(\frac{\partial A_1}{\partial z} - \frac{\partial A_3}{\partial x}\right)$$

$$+ B_3\left(\frac{\partial A_2}{\partial x} - \frac{\partial A_1}{\partial y}\right) - A_1\left(\frac{\partial B_3}{\partial y} - \frac{\partial B_2}{\partial z}\right) - A_2\left(\frac{\partial B_1}{\partial z} - \frac{\partial B_3}{\partial x}\right)$$

$$- A_3\left(\frac{\partial B_2}{\partial x} - \frac{\partial B_1}{\partial y}\right)$$

$$= \mathbf{B} \cdot \nabla \times \mathbf{A} - \mathbf{A} \cdot \nabla \times \mathbf{B}$$

Two additional relationships are

$$\nabla \cdot \mathbf{r} = 3$$
$$\nabla \times \mathbf{r} = 0$$

They can be established with rectangular coordinates; but once proven they are plainly valid for any coordinate system.

EXERCISES

1. Prove that $\nabla \cdot \mathbf{r} = 3$, where $\mathbf{r}$ is the radius vector from the origin of coordinates.

2. Prove that $\nabla \times \mathbf{r} = 0$.

In Exercises 3, 4, and 5, let

$$\phi = xyz, \quad \mathbf{A} = y\mathbf{i} + z\mathbf{j} + x\mathbf{k}, \quad \mathbf{B} = x\mathbf{i} - y\mathbf{j}$$

3. Verify that $\nabla \cdot (\phi \mathbf{A}) = \phi \nabla \cdot \mathbf{A} + \mathbf{A} \cdot \nabla \phi$.

4. Verify that $\nabla \times (\phi \mathbf{A}) = \phi \nabla \times \mathbf{A} + \nabla \phi \times \mathbf{A}$.

5. Verify that $\nabla \cdot (\mathbf{A} \times \mathbf{B}) = \mathbf{B} \cdot \nabla \times \mathbf{A} - \mathbf{A} \cdot \nabla \times \mathbf{B}$.

6. For any two differentiable vectors $\mathbf{A}$ and $\mathbf{B}$ show that

$$\nabla \cdot (\mathbf{A} \times \mathbf{B}) = \begin{vmatrix} \dfrac{\partial}{\partial x} & \dfrac{\partial}{\partial y} & \dfrac{\partial}{\partial z} \\ A_1 & A_2 & A_3 \\ B_1 & B_2 & B_3 \end{vmatrix}$$

$$= \begin{vmatrix} B_1 & B_2 & B_3 \\ \dfrac{\partial}{\partial x} & \dfrac{\partial}{\partial y} & \dfrac{\partial}{\partial z} \\ A_1 & A_2 & A_3 \end{vmatrix} - \begin{vmatrix} A_1 & A_2 & A_3 \\ \dfrac{\partial}{\partial x} & \dfrac{\partial}{\partial y} & \dfrac{\partial}{\partial z} \\ B_1 & B_2 & B_3 \end{vmatrix}$$

6-2. Relations Valid in Rectangular Coordinates

A vector **A** and the operator ∇ can be combined in rectangular coordinate form to yield a new operator which is often useful. The new operator is given by

$$\mathbf{A} \cdot \nabla = A_1 \frac{\partial}{\partial x} + A_2 \frac{\partial}{\partial y} + A_3 \frac{\partial}{\partial z} \tag{6-4}$$

and is in the form of a scalar operating from the left. Applied to a scalar ϕ, the operator gives

$$(\mathbf{A} \cdot \nabla)\phi = A_1 \frac{\partial \phi}{\partial x} + A_2 \frac{\partial \phi}{\partial y} + A_3 \frac{\partial \phi}{\partial z}$$

From this one sees immediately that

$$(\mathbf{A} \cdot \nabla)\phi = \mathbf{A} \cdot (\nabla \phi)$$

One can, therefore, write simply $\mathbf{A} \cdot \nabla \phi$.

As applied to a vector **B**, $\mathbf{A} \cdot \nabla$ operates upon each component, yielding

$$\begin{aligned}
(\mathbf{A} \cdot \nabla)\mathbf{B} &= \left(A_1 \frac{\partial B_1}{\partial x} + A_2 \frac{\partial B_1}{\partial y} + A_3 \frac{\partial B_1}{\partial z} \right) \mathbf{i} \\
&+ \left(A_1 \frac{\partial B_2}{\partial x} + A_2 \frac{\partial B_2}{\partial y} + A_3 \frac{\partial B_2}{\partial z} \right) \mathbf{j} \\
&+ \left(A_1 \frac{\partial B_3}{\partial x} + A_2 \frac{\partial B_3}{\partial y} + A_3 \frac{\partial B_3}{\partial z} \right) \mathbf{k} \\
&= \mathbf{A} \cdot \nabla B_1 \mathbf{i} + \mathbf{A} \cdot \nabla B_2 \mathbf{j} + \mathbf{A} \cdot \nabla B_3 \mathbf{k}
\end{aligned}$$

In analogy with (6-4), $\nabla \cdot \nabla$ or ∇^2 is defined as

$$\nabla \cdot \nabla = \nabla^2 = \frac{\partial^2}{\partial x^2} + \frac{\partial^2}{\partial y^2} + \frac{\partial^2}{\partial z^2} \tag{6-5}$$

In place of ∇^2, the symbol Δ is also used to denote $\nabla \cdot \nabla$. The quantity $\nabla^2 \phi$ is often called the Laplacian of ϕ.

With the definitions (6-4) and (6-5) for $\mathbf{A} \cdot \nabla$ and ∇^2, the following relations can be proven to hold in rectangular coordinates:

$$\nabla \times (\mathbf{A} \times \mathbf{B}) = (\mathbf{A}\nabla \cdot - \mathbf{A} \cdot \nabla)\mathbf{B} - (\mathbf{B}\nabla \cdot - \mathbf{B} \cdot \nabla)\mathbf{A} \tag{6-6}$$

$$\nabla(\mathbf{A} \cdot \mathbf{B}) = \mathbf{A} \cdot \nabla \mathbf{B} + \mathbf{B} \cdot \nabla \mathbf{A} + \mathbf{A} \times (\nabla \times \mathbf{B}) + \mathbf{B} \times (\nabla \times \mathbf{A}) \tag{6-7}$$

$$\nabla^2 \phi = \nabla \cdot (\nabla \phi) \tag{6-8}$$
$$= \text{div (grad } \phi)$$

$$\nabla^2 \mathbf{A} = \nabla(\nabla \cdot \mathbf{A}) - \nabla \times (\nabla \times \mathbf{A}) \tag{6-9}$$
$$= \text{grad (div } \mathbf{A}) - \text{curl (curl } \mathbf{A})$$

In each case the proof is effected simply by expanding both sides and comparing results.

As they have been introduced here, relations (6-6) to (6-9) hold only for rectangular coordinates. Note, however, that the right members of (6-8) and (6-9) have completely defined meanings which are independent of the coordinate system used. For the general case, then, (6-8) can be taken as the definition of $\nabla^2\phi$, and this will be done. Similarly, (6-9) will be taken as defining $\nabla^2\mathbf{A}$ whatever the coordinate system. These definitions are entirely consistent with the earlier definition (6-5) for ∇^2 in rectangular coordinates. Having adopted the more general definition for $\nabla^2\phi$ and $\nabla^2\mathbf{A}$, then it becomes a theorem that in rectangular coordinates ∇^2 may be thought of as the operator (6-5).

EXERCISES

1. Establish (6-6).

2. Establish (6-7).

3. Using (6-5) for ∇^2, establish (6-8) in rectangular coordinates.

4. Using (6-5) for ∇^2, establish (6-9) in rectangular coordinates.

5. Let ϕ, ψ, and their derivatives be differentiable. Prove that

$$\nabla \cdot (\phi\nabla\psi) = \phi\nabla^2\psi + \nabla\phi \cdot \nabla\psi$$
$$\nabla \cdot (\phi\nabla\psi - \psi\nabla\phi) = \phi\nabla^2\psi - \psi\nabla^2\phi$$

6. Let ϕ and ψ have continuous second derivatives in a region containing the closed region R. Prove Green's first theorem:

$$\oint_{\substack{\text{bdy} \\ \text{of } R}} \phi\nabla\psi \cdot d\mathbf{S} = \int_R [\phi\nabla^2\psi + \nabla\phi \cdot \nabla\psi]\, dV$$

7. Under the condition of Exercise 6, prove Green's second theorem:

$$\oint_{\substack{\text{bdy} \\ \text{of } R}} [\phi\nabla\psi - \psi\nabla\phi] \cdot d\mathbf{S} = \int_R [\phi\nabla^2\psi - \psi\nabla^2\phi]\, dV$$

REFERENCES

Joos, G.: "Theoretical Physics," translated by I. M. Freeman, G. E. Stechert & Company, New York, 1934.

Phillips, H. B.: "Vector Analysis," John Wiley & Sons, Inc., New York, 1933.

CHAPTER 7

CURVILINEAR COORDINATES

7-1. Coordinate Systems

The concepts of vector, gradient, divergence, and curl do not depend upon the system of reference used in calculating them. Also many of the interrelationships among the various quantities hold quite generally without reference to any special coordinates. Operations involving such quantities and relationships can accordingly be carried out independently of any coordinate system, and when completed, the final result can be expressed in terms of the most convenient coordinates, which often are not rectangular.

Ordinary cartesian coordinates possess many simple features which recommend their frequent use. The coordinate surfaces

$$x = \text{constant}$$
$$y = \text{constant}$$
$$z = \text{constant}$$

are mutually orthogonal planes. The coordinate lines, namely,

$$x \text{ lines:} \begin{cases} y = \text{constant} \\ z = \text{constant} \end{cases}$$

$$y \text{ lines:} \begin{cases} z = \text{constant} \\ x = \text{constant} \end{cases}$$

$$z \text{ lines:} \begin{cases} x = \text{constant} \\ y = \text{constant} \end{cases}$$

are straight lines. Furthermore all x lines have the same direction; so do all the y lines and all z lines. Also, any x line, any y line, and any z line form a mutually orthogonal set. Finally the elemental volumes in a fundamental mesh are rectangular boxes. The ease with which such coordinates can be visualized is a great advantage. But the properties of simplicity possessed by cartesian coordinates are not the essential characteristics required of a coordinate system.

83

The principal feature that a system of coordinates must possess is that there be a one-to-one continuous correspondence between all the points of the region under study and the sets of coordinate numbers used. In the case of cartesian coordinates such a biunique correspondence extends throughout all space, or in two dimensions to the entire plane. For ordinary cylindrical and spherical coordinates the one-to-one correspondence fails along a singular line, but holds elsewhere. In practice the existence of a singular line causes no difficulties, but should be kept in mind.

Let (u_1, u_2, u_3) be general coordinates for points in a region R of space. In this general case the coordinate surfaces

$$u_1 = \text{constant}$$
$$u_2 = \text{constant}$$
$$u_3 = \text{constant}$$

are not necessarily planes, and are not necessarily orthogonal. Nor are the u_ν surfaces for a given value of ν necessarily parallel. In general the u_ν lines are curved, giving rise to the phrase *curvilinear coordinates*, and are not always orthogonal. On the other hand, since there exists a biunique continuous correspondence between the points of R and the curvilinear coordinates, there must be a set of relations

$$x = x(u_1, u_2, u_3)$$
$$y = y(u_1, u_2, u_3) \tag{7-1}$$
$$z = z(u_1, u_2, u_3)$$

transforming the triples (u_1, u_2, u_3) into the cartesian coordinate triples (x, y, z), in which the functions on the right are continuous. Moreover, relations (7-1) must be solvable for the u_ν:

$$u_1 = u_1(x, y, z)$$
$$u_2 = u_2(x, y, z) \tag{7-2}$$
$$u_3 = u_3(x, y, z)$$

where again the functions on the right are continuous in their arguments.

Practically, the most useful general coordinates are those for which the functions in (7-1) and (7-2) have continuous first partial derivatives. Such is the case, for example, with cylindrical and spherical coordinates, except along the singular lines. Henceforth the curvilinear coordinate systems used in this text will be assumed to be related to cartesian coordinates by transformations of the form (7-1) and (7-2) in which the functions on the right possess continuous first partial derivatives.

EXERCISES†

1. Draw a figure illustrating spherical polar coordinates. Which is the singular line referred to in the text? How is it singular? Obtain the transformation from spherical to rectangular coordinates, and vice versa.

2. Draw a figure illustrating cylindrical polar coordinates. Which is the singular line referred to in the text? How is it singular? Obtain the transformation from cylindrical to rectangular coordinates, and vice versa.

3. Let P have the rectangular coordinates (x,y,z). Let r_1 and r_2 be the distances from $(c,0,0)$ to $(x,y,0)$ and from $(-c,0,0)$ to $(x,y,0)$ respectively, where $c > 0$. Then u_1, u_2, u_3, defined by

$$u_1 = \frac{r_1 + r_2}{2c}$$

$$u_2 = \frac{r_1 - r_2}{2c}$$

$$u_3 = z$$

are called elliptic coordinates for P. (a) Describe the coordinate system, drawing an illustrative figure. (b) Give the transformation from elliptic to rectangular coordinates, and the inverse.

4. Let the point P have the cylindrical coordinates (r,θ,z). Then

$$u_1 = \sqrt{2r}\,\sin\frac{\theta}{2}$$

$$u_2 = \sqrt{2r}\,\cos\frac{\theta}{2}$$

$$u_3 = -z$$

are called parabolic coordinates of P. (a) Describe the coordinate system, drawing an illustrative figure. (b) Give the transformation from parabolic to rectangular coordinates, and the inverse.

5. Let P have the rectangular coordinates (x,y,z). Show how to set up a system of coordinates (u_1,u_2,u_3) for P where

$$(x - a\coth u_1)^2 + y^2 = a^2\operatorname{csch}^2 u_1$$
$$x^2 + (y - a\operatorname{ctn} u_2)^2 = a^2\csc^2 u_2$$
$$u_3 = z$$

† Many of the exercises in this chapter were suggested by the excellent review of some orthogonal coordinate systems given in Sec. 1.18 of J. A. Stratton: "Electromagnetic Theory," McGraw-Hill Book Company, Inc., New York, 1941.

Such coordinates are called bipolar coordinates. (*a*) Describe the coordinate system, drawing an illustrative figure. (*b*) Give the transformation from bipolar to rectangular coordinates, and the inverse.

6. Let a system of confocal ellipses and hyperbolas in the xy plane, with foci on the x axis and center at (0,0), be rotated about the x axis. Using u_1 and u_2 as in elliptic coordinates (Exercise 3) but replacing $u_3 = z$ by $u_3 = \phi$, where ϕ is the angle of rotation about the x axis, one can set up what are known as spheroidal coordinates. (*a*) Describe the coordinate system, drawing an illustrative figure. (*b*) Give the transformation from spheroidal to rectangular coordinates, and the inverse.

7. The spheroidal coordinates of Exercise 6 were obtained by rotating a confocal system of ellipses and hyperbolas about the major axes of the ellipses. Discuss the spheroidal coordinates obtained by rotating the system about the minor axes of the ellipses.

8. Paraboloidal coordinates bear to parabolic coordinates the same relation that spheroidal coordinates do to elliptic coordinates. Discuss paraboloidal coordinates.

9. Let x, y, z be rectangular coordinates. Consider

$$\frac{x^2}{a^2 + u_1} + \frac{y^2}{b^2 + u_1} + \frac{z^2}{c^2 + u_1} = 1 \qquad (u_1 > -c^2)$$

$$\frac{x^2}{a^2 + u_2} + \frac{y^2}{b^2 + u_2} + \frac{z^2}{c^2 + u_2} = 1 \qquad (-c^2 > u_2 > -b^2)$$

$$\frac{x^2}{a^2 + u_3} + \frac{y^2}{b^2 + u_3} + \frac{z^2}{c^2 + u_3} = 1 \qquad (-b^2 > u_3 > -a^2)$$

Show that (u_1, u_2, u_3) can be used as coordinates for a point in space. Such coordinates are known as ellipsoidal coordinates. (*a*) Describe the coordinate system, drawing an illustrative figure. (*b*) Give the transformation from ellipsoidal to rectangular coordinates, and the inverse.

10. Describe the coordinate system given by

$$u_1 = x^2 - y^2$$
$$u_2 = x y$$
$$u_3 = z$$

11. Describe the coordinate system given by

$$u_1 = y$$
$$u_2 = y - x^2$$
$$u_3 = z$$

12. Describe the coordinate system given by

$$x = u_1$$
$$y = u_1 \tan u_2$$
$$z = u_3$$

13. Describe the coordinate system given by

$$u_1 = z - x$$
$$u_2 = y - z$$
$$u_3 = x + y + z$$

7-2. Fundamental Vectors in General Coordinates

For representing vectors in a rectangular coordinate system it was found convenient to introduce a set of mutually orthogonal unit vectors **i**, **j**, **k**, parallel to the x, y, and z axes respectively. In such a reference system the base vectors maintain a fixed orientation in space, and it is a matter of indifference whether the fundamental vectors are thought of as attached to the origin of coordinates or to the point under study.

Again in the case of curvilinear coordinates it is convenient to introduce fundamental sets of vectors as bases for representing vectors in general. In the most general case, at each point P there are two sets which recommend themselves. First, there is the set $\mathbf{i}_1$, $\mathbf{i}_2$, $\mathbf{i}_3$ of unit vectors tangent at P to the coordinate lines through P, as drawn in Fig. 7-1. Second, there are the unit vectors $\mathbf{e}_1$, $\mathbf{e}_2$, $\mathbf{e}_3$ normal at P to the coordinate surfaces through P. Both $\mathbf{i}_\alpha$ and $\mathbf{e}_\alpha$ will be taken in the direction of increasing u_α. Generally, the fundamental vectors vary in orientation from point to point; hence, it is customary to think of them as attached to the point under study, rather than to the origin of coordinates. Only in the case of orthogonal coordinates do the two fundamental sets coalesce into one set.

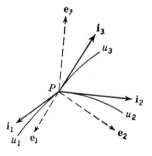

FIG. 7-1. Base vectors for general coordinates.

Figure 7-2 shows the vectors $\mathbf{i}_1$, $\mathbf{i}_2$, $\mathbf{i}_3$ in the directions of increasing r, θ, and ϕ respectively for spherical polar coordinates; in this case the set $\mathbf{e}_1$, $\mathbf{e}_2$, $\mathbf{e}_3$ coincides with $\mathbf{i}_1$, $\mathbf{i}_2$, $\mathbf{i}_3$.

Let **r** be the vector from the origin of rectangular coordinates to the point $P:(x,y,z)$. In terms of the fundamental vectors **r** can be written as

$$\mathbf{r} = x\mathbf{i} + y\mathbf{j} + z\mathbf{k} = \mathbf{r}(x,y,z)$$

By using (7-1), $\mathbf{r}$ can also be expressed as a function of u_1, u_2, and u_3:

$$\mathbf{r} = \mathbf{r}(u_1, u_2, u_3)$$

where (u_1, u_2, u_3) are general coordinates of P.

Starting from P let u_1 vary by an amount Δu_1, with u_2, u_3 fixed. As shown in Fig. 7-3, the vector $\mathbf{r}$ changes by $\Delta_{u_1}\mathbf{r}$ which subtends an arc of the u_1 curve. Plainly, the vector

$$\frac{\partial \mathbf{r}}{\partial u_1} = \lim_{\Delta u_1 \to 0} \frac{\Delta_{u_1}\mathbf{r}}{\Delta u_1} \tag{7-3}$$

is tangent at P to the u_1 curve through P. Also (7-3) is tangent at P to the u_2 and u_3 surfaces through P.

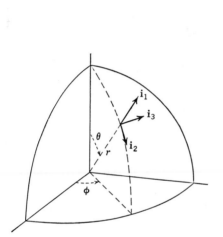

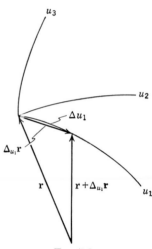

FIG. 7-2. Base vectors for spherical polar coordinates.

FIG. 7-3.

Similarly, $\partial \mathbf{r}/\partial u_2$ and $\partial \mathbf{r}/\partial u_3$ are tangent to the u_2 and u_3 curves. Also $\partial \mathbf{r}/\partial u_2$ is tangent to the u_3 and u_1 surfaces, while $\partial \mathbf{r}/\partial u_3$ is tangent to the u_1 and u_2 surfaces. Finally, $\partial \mathbf{r}/\partial u_1$, $\partial \mathbf{r}/\partial u_2$, and $\partial \mathbf{r}/\partial u_3$ are parallel respectively to $\mathbf{i}_1$, $\mathbf{i}_2$, and $\mathbf{i}_3$, of the fundamental set at P.

The vectors ∇u_1, ∇u_2, and ∇u_3 are normal respectively to the u_1, u_2, and u_3 surfaces. Hence they are parallel respectively to the fundamental vectors $\mathbf{e}_1$, $\mathbf{e}_2$, and $\mathbf{e}_3$.

One has immediately

$$\frac{\partial \mathbf{r}}{\partial u_\alpha} \cdot \nabla u_\beta = 0$$

as long as $\alpha \neq \beta$. Since, from the definition of ∇u_α,

$$d\mathbf{r} \cdot \nabla u_\alpha = du_\alpha$$

it is plain that

$$\frac{\partial \mathbf{r}}{\partial u_\alpha} \cdot \nabla u_\alpha = 1$$

Summarizing,

$$\frac{\partial \mathbf{r}}{\partial u_\alpha} \cdot \nabla u_\beta = \delta_{\alpha\beta} \tag{7-4}$$

where $\delta_{\alpha\beta}$ is unity if $\alpha = \beta$, and is zero otherwise. Thus the vectors $\partial \mathbf{r}/\partial u_\alpha$, where $\alpha = 1, 2, 3$, and the vectors ∇u_β, where $\beta = 1, 2, 3$, form reciprocal sets. They possess, therefore, the properties of reciprocal sets discussed in Sec. 1-15.

Note that whereas (7-4) does mean that $\partial \mathbf{r}/\partial u_\alpha$ and ∇u_β, for $\alpha \neq \beta$, are perpendicular, the relation does not imply that $\partial \mathbf{r}/\partial u_\alpha$ and ∇u_α are parallel. This would be true if and only if the coordinate surfaces were mutually orthogonal. It should also be observed that $\partial \mathbf{r}/\partial u_\alpha$ and ∇u_β are in general not unit vectors.

Illustrative Example

By way of illustration, return to Fig. 7-2 depicting spherical polar coordinates. Let $u_1 = r$, $u_2 = \theta$, $u_3 = \phi$.
Then

$$\begin{cases} x = u_1 \sin u_2 \cos u_3 \\ y = u_1 \sin u_2 \sin u_3 \\ z = u_1 \cos u_2 \end{cases}$$

and

$$u_1 = \sqrt{x^2 + y^2 + z^2}$$
$$u_2 = \arctan \frac{\sqrt{x^2 + y^2}}{z} \tag{7-5}$$
$$u_3 = \arctan \frac{y}{x}$$

Thus

$$\mathbf{r} = u_1 \sin u_2 \cos u_3 \mathbf{i} + u_1 \sin u_2 \sin u_3 \mathbf{j} + u_1 \cos u_2 \mathbf{k}$$
$$\frac{\partial \mathbf{r}}{\partial u_1} = \sin u_2 \cos u_3 \mathbf{i} + \sin u_2 \sin u_3 \mathbf{j} + \cos u_2 \mathbf{k}$$
$$\frac{\partial \mathbf{r}}{\partial u_2} = u_1 \cos u_2 \cos u_3 \mathbf{i} + u_1 \cos u_2 \sin u_3 \mathbf{j} - u_1 \sin u_2 \mathbf{k}$$
$$\frac{\partial \mathbf{r}}{\partial u_3} = -u_1 \sin u_2 \sin u_3 \mathbf{i} + u_1 \sin u_2 \cos u_3 \mathbf{j}$$

Now,

$$\left| \frac{\partial \mathbf{r}}{\partial u_1} \right| = \left[\frac{\partial \mathbf{r}}{\partial u_1} \cdot \frac{\partial \mathbf{r}}{\partial u_1} \right]^{1/2} = 1$$
$$\left| \frac{\partial \mathbf{r}}{\partial u_2} \right| = u_1 = r$$
$$\left| \frac{\partial \mathbf{r}}{\partial u_3} \right| = u_1 \sin u_2 = r \sin \theta$$

Thus

$$i_1 = \frac{\partial r/\partial u_1}{|\partial r/\partial u_1|} = \sin u_2 \cos u_3 i + \sin u_2 \sin u_3 j + \cos u_2 k$$

$$i_2 = \cos u_2 \cos u_3 i + \cos u_2 \sin u_3 j - \sin u_2 k$$

$$i_3 = -\sin u_3 i + \cos u_3 j$$

$$i_1 \cdot i_2 = \sin u_2 \cos u_2 \cos^2 u_3 + \sin u_2 \cos u_2 \sin^2 u_3 - \sin u_2 \cos u_2 = 0$$

$$i_2 \cdot i_3 = -\cos u_2 \sin u_3 \cos u_3 + \cos u_2 \sin u_3 \cos u_3 = 0$$

$$i_3 \cdot i_1 = -\sin u_2 \sin u_3 \cos u_3 + \sin u_2 \sin u_3 \cos u_3 = 0$$

Hence i_1, i_2, i_3 are mutually orthogonal.

From (7-5),

$$\nabla u_1 = \frac{1}{\sqrt{x^2 + y^2 + z^2}} [xi + yj + zk]$$

$$\nabla u_2 = \frac{1}{\sqrt{x^2 + y^2}\,(x^2 + y^2 + z^2)} [zxi + zyj - (x^2 + y^2)k]$$

$$\nabla u_3 = \frac{1}{x^2 + y^2} [-yi + xj]$$

$$|\nabla u_1| = 1$$

$$|\nabla u_2| = \frac{1}{\sqrt{x^2 + y^2 + z^2}} = \frac{1}{r}$$

$$|\nabla u_3| = \frac{1}{\sqrt{x^2 + y^2}} = \frac{1}{r \sin \theta}$$

Hence

$$e_1 = \frac{\nabla u_1}{|\nabla u_1|} = \frac{1}{\sqrt{x^2 + y^2 + z^2}} [xi + yj + zk]$$

$$= \sin u_2 \cos u_3 i + \sin u_2 \sin u_3 j + \cos u_2 k$$

$$= i_1$$

$$e_2 = i_2$$

$$e_3 = i_3$$

The fact that e_1, e_2, e_3 would turn out to be identical with the set i_1, i_2, i_3 could have been predicted from the fact that the i_1, i_2, i_3 are mutually orthogonal.

EXERCISES

1. Verify for spherical polar coordinates that the vectors $\frac{\partial r}{\partial u_\alpha}$, where $\alpha = 1, 2, 3$, and the vectors ∇u_β, where $\beta = 1, 2, 3$, form reciprocal sets.

2. Prove that a necessary and sufficient condition that the vectors e_1, e_2, e_3 coincide with the vectors i_1, i_2, i_3, is that either set consist of mutually orthogonal vectors.

3. Repeat for cylindrical polar coordinates, the calculations carried out at the end of Sec. 7-2 for spherical polar coordinates.

Prove that the following coordinate systems are orthogonal:
 4. Elliptic coordinates
 5. Parabolic coordinates
 6. Bipolar coordinates
 7. Spheroidal coordinates
 8. Paraboloidal coordinates
 9. Ellipsoidal coordinates

10. From (7-4) one concludes that the vectors $\dfrac{\partial \mathbf{r}}{\partial u_\alpha}$, where $\alpha = 1, 2, 3$, and the vectors ∇u_β, where $\beta = 1, 2, 3$, form reciprocal sets. Applying the results of Sec. 1-15, show how to calculate the ∇u_β from the $\dfrac{\partial \mathbf{r}}{\partial u_\alpha}$, and vice versa.

7-3. Relations between the $\partial \mathbf{r}/\partial u_\alpha$ and the ∇u_β

Since the vectors $\partial \mathbf{r}/\partial u_\alpha$, where $\alpha = 1, 2, 3$, and the vectors ∇u_β, where $\beta = 1, 2, 3$, form reciprocal sets, the results of Sec. 1-15 can be applied to them. One has at once

$$d = \frac{\partial \mathbf{r}}{\partial u_1} \cdot \frac{\partial \mathbf{r}}{\partial u_2} \times \frac{\partial \mathbf{r}}{\partial u_3} \neq 0 \tag{7-6}$$

and

$$D = \nabla u_1 \cdot \nabla u_2 \times \nabla u_3 = \frac{1}{d} \tag{7-7}$$

Also,

$$\frac{\partial \mathbf{r}}{\partial u_1} = \frac{\nabla u_2 \times \nabla u_3}{D}$$
$$\frac{\partial \mathbf{r}}{\partial u_2} = \frac{\nabla u_3 \times \nabla u_1}{D} \tag{7-8}$$
$$\frac{\partial \mathbf{r}}{\partial u_3} = \frac{\nabla u_1 \times \nabla u_2}{D}$$

and

$$\nabla u_1 = \frac{1}{d}\left[\frac{\partial \mathbf{r}}{\partial u_2} \times \frac{\partial \mathbf{r}}{\partial u_3}\right]$$
$$\nabla u_2 = \frac{1}{d}\left[\frac{\partial \mathbf{r}}{\partial u_3} \times \frac{\partial \mathbf{r}}{\partial u_1}\right] \tag{7-9}$$
$$\nabla u_3 = \frac{1}{d}\left[\frac{\partial \mathbf{r}}{\partial u_1} \times \frac{\partial \mathbf{r}}{\partial u_2}\right]$$

EXERCISES

Evaluate the determinant d for:
1. Cylindrical polar coordinates
2. Spherical polar coordinates
3. Elliptic coordinates
4. Parabolic coordinates
5. Bipolar coordinates
6. Spheroidal coordinates
7. Paraboloidal coordinates
8. Ellipsoidal coordinates
9. The coordinates of Exercise 10, Sec. 7-1
10. The coordinates of Exercise 11, Sec. 7-1
11. The coordinates of Exercise 12, Sec. 7-1
12. The coordinates of Exercise 13, Sec. 7-1

Calculate the vectors ∇u_β from the vectors $\dfrac{\partial \mathbf{r}}{\partial u_\alpha}$ for.

13. Cylindrical polar coordinates
14. Spherical polar coordinates
15. Parabolic coordinates

7-4. Representation of an Arbitrary Vector in Terms of the $\partial \mathbf{r}/\partial u_\alpha$ and the ∇u_β

Since both the $\partial \mathbf{r}/\partial u_\alpha$ and the ∇u_β are sets of noncoplanar vectors, they may be used as bases for representing the general vector $\mathbf{A}$. But it should be emphasized that the vectors $\partial \mathbf{r}/\partial u_\alpha$ and ∇u_β may not be unit vectors, will in general vary from point to point, and are not necessarily orthogonal. With such base vectors, in moving from one point to another in a vector field $\mathbf{A}$, not only the coefficients of the base vectors but also the base vectors themselves will vary.

Express $\mathbf{A}$ in the form

$$\mathbf{A} = A_1 \frac{\partial \mathbf{r}}{\partial u_1} + A_2 \frac{\partial \mathbf{r}}{\partial u_2} + A_3 \frac{\partial \mathbf{r}}{\partial u_3}$$

Using (7-4),

$$\mathbf{A} \cdot \nabla u_1 = A_1$$
$$\mathbf{A} \cdot \nabla u_2 = A_2$$
$$\mathbf{A} \cdot \nabla u_3 = A_3$$

Hence finally

$$\mathbf{A} = \sum_{\alpha=1}^{3} (\mathbf{A} \cdot \nabla u_\alpha) \frac{\partial \mathbf{r}}{\partial u_\alpha} \qquad (7\text{-}10)$$

In similar fashion

$$\mathbf{A} = \sum_{\alpha=1}^{3} \left(\mathbf{A} \cdot \frac{\partial \mathbf{r}}{\partial u_\alpha} \right) \nabla u_\alpha \qquad (7\text{-}11)$$

Sometimes it is convenient to use the unit vectors $\mathbf{i}_\alpha$ and $\mathbf{e}_\beta$ instead of the $\dfrac{\partial \mathbf{r}}{\partial u_\alpha}$ and ∇u_β. Set

$$g_{\alpha\beta} = \frac{\partial \mathbf{r}}{\partial u_\alpha} \cdot \frac{\partial \mathbf{r}}{\partial u_\beta} \qquad (7\text{-}12)$$

and

$$G_{\alpha\beta} = \nabla u_\alpha \cdot \nabla u_\beta \qquad (7\text{-}13)$$

Then

$$\mathbf{i}_\alpha = \frac{1}{\sqrt{g_{\alpha\alpha}}} \frac{\partial \mathbf{r}}{\partial u_\alpha} \qquad \alpha = 1, 2, 3 \qquad (7\text{-}14)$$

and

$$\mathbf{e}_\alpha = \frac{1}{\sqrt{G_{\alpha\alpha}}} \nabla u_\alpha \qquad \alpha = 1, 2, 3 \qquad (7\text{-}15)$$

Hence (7-10) and (7-11) can be rewritten as

$$\mathbf{A} = \sum_{\alpha=1}^{3} \sqrt{g_{\alpha\alpha} G_{\alpha\alpha}} \, (\mathbf{A} \cdot \mathbf{e}_\alpha) \mathbf{i}_\alpha \qquad (7\text{-}16)$$

and

$$\mathbf{A} = \sum_{\alpha=1}^{3} \sqrt{g_{\alpha\alpha} G_{\alpha\alpha}} \, (\mathbf{A} \cdot \mathbf{i}_\alpha) \mathbf{e}_\alpha \qquad (7\text{-}17)$$

Illustrative Example

As an example, consider the representation of

$$\mathbf{A} = z\mathbf{i}$$

in spherical coordinates. Using the results of Sec. 7-2, one has

$$\mathbf{A} \cdot \nabla u_1 = \frac{xz}{\sqrt{x^2 + y^2 + z^2}} = u_1 \sin u_2 \cos u_2 \cos u_3$$

$$\mathbf{A} \cdot \nabla u_2 = \frac{xz^2}{\sqrt{x^2 + y^2}\,(x^2 + y^2 + z^2)} = \cos^2 u_2 \cos u_3$$

$$\mathbf{A} \cdot \nabla u_3 = \frac{-yz}{x^2 + y^2} = -\operatorname{ctn} u_2 \sin u_3$$

Hence

$$\mathbf{A} = u_1 \sin u_2 \cos u_2 \cos u_3 \frac{\partial \mathbf{r}}{\partial u_1} + \cos^2 u_2 \cos u_3 \frac{\partial \mathbf{r}}{\partial u_2} - \operatorname{ctn} u_2 \sin u_3 \frac{\partial \mathbf{r}}{\partial u_3}$$

$$= u_1 \sin u_2 \cos u_2 \cos u_3 \mathbf{i}_1 + u_1 \cos^2 u_2 \cos u_3 \mathbf{i}_2 - u_1 \cos u_2 \sin u_3 \mathbf{i}_3$$

94 VECTOR ANALYSIS

Also,

$$g_{11} = 1$$
$$g_{22} = u_1{}^2 = r^2$$
$$g_{33} = u_1{}^2 \sin^2 u_2 = r^2 \sin^2 \theta$$
$$g_{12} = g_{21} = g_{13} = g_{31} = g_{23} = g_{32} = 0$$

EXERCISES

1. Obtain the representation of the vector $\mathbf{A} = z\mathbf{i}$ in terms of $\mathbf{i}_1, \mathbf{i}_2, \mathbf{i}_3$ for cylindrical polar coordinates.

Obtain the $g_{\alpha\beta}$ for:
2. Cylindrical polar coordinates
3. Elliptic coordinates
4. Parabolic coordinates
5. Bipolar coordinates
6. Spheroidal coordinates
7. Paraboloidal coordinates
8. Ellipsoidal coordinates
9. The coordinates of Exercise 10, Sec. 7-1
10. The coordinates of Exercise 11, Sec. 7-1
11. The coordinates of Exercise 12, Sec. 7-1
12. The coordinates of Exercise 13, Sec. 7-1

13. Prove that

$$g_{\alpha\beta} = \frac{G_{\alpha\gamma}G_{\beta\gamma} - G_{\alpha\beta}G_{\gamma\gamma}}{D^2} \tag{7-18}$$

where α, β, γ is any permutation of 1, 2, 3.
14. Prove that

$$g_{\alpha\alpha} = \frac{G_{\beta\beta}G_{\gamma\gamma} - G^2{}_{\beta\gamma}}{D^2} \tag{7-19}$$

where α, β, γ is any permutation of 1, 2, 3.
15. Derive relations, similar to (7-18) and (7-19), giving the $G_{\alpha\beta}$, where $\alpha, \beta = 1, 2, 3$, in terms of d and the $g_{\alpha\beta}$, where $\alpha, \beta = 1, 2, 3$.
16. Let

$$g = |g_{\alpha\beta}| = \begin{vmatrix} g_{11} & g_{12} & g_{13} \\ g_{21} & g_{22} & g_{23} \\ g_{31} & g_{32} & g_{33} \end{vmatrix}$$

Prove that

$$g = d^2$$

Evaluate the determinant g for
17. Cylindrical polar coordinates
18. Spherical polar coordinates

19. Elliptic coordinates
20. Parabolic coordinates
21. Bipolar coordinates
22. Spheroidal coordinates
23. Paraboloidal coordinates
24. Ellipsoidal coordinates
25. The coordinates of Exercise 10, Sec. 7-1
26. The coordinates of Exercise 11, Sec. 7-1
27. The coordinates of Exercise 12, Sec. 7-1
28. The coordinates of Exercise 13, Sec. 7-1

29. Let
$$G = |G_{\alpha\beta}|$$
Prove that $G = 1/g$.

30. Let i_1, i_2, i_3 be mutually orthogonal. Prove that

$$g_{\alpha\alpha} = \frac{1}{G_{\alpha\alpha}}$$

7-5. Differential Elements of Volume and Arc Length in General Coordinates

With the notation of (7-10) and (7-6) for $g_{\alpha\beta}$ and d it can be shown that

$$d = \pm \sqrt{g} \tag{7-20}$$

where g is the determinant $|g_{\alpha\beta}|$. The plus and minus signs correspond respectively to right-handed and left-handed coordinate systems. Henceforth, unless explicitly stated otherwise, only right-handed coordinates will be considered, so that the positive root in (7-20) should be used. The student ought, however, to consider what effect left-handedness of the coordinate system would have upon the discussions to follow and upon the formulas derived.

The differential element of volume is a parallelepiped, three adjacent sides of which are the vectors

$$\frac{\partial \mathbf{r}}{\partial u_1} du_1 \qquad \frac{\partial \mathbf{r}}{\partial u_2} du_2 \qquad \frac{\partial \mathbf{r}}{\partial u_3} du_3 \tag{7-21}$$

The volume dV thereof is given by

$$dV = \frac{\partial \mathbf{r}}{\partial u_1} \cdot \frac{\partial \mathbf{r}}{\partial u_2} \times \frac{\partial \mathbf{r}}{\partial u_3} du_1\, du_2\, du_3$$
$$= d\, du_1\, du_2\, du_3$$

or

$$dV = \sqrt{g}\, du_1\, du_2\, du_3 \tag{7-22}$$

Using (7-10) the vector element of arc, $d\mathbf{r}$, can be put in the form

$$d\mathbf{r} = \sum_{\alpha=1}^{3} (d\mathbf{r} \cdot \nabla u_\alpha) \frac{\partial \mathbf{r}}{\partial u_\alpha}$$

$$d\mathbf{r} = \sum_{\alpha=1}^{3} \frac{\partial \mathbf{r}}{\partial u_\alpha} du_\alpha \qquad (7\text{-}23)$$

Accordingly, the differential element of arc length is given by

$$ds^2 = d\mathbf{r} \cdot d\mathbf{r} = \sum_{\alpha=1}^{3} \frac{\partial \mathbf{r}}{\partial u_\alpha} du_\alpha \cdot \sum_{\beta=1}^{3} \frac{\partial \mathbf{r}}{\partial u_\beta} du_\beta$$

$$ds^2 = \sum_{\alpha,\beta=1}^{3} g_{\alpha\beta} \, du_\alpha \, du_\beta \qquad (7\text{-}24)$$

Illustrative Example

In the case of spherical polar coordinates, for example, one has, using the results at the end of Sec. 7-4,

$$g = \begin{vmatrix} 1 & 0 & 0 \\ 0 & u_1{}^2 & 0 \\ 0 & 0 & u_1{}^2 \sin^2 u_2 \end{vmatrix} = u_1{}^4 \sin^2 u_2 = r^4 \sin^2 \theta$$

$$dV = u_1{}^2 \sin u_2 \, du_1 \, du_2 \, du_3$$
$$= r^2 \sin \theta \, dr \, d\theta \, d\phi$$
$$ds^2 = du_1{}^2 + u_1{}^2 \, du_2{}^2 + u_1{}^2 \sin^2 u_2 \, du_3{}^2$$
$$= dr^2 + r^2 \, d\theta^2 + r^2 \sin^2 \theta \, d\phi^2$$

EXERCISES

Obtain dV and ds^2 for the following coordinate systems:
1. Cylindrical polar coordinates
2. Elliptic coordinates
3. Parabolic coordinates
4. Bipolar coordinates
5. Spheroidal coordinates
6. Paraboloidal coordinates
7. Ellipsoidal coordinates
8. The coordinates of Exercise 10, Sec. 7-1
9. The coordinates of Exercise 11, Sec. 7-1
10. The coordinates of Exercise 12, Sec. 7-1
11. The coordinates of Exercise 13, Sec. 7-1

12. Define element of area on a coordinate surface. Using (7-23) obtain an expression for the element of area on a coordinate surface.

13. Using the definition of Exercise 12, obtain an expression in spherical coordinates for the element of area on the surface of a sphere of radius r.

7-6. Gradient in General Coordinates

The gradient of a differentiable scalar function can be expressed as in (7-11) by

$$\nabla\Phi = \sum_{\alpha=1}^{3} \left(\nabla\Phi \cdot \frac{\partial \mathbf{r}}{\partial u_\alpha}\right) \nabla u_\alpha$$

or

$$\nabla\Phi = \sum_{\alpha=1}^{3} \frac{\partial \Phi}{\partial u_\alpha} \nabla u_\alpha \tag{7-25}$$

Illustrative Example

In spherical polar coordinates, from the results at the end of Sec. 7-2:

$$\nabla u_1 = \mathbf{e}_1 = \mathbf{i}_1$$
$$\nabla u_2 = \frac{\mathbf{e}_2}{u_1} = \frac{\mathbf{i}_2}{u_1}$$
$$\nabla u_3 = \frac{\mathbf{e}_3}{u_1 \sin u_2} = \frac{\mathbf{i}_3}{u_1 \sin u_2}$$

Thus,

$$\nabla\Phi = \frac{\partial \Phi}{\partial u_1} \mathbf{i}_1 + \frac{1}{u_1} \frac{\partial \Phi}{\partial u_2} \mathbf{i}_2 + \frac{1}{u_1 \sin u_2} \frac{\partial \Phi}{\partial u_3} \mathbf{i}_3$$
$$= \frac{\partial \Phi}{\partial r} \mathbf{i}_1 + \frac{1}{r} \frac{\partial \Phi}{\partial \theta} \mathbf{i}_2 + \frac{1}{r \sin \theta} \frac{\partial \Phi}{\partial \phi} \mathbf{i}_3$$

EXERCISES

Calculate grad Φ in:
1. Cylindrical polar coordinates
2. Elliptic coordinates
3. Parabolic coordinates
4. Bipolar coordinates
5. Spheroidal coordinates
6. Paraboloidal coordinates
7. Ellipsoidal coordinates

8. The coordinates of Exercise 10, Sec. 7-1
9. The coordinates of Exercise 11, Sec. 7-1
10. The coordinates of Exercise 12, Sec. 7-1
11. The coordinates of Exercise 13, Sec. 7-1

7-7. Divergence in General Coordinates

Using (7-8), (7-7), and (7-20), relations (7-14) can be put in the form

$$\mathbf{i}_1 = \sqrt{\frac{g}{g_{11}}}\, \nabla u_2 \times \nabla u_3$$

$$\mathbf{i}_2 = \sqrt{\frac{g}{g_{22}}}\, \nabla u_3 \times \nabla u_1$$

$$\mathbf{i}_3 = \sqrt{\frac{g}{g_{33}}}\, \nabla u_1 \times \nabla u_2$$

With these an arbitrary vector $\mathbf{A}$ can be expressed as

$$\mathbf{A} = A_1 \mathbf{i}_1 + A_2 \mathbf{i}_2 + A_3 \mathbf{i}_3$$

or

$$\mathbf{A} = \left(A_1 \sqrt{\frac{g}{g_{11}}} \right) \nabla u_2 \times \nabla u_3 + \left(A_2 \sqrt{\frac{g}{g_{22}}} \right) \nabla u_3 \times \nabla u_1$$
$$+ \left(A_3 \sqrt{\frac{g}{g_{33}}} \right) \nabla u_1 \times \nabla u_2$$

If $\mathbf{A}$ is differentiable, the **divergence exists** and is given by

$$\nabla \cdot \mathbf{A} = \nabla \left(A_1 \sqrt{\frac{g}{g_{11}}} \right) \cdot \nabla u_2 \times \nabla u_3 + \nabla \left(A_2 \sqrt{\frac{g}{g_{22}}} \right) \cdot \nabla u_3 \times \nabla u_1$$
$$+ \nabla \left(A_3 \sqrt{\frac{g}{g_{33}}} \right) \cdot \nabla u_1 \times \nabla u_2 + \left(A_1 \sqrt{\frac{g}{g_{11}}} \right) \nabla \cdot (\nabla u_2 \times \nabla u_3)$$
$$+ \left(A_2 \sqrt{\frac{g}{g_{22}}} \right) \nabla \cdot (\nabla u_3 \times \nabla u_1) + \left(A_3 \sqrt{\frac{g}{g_{33}}} \right) \nabla \cdot (\nabla u_1 \times \nabla u_2)$$

making use of the relation

$$\nabla \cdot (\phi \mathbf{B}) = \nabla \phi \cdot \mathbf{B} + \phi \nabla \cdot \mathbf{B}$$

In Exercise 3 of Sec. 4-2 it was shown that

$$\nabla \cdot (\nabla \phi \times \nabla \psi) \equiv 0$$

Hence the last three terms in the expression for $\nabla \cdot \mathbf{A}$ vanish.

Now using (7-25) for the gradient of a scalar function, one gets

$$\nabla \cdot \mathbf{A} = \sum_{\alpha=1}^{3} \left[\frac{\partial}{\partial u_\alpha} \left(A_1 \sqrt{\frac{g}{g_{11}}} \right) \right] \nabla u_\alpha \cdot \nabla u_2 \times \nabla u_3$$

$$+ \sum_{\alpha=1}^{3} \left[\frac{\partial}{\partial u_\alpha} \left(A_2 \sqrt{\frac{g}{g_{22}}} \right) \right] \nabla u_\alpha \cdot \nabla u_3 \times \nabla u_1$$

$$+ \sum_{\alpha=1}^{3} \left[\frac{\partial}{\partial u_\alpha} \left(A_3 \sqrt{\frac{g}{g_{33}}} \right) \right] \nabla u_\alpha \cdot \nabla u_1 \times \nabla u_2$$

Finally,

$$\nabla \cdot \mathbf{A} = \frac{1}{\sqrt{g}} \sum_{\alpha=1}^{3} \frac{\partial}{\partial u_\alpha} \left(A_\alpha \sqrt{\frac{g}{g_{\alpha\alpha}}} \right) \tag{7-26}$$

By way of caution it should be emphasized that the A_α in (7-26) must be the coefficients in the representation of the vector $\mathbf{A}$ in terms of the base vectors $\mathbf{i}_\alpha$ tangent to the coordinate lines.

Illustrative Example

For spherical polar coordinates

$$\nabla \cdot \mathbf{A} = \frac{1}{u_1{}^2 \sin u_2} \left[\frac{\partial}{\partial u_1} \left(A_1 \frac{u_1{}^2 \sin u_2}{1} \right) \right.$$

$$\left. + \frac{\partial}{\partial u_2} \left(A_2 \frac{u_1{}^2 \sin u_2}{u_1} \right) + \frac{\partial}{\partial u_3} \left(A_3 \frac{u_1{}^2 \sin u_2}{u_1 \sin u_2} \right) \right]$$

$$= \frac{1}{u_1{}^2} \frac{\partial}{\partial u_1} (u_1{}^2 A_1) + \frac{1}{u_1 \sin u_2} \frac{\partial}{\partial u_2} (A_2 \sin u_2) + \frac{1}{u_1 \sin u_2} \frac{\partial A_3}{\partial u_3}$$

$$= \frac{1}{r^2} \frac{\partial}{\partial r} (r^2 A_1) + \frac{1}{r \sin \theta} \frac{\partial}{\partial \theta} (A_2 \sin \theta) + \frac{1}{r \sin \theta} \frac{\partial A_3}{\partial \phi}$$

If $\mathbf{A}$ is the vector $\mathbf{r}$, then $\nabla \cdot \mathbf{A}$ should turn out to be 3, as was shown in Exercise 1 of Sec. 6-1. This can be verified by noting that

$$\mathbf{A} = r\mathbf{i}_1$$

whence

$$\nabla \cdot \mathbf{A} = \frac{1}{r^2} \frac{\partial}{\partial r} (r^3) = 3$$

EXERCISES

Calculate $\nabla \cdot \mathbf{A}$ for
1. Cylindrical polar coordinates
2. Elliptic coordinates

7-8. Curl in General Coordinates

Using (7-11) and (7-14) a vector $\mathbf{A}$ can be written in the form

$$\mathbf{A} = \sum_{\alpha=1}^{3} \sqrt{g_{\alpha\alpha}} \, (\mathbf{A} \cdot \mathbf{i}_\alpha) \, \nabla u_\alpha$$

Then from (6-2) and Exercise 4 of Sec. 4-7:

$$\nabla \times \mathbf{A} = \sum_{\alpha=1}^{3} \nabla(\sqrt{g_{\alpha\alpha}} \, (\mathbf{A} \cdot \mathbf{i}_\alpha)) \times \nabla u_\alpha$$

Using (7-25) for the gradients, the above becomes

$$\nabla \times \mathbf{A} = \sum_{\alpha=1}^{3} \left[\sum_{\beta=1}^{3} \frac{\partial}{\partial u_\beta} (\sqrt{g_{\alpha\alpha}} \, (\mathbf{A} \cdot \mathbf{i}_\alpha)) \, \nabla u_\beta \right] \times \nabla u_\alpha \qquad (7\text{-}27)$$

Finally with (7-8), (7-7), (7-14), and (7-20), Eq. (7-27) can be reduced to

$$\nabla \times \mathbf{A} = \sqrt{\frac{g_{11}}{g}} \left[\frac{\partial}{\partial u_2} (\sqrt{g_{33}} \, (\mathbf{A} \cdot \mathbf{i}_3)) - \frac{\partial}{\partial u_3} (\sqrt{g_{22}} \, (\mathbf{A} \cdot \mathbf{i}_2)) \right] \mathbf{i}_1$$
$$+ \sqrt{\frac{g_{22}}{g}} \left[\frac{\partial}{\partial u_3} (\sqrt{g_{11}} \, (\mathbf{A} \cdot \mathbf{i}_1)) - \frac{\partial}{\partial u_1} (\sqrt{g_{33}} \, (\mathbf{A} \cdot \mathbf{i}_3)) \right] \mathbf{i}_2$$
$$+ \sqrt{\frac{g_{33}}{g}} \left[\frac{\partial}{\partial u_1} (\sqrt{g_{22}} \, (\mathbf{A} \cdot \mathbf{i}_2)) - \frac{\partial}{\partial u_2} (\sqrt{g_{11}} \, (\mathbf{A} \cdot \mathbf{i}_1)) \right] \mathbf{i}_3$$

which is equivalent to

$$\nabla \times \mathbf{A} = \frac{1}{\sqrt{g}} \begin{vmatrix} \sqrt{g_{11}} \, \mathbf{i}_1 & \sqrt{g_{22}} \, \mathbf{i}_2 & \sqrt{g_{33}} \, \mathbf{i}_3 \\ \dfrac{\partial}{\partial u_1} & \dfrac{\partial}{\partial u_2} & \dfrac{\partial}{\partial u_3} \\ \sqrt{g_{11}} \, (\mathbf{A} \cdot \mathbf{i}_1) & \sqrt{g_{22}} \, (\mathbf{A} \cdot \mathbf{i}_2) & \sqrt{g_{33}} \, (\mathbf{A} \cdot \mathbf{i}_3) \end{vmatrix} \qquad (7\text{-}28)$$

Illustrative Example

For spherical polar coordinates, setting

$$\mathbf{A} = A_1\mathbf{i}_1 + A_2\mathbf{i}_2 + A_3\mathbf{i}_3$$

(7-28) becomes

$$\nabla \times \mathbf{A} = \frac{1}{u_1{}^2 \sin u_2} \begin{vmatrix} \mathbf{i}_1 & u_1\mathbf{i}_2 & u_1 \sin u_2\mathbf{i}_3 \\ \dfrac{\partial}{\partial u_1} & \dfrac{\partial}{\partial u_2} & \dfrac{\partial}{\partial u_3} \\ A_1 & u_1 A_2 & u_1 \sin u_2 A_3 \end{vmatrix}$$

$$\nabla \times \mathbf{A} = \frac{1}{r^2 \sin \theta} \begin{vmatrix} \mathbf{i}_1 & r\mathbf{i}_2 & r \sin \theta\mathbf{i}_3 \\ \dfrac{\partial}{\partial r} & \dfrac{\partial}{\partial \theta} & \dfrac{\partial}{\partial \phi} \\ A_1 & rA_2 & r \sin \theta A_3 \end{vmatrix} \qquad (7\text{-}29)$$

EXERCISES

1. Let $\mathbf{A} = z\mathbf{i}$. Then $\nabla \times \mathbf{A} = \mathbf{j}$. Express $\mathbf{A}$ in spherical polar coordinates. Then use (7-29) to calculate $\nabla \times \mathbf{A}$. Transform the result back to cartesian coordinates, and thereby verify that $\nabla \times \mathbf{A}$ as calculated from (7-29) is the same as the value $\mathbf{j}$ obtained in rectangular coordinates.

Calculate curl $\mathbf{A}$ for
   2. Cylindrical polar coordinates
   3. Elliptic coordinates
   4. Parabolic coordinates
   5. Bipolar coordinates
   6. Spheroidal coordinates
   7. Paraboloidal coordinates
   8. Ellipsoidal coordinates
   9. The coordinates of Exercise 10, Sec. 7-1
   10. The coordinates of Exercise 11, Sec. 7-1
   11. The coordinates of Exercise 12, Sec. 7-1
   12. The coordinates of Exercise 13, Sec. 7-1

7-9. The Laplacian $\nabla^2\Phi$ in General Coordinates

If Φ is a differentiable scalar, then $\nabla^2\Phi$ is defined as

$$\nabla^2\Phi = \nabla \cdot (\nabla\Phi) = \text{div (grad } \Phi)$$

The calculation of $\nabla^2\Phi$, which is known as the Laplacian of Φ, has already been carried out for rectangular coordinates in Sec. 6-2. For the general case, using (7-10) and (7-14) one can put $\nabla\Phi$ in the form

$$\nabla\Phi = \sum_{\alpha=1}^{3} \sqrt{g_{\alpha\alpha}} \, (\nabla\Phi \cdot \nabla u_\alpha)\mathbf{i}_\alpha$$

Then (7-26) gives

$$\nabla \cdot (\nabla\phi) = \frac{1}{\sqrt{g}} \sum_{\alpha=1}^{3} \frac{\partial}{\partial u_\alpha} \left[\sqrt{g_{\alpha\alpha}} \, (\nabla\Phi \cdot \nabla u_\alpha) \sqrt{\frac{g}{g_{\alpha\alpha}}} \right]$$

$$\nabla^2\Phi = \frac{1}{\sqrt{g}} \sum_{\alpha=1}^{3} \frac{\partial}{\partial u_\alpha} [\sqrt{g} \, \nabla\Phi \cdot \nabla u_\alpha]$$

From (7-25)

$$\nabla\Phi = \sum_{\beta=1}^{3} \frac{\partial\Phi}{\partial u_\beta} \nabla u_\beta$$

whence

$$\nabla^2\Phi = \frac{1}{\sqrt{g}} \sum_{\alpha=1}^{3} \frac{\partial}{\partial u_\alpha} \left(\sqrt{g} \sum_{\beta=1}^{3} \frac{\partial\Phi}{\partial u_\beta} \nabla u_\beta \cdot \nabla u_\alpha \right) \qquad (7\text{-}30)$$

Illustrative Example

For spherical polar coordinates, $\nabla u_\beta \cdot \nabla u_\alpha$ vanishes when $\beta \neq \alpha$. Hence

$$\nabla^2\Phi = \frac{1}{\sqrt{g}} \sum_{\alpha=1}^{3} \frac{\partial}{\partial u_\alpha} \left(\sqrt{g} \, (\nabla u_\alpha)^2 \frac{\partial\Phi}{\partial u_\alpha} \right)$$

$$= \frac{1}{u_1{}^2 \sin u_2} \left[\frac{\partial}{\partial u_1} \left(\frac{u_1{}^2 \sin u_2}{1} \frac{\partial\Phi}{\partial u_1} \right) + \frac{\partial}{\partial u_2} \left(\frac{u_1{}^2 \sin u_2}{u_1{}^2} \frac{\partial\Phi}{\partial u_2} \right) \right.$$
$$\left. + \frac{\partial}{\partial u_3} \left(\frac{u_1{}^2 \sin u_2}{u_1{}^2 \sin^2 u_2} \frac{\partial\Phi}{\partial u_3} \right) \right]$$

using the values obtained in Sec. 7-6 for the vectors ∇u_α.   Thus

$$\nabla^2\Phi = \frac{1}{u_1{}^2} \frac{\partial}{\partial u_1} \left(u_1{}^2 \frac{\partial\Phi}{\partial u_1} \right) + \frac{1}{u_1{}^2 \sin u_2} \frac{\partial}{\partial u_2} \left(\sin u_2 \frac{\partial\Phi}{\partial u_2} \right) + \frac{1}{u_1{}^2 \sin^2 u_2} \frac{\partial^2\Phi}{\partial u_3{}^2}$$

$$\nabla^2\Phi = \frac{1}{r^2} \frac{\partial}{\partial r} \left(r^2 \frac{\partial\Phi}{\partial r} \right) + \frac{1}{r^2 \sin\theta} \frac{\partial}{\partial\theta} \left(\sin\theta \frac{\partial\Phi}{\partial\theta} \right) + \frac{1}{r^2 \sin^2\theta} \frac{\partial^2\Phi}{\partial\phi^2} \qquad (7\text{-}31)$$

If Φ is the function

$$\frac{x^2 + y^2 + z^2}{2}$$

then

$$\nabla^2\Phi = 3$$

This may be verified in (7-31) after noting that

$$\Phi = \frac{r^2}{2}$$

Then

$$\nabla^2\Phi = \frac{1}{r^2}\frac{\partial}{\partial r}(r^2 r) = 3$$

EXERCISES

Calculate $\nabla^2\Phi$ for
1. Cylindrical polar coordinates
2. Elliptic coordinates
3. Parabolic coordinates
4. Bipolar coordinates
5. Spheroidal coordinates
6. Paraboloidal coordinates
7. Ellipsoidal coordinates
8. The coordinates of Exercise 10, Sec. 7-1
9. The coordinates of Exercise 11, Sec. 7-1
10. The coordinates of Exercise 12, Sec. 7-1
11. The coordinates of Exercise 13, Sec. 7-1

7-10. Orthogonal Coordinates

The relations (7-25), (7-26), (7-29), and (7-30) for $\nabla\phi$, $\nabla \cdot \mathbf{A}$, $\nabla \times \mathbf{A}$, and $\nabla^2\phi$ respectively, are valid in both orthogonal and nonorthogonal coordinate systems. They are, accordingly, quite general. In practice, however, one usually employs orthogonal coordinates, and it is worthwhile to revamp the various relations for the special case of orthogonal coordinates.

Suppose that the vectors $\mathbf{i}_1$, $\mathbf{i}_2$, $\mathbf{i}_3$ form an orthogonal set. Then $g_{\alpha\beta} = 0$ unless $\alpha = \beta$. Set

$$h_\alpha = \sqrt{g_{\alpha\alpha}} \tag{7-32}$$

Then

$$\frac{\partial \mathbf{r}}{\partial u_\alpha} = h_\alpha \mathbf{i}_\alpha \qquad \alpha = 1, 2, 3 \tag{7-33}$$

It follows from (7-11) that ∇u_α is parallel to $\mathbf{i}_\alpha$. For

$$\mathbf{i}_\alpha = \sum_\beta \left(\mathbf{i}_\alpha \cdot \frac{\partial \mathbf{r}}{\partial u_\beta}\right) \nabla u_\beta$$

$$= h_\alpha \nabla u_\alpha$$

Hence

$$\nabla u_\alpha = \frac{1}{h_\alpha}\mathbf{i}_\alpha \tag{7-34}$$

From the definition of g,

$$\sqrt{g} = h_1 h_2 h_3 \tag{7-35}$$

The expressions for grad ϕ, div $\mathbf{A}$, curl $\mathbf{A}$, and $\nabla^2\phi$ in general coordinates, can now be simplified for the orthogonal case. Eq. (7-25) becomes

$$\nabla\phi = \sum_{\alpha=1}^{3} \frac{1}{h_\alpha} \frac{\partial\phi}{\partial u_\alpha} \mathbf{i}_\alpha \tag{7-36}$$

Setting $\mathbf{A} = \Sigma A_\alpha \mathbf{i}_\alpha$, Eqs. (7-26) and (7-28) become

$$\nabla \cdot \mathbf{A} = \frac{1}{h_1 h_2 h_3} \sum_{\alpha=1}^{3} \frac{\partial}{\partial u_\alpha} \left[\frac{h_1 h_2 h_3}{h_\alpha} A_\alpha \right] \tag{7-37}$$

and

$$\nabla \times \mathbf{A} = \frac{1}{h_1 h_2 h_3} \begin{vmatrix} h_1 \mathbf{i}_1 & h_2 \mathbf{i}_2 & h_3 \mathbf{i}_3 \\ \dfrac{\partial}{\partial u_1} & \dfrac{\partial}{\partial u_2} & \dfrac{\partial}{\partial u_3} \\ h_1 A_1 & h_2 A_2 & h_3 A_3 \end{vmatrix} \tag{7-38}$$

Finally, using (7-34), relation (7-30) becomes

$$\nabla^2\phi = \frac{1}{h_1 h_2 h_3} \sum_{\alpha=1}^{3} \frac{\partial}{\partial u_\alpha} \left[\frac{h_1 h_2 h_3}{h_\alpha^2} \frac{\partial\phi}{\partial u_\alpha} \right] \tag{7-39}$$

EXERCISES

1. Calculate the h_α, where $\alpha = 1, 2, 3$, for the various orthogonal coordinate systems introduced in the exercises of Sec. 7-1.

2. Use (7-36) to verify earlier determinations of grad ϕ in various orthogonal coordinate systems.

3. Use (7-37) to verify earlier determinations of div $\mathbf{A}$ in various orthogonal coordinate systems.

4. Use (7-38) to check previous calculations of curl $\mathbf{A}$ in various orthogonal coordinate systems.

5. Use (7-39) to check previous calculations of $\nabla^2\phi$ for various orthogonal coordinate systems.

REFERENCES

Phillips, H. B.: "Vector Analysis," John Wiley & Sons, Inc., New York, 1933.

Stratton, J. A.: "Electromagnetic Theory," McGraw-Hill Book Company, Inc., New York, 1941.

CHAPTER 8

GENERAL THEOREMS AND POTENTIAL THEORY

8-1. Irrotational Vectors

If the vector curl $\mathbf{A}$ vanishes everywhere within a region R, then $\mathbf{A}$ is said to be irrotational within R. Because of the connection between circulation in the field and curl $\mathbf{A}$, the definition is a natural one.

Let $\mathbf{A}$ have continuous first derivatives within a simply connected region R. Then a necessary and sufficient condition that curl $\mathbf{A}$ vanish everywhere within R is that $\mathbf{A}$ be of the form $\nabla\phi$. Such a function ϕ is called a *scalar potential* of the vector $\mathbf{A}$.

First suppose that

$$\mathbf{A} = \nabla\phi = \mathbf{i}\,\frac{\partial\phi}{\partial x} + \mathbf{j}\,\frac{\partial\phi}{\partial y} + \mathbf{k}\,\frac{\partial\phi}{\partial z}$$

Then

$$\text{curl } \mathbf{A} = \begin{vmatrix} \mathbf{i} & \mathbf{j} & \mathbf{k} \\ \dfrac{\partial}{\partial x} & \dfrac{\partial}{\partial y} & \dfrac{\partial}{\partial z} \\ \dfrac{\partial\phi}{\partial x} & \dfrac{\partial\phi}{\partial y} & \dfrac{\partial\phi}{\partial z} \end{vmatrix}$$

$$= \mathbf{i}\left(\frac{\partial^2\phi}{\partial y\,\partial z} - \frac{\partial^2\phi}{\partial z\,\partial y}\right) + \mathbf{j}\left(\frac{\partial^2\phi}{\partial z\,\partial x} - \frac{\partial^2\phi}{\partial x\,\partial z}\right) + \mathbf{k}\left(\frac{\partial^2\phi}{\partial x\,\partial y} - \frac{\partial^2\phi}{\partial y\,\partial x}\right)$$

$$\equiv 0$$

Next suppose that $\nabla \times \mathbf{A} \equiv 0$. Then for every simple closed curve C in R,

$$\oint_C \mathbf{A} \cdot d\mathbf{r} = \int_S \nabla \times \mathbf{A} \cdot d\mathbf{S} = 0$$

where S is a simple surface spanning C. Hence the integral

$$\phi = \int_{P_0}^{P} \mathbf{A} \cdot d\mathbf{r}$$

is independent of the path followed from P_0 to P in R. With P_0 fixed, ϕ is a function only of P. Since then

$$d\phi = \mathbf{A} \cdot d\mathbf{r} = \nabla\phi \cdot d\mathbf{r}$$

for every $d\mathbf{r}$, it follows that

$$\mathbf{A} = \nabla\phi$$

Let $\mathbf{A}$ have continuous first derivatives within a simply connected region R. Then a necessary and sufficient condition that $\mathbf{A}$ be of the form $\nabla\phi$ is that for every simple closed curve C in R

$$\oint_C \mathbf{A} \cdot d\mathbf{r} = 0$$

The truth of this theorem follows directly from the preceding discussion.

One can now say that in a simply connected region R in which $\mathbf{A}$ has continuous first derivatives, any one of the following three conditions is necessary and sufficient that $\mathbf{A}$ should be irrotational:

(a) $\nabla \times \mathbf{A} \equiv 0$

(b) $\mathbf{A}$ is of the form $\nabla\phi$

(c)   For every simple closed curved C in R, $\oint_C \mathbf{A} \cdot d\mathbf{r}$ vanishes

EXERCISES

1. Prove that if $\nabla\phi$ vanishes identically, then ϕ is a constant.

2. Let $\mathbf{A}$ have continuous first derivatives in a simply connected region R. Prove that a necessary and sufficient condition that $\mathbf{A}$ be of the form $\nabla\phi$ is that for every simple closed curve C in R

$$\oint_C \mathbf{A} \cdot d\mathbf{r} = 0$$

3. Which of the following are irrotational?

a. $x\mathbf{i} + y\mathbf{j} + z\mathbf{k}$

b. $xy\mathbf{i} + yz\mathbf{j} + zx\mathbf{k}$

c. $2xye^z\mathbf{i} + x^2e^z\mathbf{j} + x^2ye^z\mathbf{k}$

4. Show that the earth's gravitational field is irrotational.

5. Two electrons are fixed at a distance d apart. Show that the field which at each point P is the force which would be exerted by the electrons on a proton at P, is irrotational.

6. The vector $\mathbf{r} = x\mathbf{i} + y\mathbf{j} + z\mathbf{k}$ is irrotational. Obtain a scalar potential ϕ of $\mathbf{r}$.

7. Verify that

$$\mathbf{A} = e^x \sin(yz)\mathbf{i} + ze^x \cos(yz)\mathbf{j} + ye^x \cos(yz)\mathbf{k}$$

is irrotational. Determine a scalar potential ϕ for $\mathbf{A}$.

8. Show that the scalar potential ϕ of an irrotational vector must satisfy Poisson's equation:

$$\nabla^2 \phi = a$$

where a is some function of position.

9. Given that

$$\nabla \times \mathbf{A} = \nabla \times \mathbf{B}$$

Prove that $\mathbf{A}$ and $\mathbf{B}$ are related by an equation of the form

$$\mathbf{A} = \mathbf{B} + \nabla \phi$$

8-2. Field Lines

Let the vector $\mathbf{A}$ be continuous and single-valued everywhere within a region R of space. The vectors $\mathbf{A}$ depend upon position P in R and form what is called a field of vectors. The *field lines* are those curves which are everywhere tangent to the field vectors. Thus at point P the vector $\mathbf{A}(P)$ is tangent to the field line which passes through P. Because of the single-valued nature of $\mathbf{A}$, no two field lines can cross each other at a nonzero angle.

The field lines must satisfy the differential equations

$$\frac{dx}{A_1} = \frac{dy}{A_2} = \frac{dz}{A_3} \tag{8-1}$$

Under the specified conditions these have solutions

$$u_1(x,y,z) = c_1 \tag{8-2}$$
$$u_2(x,y,z) = c_2 \tag{8-3}$$

where the constants c_1 and c_2 are constants of integration. The field lines are the curves of intersection of the surfaces (8-2) with the surfaces (8-3). Hence they comprise a two-parameter family of curves.

Now the vectors $\mathbf{A}$ are parallel to the field lines. So are the vectors

$$\nabla u_1 \times \nabla u_2$$

which follows from the earlier observation that the field lines are the intersections of (8-2) with (8-3). Hence

$$\mathbf{A} = K \nabla u_1 \times \nabla u_2 \tag{8-4}$$

where K is some scalar function of position in R.

Fix attention upon a point P in R, and imagine a small plane area S containing P and normal to the vector $\mathbf{A}(P)$. The field lines passing through S form a small bundle in the region R. The side surface of this bundle is a tube consisting of field lines, hence nowhere is there a component of **A** normal to the sides. There is, accordingly, no flux of **A** through the sides of the tube; the entire flux of **A** across S continues along the tube.

If **A** is the velocity of flow of some fluid, then the field lines are lines of instantaneous flow. They are called streamlines, and a bundle of streamlines, such as the bundle of field lines considered above, might be called a stream-tube. In the steady-state case, in which the flow does not change with time, the streamlines are the actual trajectories of the fluid particles. This is not necessarily true, however, for the general case in which the velocity vector $\mathbf{A}(P,t)$ changes with time. In such a case the streamlines and the fluid trajectories may differ markedly.

EXERCISES

1. Prove that the field lines of the vector field $\mathbf{A}(x,y,z)$ must satisfy the differential equations (8-1).

2. Determine the field lines of the gravitational force field due to a mass particle at the origin of coordinates.

3. Determine the field lines of the field $\mathbf{A} = y\mathbf{i} - x\mathbf{j}$.

4. Determine the field lines of the field $\mathbf{A} = x\mathbf{i} - y\mathbf{j}$.

5. Let $\mathbf{v}(P,t)$ be the velocity of flow of a fluid. According to (8-1) the streamlines are given by

$$\frac{dx}{v_1} = \frac{dy}{v_2} = \frac{dz}{v_3} \qquad (t \text{ fixed})$$

Show that the particle trajectories are given by

$$\frac{dx}{v_1} = \frac{dy}{v_2} = \frac{dz}{v_3} = dt \qquad (8\text{-}5)$$

6. Let the velocity of flow of a fluid be given by

$$\mathbf{v} = 3t^2 x\mathbf{i} + y\mathbf{j} + z\mathbf{k}$$

Find the streamlines and particle trajectories.

7. The velocity of flow of a fluid is

$$\mathbf{v} = 2t\mathbf{i} + \mathbf{j}$$

Find the fluid streamlines and trajectories.

8-3. Solenoidal Vectors

Throughout this section suppose that the vector **A** has continuous first derivatives in a region R. If div **A** vanishes everywhere within R, then the field **A** is free of sources and sinks. Such a field is said to be solenoidal.

Let V be a volume within R, and suppose that $\nabla \cdot \mathbf{A}$ is identically zero. From Gauss' theorem one has

$$\oint_{\substack{\text{bdy} \\ \text{of } V}} \mathbf{A} \cdot d\mathbf{S} = \int_V \nabla \cdot \mathbf{A} \, dV = 0 \qquad (8\text{-}6)$$

Hence the flux of $\mathbf{A}$ into V is exactly balanced by the flux of $\mathbf{A}$ out of V.

Now let V in (8-6) be a section cut from a tube of field lines by two plane areas S_1 and S_2 normal to the tube, as shown in Fig. 8-1. Since the sides of the tube consist entirely of field lines, there is no flux of $\mathbf{A}$ through the sides. Hence any flow of $\mathbf{A}$ into and out of V must be through S_1 and S_2. By virtue of (8-6) however, if there is a flux of $\mathbf{A}$ through S_1 into V there must be an equal flow through S_2 out of V. More generally, one concludes that the same total flux of $\mathbf{A}$ must transverse any

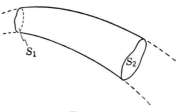

FIG. 8-1.

two cross-sectional areas S_1 and S_2 of the tube of field lines. This is a principal characteristic of solenoidal fields.

A second important characteristic of a solenoidal field is expressed in the following theorem. A necessary and sufficient condition that div $\mathbf{A}$ vanish identically is that $\mathbf{A}$ be the curl of some vector. The sufficiency is easily proved. For if $\mathbf{A} = \nabla \times \mathbf{B}$, then

$$\nabla \cdot \mathbf{A} = \frac{\partial}{\partial x}\left[\frac{\partial B_3}{\partial y} - \frac{\partial B_2}{\partial z}\right] + \frac{\partial}{\partial y}\left[\frac{\partial B_1}{\partial z} - \frac{\partial B_3}{\partial x}\right] + \frac{\partial}{\partial z}\left[\frac{\partial B_2}{\partial x} - \frac{\partial B_1}{\partial y}\right] \equiv 0$$

Now suppose that $\nabla \cdot \mathbf{A}$ vanishes identically. Write $\mathbf{A}$ in the form (8-4). Then K must be constant along a field line, for otherwise $\nabla \cdot \mathbf{A}$ could not vanish. This can be shown as follows.

Choose a differentiable function $u_3(x,y,z)$ such that the surfaces

$$u_3(x,y,z) = c_3$$

cut across the field lines. Then u_1 and u_2 of (8-2) and (8-3), together with u_3 can be used as general coordinates of the points of R. For these coordinates, the u_3 lines coincide with the field lines. Also,

$$\nabla u_1 \times \nabla u_2 \cdot \nabla u_3 \neq 0 \qquad (8\text{-}7)$$

Consider $\nabla \cdot \mathbf{A}$. From (8-4),

$$\begin{aligned}
\nabla \cdot \mathbf{A} &= \nabla \cdot [K \nabla u_1 \times \nabla u_2] \\
&= \nabla K \cdot \nabla u_1 \times \nabla u_2 + K \nabla \cdot [\nabla u_1 \times \nabla u_2]
\end{aligned}$$

where the second term on the right drops out since, as was shown earlier, the divergence of the cross product of two gradients vanishes. Thus

$$\nabla \cdot \mathbf{A} = \sum_{\alpha=1}^{3} \frac{\partial K}{\partial u_\alpha} \nabla u_\alpha \cdot \nabla u_1 \times \nabla u_2$$
$$= \frac{\partial K}{\partial u_3} \nabla u_3 \cdot \nabla u_1 \times \nabla u_2$$

Since $\nabla \cdot \mathbf{A}$ vanishes identically, while from (8-7) the determinant $\nabla u_3 \cdot \nabla u_1 \times \nabla u_2$ is never zero, it follows that

$$\frac{\partial K}{\partial u_3} \equiv 0$$

Thus K does not depend upon u_3; hence

$$K = K(u_1, u_2)$$

Form a new function $\phi(u_1, u_2)$ by integrating $K(u_1, u_2)$ along a u_1 line:

$$\phi(u_1, u_2) = \int^{u_1} K(u_1, u_2)\, du_1 \tag{8-8}$$

As indicated, ϕ is also independent of u_3. Now consider

$$\nabla \times (\phi \nabla u_2) = \nabla \phi \times \nabla u_2 + \phi \nabla \times \nabla u_2$$

Since the curl of a gradient vanishes identically, the second term on the right drops out. Thus

$$\nabla \times (\phi \nabla u_2) = \frac{\partial \phi}{\partial u_1} \nabla u_1 \times \nabla u_2 + \frac{\partial \phi}{\partial u_2} \nabla u_2 \times \nabla u_2 + \frac{\partial \phi}{\partial u_3} \nabla u_3 \times \nabla u_2$$

The second term on the right obviously drops out, while the last term vanishes because ϕ is independent of u_3. Evaluating $\partial \phi / \partial u_1$ from (8-8), one gets finally

$$\nabla \times (\phi \nabla u_2) = K \nabla u_1 \times \nabla u_2$$
$$= \mathbf{A}$$

This completes the proof of the theorem. In closing, however, it is well to note that the vector of which $\mathbf{A}$ is the curl is not unique. For if ψ is any differentiable function, one has

$$\nabla \times [\phi \nabla u_2 + \nabla \psi] = \mathbf{A}$$

since $\nabla \times \nabla \psi$ vanishes.

EXERCISES

1. Which of the following vectors can, and which cannot, be expressed as the curl of a vector:

a. $x\mathbf{i} + y\mathbf{j} + z\mathbf{k}$

b. $y\mathbf{i} + z\mathbf{j} + x\mathbf{k}$

c. $[e^y - x \cos (xz)]\mathbf{i} + [z \cos (xz)]\mathbf{k}$

2. $\mathbf{A} = \nabla \times \mathbf{B}$, where

$$\mathbf{B} = 2xy^2z\mathbf{i} + yz\mathbf{j} + x\mathbf{k}$$

Express $\mathbf{A}$ as the curl of a vector $\mathbf{C}$ which is everywhere normal to the x direction.

3. Show that a vector which is both irrotational and solenoidal has a scalar potential ϕ which must satisfy Laplace's equation:

$$\nabla^2\phi = 0$$

8-4. The Scalar Potential of an Irrotational Field

In Sec. 8-1 it was shown that an irrotational field $\mathbf{A}$ has a scalar potential ϕ such that

$$\mathbf{A} = \nabla\phi \tag{8-9}$$

The potential is unique to within an arbitrary additive constant K. For if ϕ satisfies (8-9), then so does $\phi + K$. Also, if ϕ_1 and ϕ both satisfy (8-9), then

$$\begin{aligned} \nabla(\phi_1 - \phi) &= \nabla\phi_1 - \nabla\phi \\ &= \mathbf{A} - \mathbf{A} \\ &= 0 \end{aligned}$$

Hence

$$\phi_1 - \phi = K$$
$$\phi_1 = \phi + K$$

where K is a constant.

Suppose that $\mathbf{A}$ has continuous first derivatives. Setting

$$\nabla \cdot \mathbf{A} = a \tag{8-10}$$

one has from (8-9) that

$$\nabla^2\phi = a \tag{8-11}$$

The relation (8-11) is known as Poisson's equation. It must be satisfied by the scalar potential.

The points at which a in (8-10) is positive are called sources of $\mathbf{A}$. Those at which a is negative are referred to as sinks. For convenience, however, the term sources will be extended here and henceforth to include both sources and sinks. At the sources of **A**, then, the potential ϕ satisfies Poisson's equation. At all other points a vanishes, and ϕ satisfies Laplace's equation:

$$\nabla^2\phi = 0 \qquad (8\text{-}12)$$

In particular, if all the sources of **A** are within some finite distance of the origin, then ϕ satisfies (8-12) for all points outside of some sphere about the origin as center.

The potential ϕ is said to be regular at infinity if

$$\phi = O\left(\frac{1}{r}\right)$$

as $r \rightarrow \infty$, where r is distance from some fixed finite point. By this notation is meant that $r\phi$ is bounded as r becomes infinite. If the irrotational vector **A** is $O(1/r^2)$ as $r \rightarrow \infty$, then **A** has a unique potential ϕ which is regular at infinity. In fact ϕ is given by

$$\phi(P) = \int_\infty^P \mathbf{A} \cdot d\mathbf{r}$$

Let P and P' be two points in space. Form the function

$$\psi(P,P') = \frac{1}{R} \qquad (8\text{-}13)$$

where R is the distance PP'. One can show readily that, except at P',

$$\nabla^2\psi = 0$$

where P' is held constant and the differentiation is carried out with respect to the coordinates of P. Similarly, except at P,

$$\nabla'^2\psi = 0$$

where the prime is used to indicate that the differentiation is carried out with respect to the coordinates of P'. In fact, one has

$$\nabla\psi = -\nabla'\psi$$

Suppose now that the vector **A** is irrotational in some region containing the closed region V, and let ϕ be a scalar potential of **A**. Let P' be any interior point of V, and consider the problem of calculating $\phi(P')$ from the sources of **A**. To this end let V' be a small sphere centered on P' and lying entirely in V. From Green's theorem, Exercise 7 of Sec. 6-2, one has, integrating over the points P of V-V',

$$\int_{V-V'} [\phi \nabla^2 \psi - \psi \nabla^2 \phi]\, dV = \oint_{\substack{\text{bdy} \\ \text{of } V}} [\phi \nabla \psi - \psi \nabla \phi] \cdot d\mathfrak{S}$$

$$+ \oint_{\substack{\text{bdy} \\ \text{of } V'}} [\phi \nabla \psi - \psi \nabla \phi] \cdot d\mathbf{S} \quad (8\text{-}14)$$

where ψ is any suitably differentiable function. The sphere V' has been excluded from the region V of integration to permit using (8-13) for the function ψ. With this choice, ψ becomes infinite when P approaches P'.

Since $\nabla^2 \psi$ vanishes, (8-14) reduces to

$$\oint_{\substack{\text{bdy} \\ \text{of } V'}} \left[\phi \nabla \left(\frac{1}{R} \right) - \frac{\nabla \phi}{R} \right] \cdot d\mathbf{S} = - \int_{V-V'} \frac{\nabla^2 \phi}{R}\, dV$$

$$+ \oint_{\substack{\text{bdy} \\ \text{of } V}} \left[\frac{\nabla \phi}{R} - \phi \nabla \left(\frac{1}{R} \right) \right] \cdot d\mathbf{S} \quad (8\text{-}15)$$

In the surface integrals the vectors $d\mathbf{S}$ point outward from V. Hence, for the integral on the left, $d\mathbf{S}$ points into the sphere V'. If $\mathbf{n}$ is the unit outer normal to the surface of V', and if ρ is the radius of the sphere, then for the surface integral on the left of (8-15)

$$d\mathbf{S} = -\mathbf{n}\, dS$$

$$\nabla \left(\frac{1}{R} \right) = - \frac{\mathbf{n}}{\rho^2}$$

Hence

$$\oint_{\substack{\text{bdy} \\ \text{of } V'}} \left[\phi \nabla \left(\frac{1}{R} \right) - \frac{\nabla \phi}{R} \right] \cdot d\mathbf{S} = \frac{1}{\rho^2} \oint_{\substack{\text{bdy} \\ \text{of } V'}} \phi\, dS + \frac{1}{\rho} \oint_{\substack{\text{bdy} \\ \text{of } V'}} (\nabla \phi \cdot \mathbf{n})\, dS$$

$$= \frac{4\pi \rho^2}{\rho^2} \bar{\phi} + \frac{4\pi \rho^2}{\rho} \overline{\nabla \phi \cdot \mathbf{n}}$$

$$= 4\pi \bar{\phi} + 4\pi \rho\, \overline{\nabla \phi \cdot \mathbf{n}}$$

where $\bar{\phi}$ is the value of ϕ at some point on the surface of V' and where $\overline{\nabla \phi \cdot \mathbf{n}}$ is the value of $\nabla \phi \cdot \mathbf{n}$ at some perhaps different point on the surface of V'. Hence

$$4\pi \bar{\phi} = - 4\pi \rho\, \overline{\nabla \phi \cdot \mathbf{n}} - \int_{V-V'} \frac{\nabla^2 \phi}{R}\, dV + \oint_{\substack{\text{bdy} \\ \text{of } V}} \left[\frac{\nabla \phi}{R} - \phi \nabla \left(\frac{1}{R} \right) \right] \cdot d\mathbf{S}$$

Replace $\nabla^2\phi$ by its value from (8-11), and let ρ diminish to zero. Since ϕ is continuous and $\nabla\phi$ is bounded, one gets, finally,

$$\phi(P') = -\frac{1}{4\pi}\int_V \frac{a}{R}\,dV + \frac{1}{4\pi}\oint_{\substack{\text{bdy}\\ \text{of } V}}\left[\frac{\nabla\phi}{R} - \phi\nabla\left(\frac{1}{R}\right)\right]\cdot d\mathbf{S} \quad (8\text{-}16)$$

In (8-16) the boundary of V may consist of a number of separate surfaces. But in the case in which $\mathbf{A}$ is everywhere differentiable and irrotational, V can be taken as a sphere about the origin large enough to include P'. Letting the radius of the sphere become infinite, one gets

$$\phi(P') = -\frac{1}{4\pi}\int_{\substack{\text{all}\\ \text{space}}} \frac{a}{R}\,dV + \lim\frac{1}{4\pi}\int_{\substack{\text{bdy}\\ \text{of } V}}\left[\frac{\nabla\phi}{R} - \phi\nabla\left(\frac{1}{R}\right)\right]\cdot d\mathbf{S} \quad (8\text{-}17)$$

If the limit of the surface integral exists, then the volume integral on the right also converges. In particular, if the limit of the surface integral is zero, one gets

$$\phi(P') = -\frac{1}{4\pi}\int_{\substack{\text{all}\\ \text{space}}} \frac{a}{R}\,dV \quad (8\text{-}18)$$

This can happen in the important case in which $\mathbf{A}$ is $O(1/r^2)$ as $r \to \infty$. For, in this case ϕ can be taken as regular at ∞. With such a choice for ϕ, the surface integral drops out of (8-17), leaving (8-18).

One can now conclude that an irrotational vector field which is $O(1/r^2)$ at ∞ is uniquely determined by its sources. For, the vector field has a unique scalar potential ϕ regular at ∞, which by the foregoing discussion must be given by (8-18). The field vector $\mathbf{A}$, then, is given uniquely by

$$\mathbf{A}(P') = \nabla'\phi$$

$$= -\frac{1}{4\pi}\int_{\substack{\text{all}\\ \text{space}}} a\nabla'\left(\frac{1}{R}\right)dV$$

or, finally

$$\mathbf{A}(P') = \frac{1}{4\pi}\int_{\substack{\text{all}\\ \text{space}}} a\nabla\left(\frac{1}{R}\right)dV \quad (8\text{-}19)$$

In the event that the sources of $\mathbf{A}$ are confined to some finite region of space, the integration in (8-19) reduces to a summation over the finite region or regions containing the sources of $\mathbf{A}$.

EXERCISES

1. Prove that if $\mathbf{A}$ is irrotational and $O\left(\dfrac{1}{r^2}\right)$ as $r \to \infty$, then $\mathbf{A}$ has a unique scalar potential regular at ∞.

2. Show that the function ψ of (8-13) satisfies Laplace's equation.

3. For the function ψ of (8-13), prove that

$$\nabla \psi = -\nabla' \psi$$

4. Let V be a sphere of radius r about the origin of coordinates, and let P' be a fixed point within V. Let ϕ be regular at ∞. Prove that

$$\lim_{r \to \infty} \int_{\substack{\text{bdy} \\ \text{of } V}} \left[\frac{\nabla \phi}{R} - \phi \nabla \left(\frac{1}{R} \right) \right] \cdot d\mathbf{S} = 0$$

where R is the distance from P' to the variable point P on the surface of integration, and where the differentiations ∇ are with respect to the coordinates of P.

5. Let $\dfrac{\partial}{\partial n}$ denote differentiation in the direction of the outer normal to the surface S. Show that

$$\int_S \left[\frac{\nabla \phi}{R} - \phi \nabla \left(\frac{1}{R} \right) \right] \cdot d\mathbf{S} = \int_S \left[\frac{1}{R} \frac{\partial \phi}{\partial n} - \phi \frac{\partial}{\partial n} \left(\frac{1}{R} \right) \right] dS$$

6. Suppose that the sources of an irrotational vector field $\mathbf{A}$ are continuous and confined to some finite region of space. Suppose further that the contribution per unit volume of the sources in any elemental volume ΔV containing the point P, to the field vector $\mathbf{A}(P')$ at a specified point P', is given by

$$\frac{\bar{a}}{4\pi R^2} \mathbf{R}^0$$

where $\mathbf{R}^0$ is the unit vector directed from P to P', R is the distance PP', and $\bar{a}$ is the source strength of $\mathbf{A}$ at some point in ΔV. Show directly that

$$\mathbf{A} = \frac{1}{4\pi} \int_{\substack{\text{all} \\ \text{sources} \\ \text{of } \mathbf{A}}} a \nabla \left(\frac{1}{R} \right) dV \tag{8-20}$$

7. For the vector field of Exercise 6, show that the scalar potential ϕ can be taken as

$$\phi = -\frac{1}{4\pi} \int_{\substack{\text{all} \\ \text{sources} \\ \text{of A}}} \frac{a}{R}\, dV \tag{8-21}$$

8. Show that ϕ of (8-21) is regular at ∞.

9. Show that **A** of (8-20) is $O\!\left(\dfrac{1}{r^2}\right)$ at ∞.

10. Let **A** be $O\!\left(\dfrac{1}{r^2}\right)$ at ∞, and let it be both irrotational and solenoidal everywhere. Prove that **A** vanishes identically.

11. Let $\phi(P')$ be given by (8-18). Suppose that a has continuous first derivatives and is $O\!\left(\dfrac{1}{r^3}\right)$ as $r \to \infty$. Prove directly that

$$\nabla'^2\,\phi = a$$

12. Let $a(P')$ be a function of position P', with continuous first derivatives. Suppose that $a(P')$ is $O\!\left(\dfrac{1}{r^3}\right)$ as $r \to \infty$. Prove that there exists a vector field **A** such that

$$\nabla' \cdot \mathbf{A} = a$$

8-5. The Vector Potential of a Solenoidal Field

Let **A** be solenoidal everywhere, and $O(1/r^2)$ at ∞. Set

$$\nabla \times \mathbf{A} = \mathbf{b}$$

where necessarily $\nabla \cdot \mathbf{b}$ vanishes. The points at which $\mathbf{b} \neq 0$ are called vortices of **A**. Suppose that the vortices of **A** have continuous first derivatives and are confined to some finite portion of space.

Consider the vector

$$\mathbf{B}(P') = \frac{1}{4\pi} \int_V \frac{\mathbf{b}}{R}\, dV \tag{8-22}$$

where V is a region containing in its interior all of the vortices of **A** and where R is the distance from P' to the variable point P of integration. This is a vector analog to (8-18). By reasoning similar to that underlying the solution of Exercise 11, Sec. 8-4, one has

$$\nabla'^2\mathbf{B} = -\mathbf{b}$$

Also,

$$\nabla' \cdot \mathbf{B} = \frac{1}{4\pi} \int_V \nabla' \cdot \left(\frac{\mathbf{b}}{R}\right) dV$$

$$= \frac{1}{4\pi} \int_V \mathbf{b} \cdot \nabla' \left(\frac{1}{R}\right) dV$$

$$= -\frac{1}{4\pi} \int_V \mathbf{b} \cdot \nabla \left(\frac{1}{R}\right) dV$$

$$= -\frac{1}{4\pi} \int_V \left[\nabla \cdot \left(\frac{\mathbf{b}}{R}\right) - \frac{\nabla \cdot \mathbf{b}}{R}\right] dV$$

$$= -\frac{1}{4\pi} \int_V \nabla \cdot \left(\frac{\mathbf{b}}{R}\right) dV$$

$$= -\frac{1}{4\pi} \int_{\substack{\text{bdy} \\ \text{of } V}} \frac{\mathbf{b}}{R} \cdot d\mathbf{S}$$

But $\mathbf{b}$ vanishes everywhere on the surface of V, whence

$$\nabla' \cdot \mathbf{B} \equiv 0$$

Now

$$\nabla' \times (\nabla' \times \mathbf{B}) = \nabla'(\nabla' \cdot \mathbf{B}) - \nabla'^2 \mathbf{B}$$
$$= \mathbf{b}$$
$$= \nabla' \times \mathbf{A}$$

It follows that from Exercise 8 of Sec. 8-1, that

$$\mathbf{A} = \nabla' \times \mathbf{B} + \nabla'\psi$$

for some ψ. But both $\mathbf{A}$ and $\mathbf{B}$ are $O(1/r^2)$ at ∞, whence so is $\nabla'\psi$. Also,

$$\nabla' \cdot \mathbf{A} = \nabla' \cdot \nabla' \times \mathbf{B} + \nabla'^2\psi$$
$$\nabla'^2\psi \equiv 0$$

Thus $\nabla'\psi$ is both irrotational and solenoidal everywhere. By Exercise 10 of Sec. 8-4, $\nabla'\psi$ vanishes everywhere. Thus,

$$\mathbf{A} = \nabla' \times \mathbf{B}$$

where $\mathbf{B}$ is given by (8-22). Hence, finally,

$$\mathbf{A}(P') = \frac{1}{4\pi} \int_V \nabla' \times \left(\frac{\mathbf{b}}{R}\right) dV$$

$$= \frac{1}{4\pi} \int_V \nabla' \left(\frac{1}{R}\right) \times \mathbf{b} \, dV$$

$$\mathbf{A}(P') = \frac{1}{4\pi} \int_V \mathbf{b} \times \nabla \left(\frac{1}{R}\right) dV \qquad (8\text{-}23)$$

The given solenoidal vector field is, therefore, uniquely determined by its vortices.

EXERCISE

Let $\mathbf{B}(P')$ be given by (8-22). Prove that

$$\nabla'^2 \mathbf{B} = -\mathbf{b}$$

8-6. Resolution of a Field into Irrotational and Solenoidal Parts

Suppose the vector field $\mathbf{A}$ to possess continuous second derivatives everywhere and to be $O(1/r^2)$ at ∞. Let

$$\nabla \cdot \mathbf{A} = a$$
$$\nabla \times \mathbf{A} = \mathbf{b}$$

where a and $\mathbf{b}$ are continuous, and where necessarily

$$\nabla \cdot \mathbf{b} = 0$$

Suppose that the sources and vortices of $\mathbf{A}$ are confined to some finite region of space.

Since irrotational and solenoidal fields have proven to be uniquely determined, the one by its sources, the other by its vortices, the question naturally arises as to whether the general field $\mathbf{A}$ above can be resolved into the sum of an irrotational field $\mathbf{B}$ with a solenoidal field $\mathbf{C}$.

Suppose that such a separation of $\mathbf{A}$ can be made:

$$\mathbf{A} = \mathbf{B} + \mathbf{C}$$

Then

$$\nabla \cdot \mathbf{A} = \nabla \cdot \mathbf{B} + \nabla \cdot \mathbf{C}$$
$$= \nabla \cdot \mathbf{B}$$

or

$$\nabla \cdot \mathbf{B} = a$$

Thus the irrotational part of $\mathbf{A}$ must have the same sources as $\mathbf{A}$. There is one and only one such vector $\mathbf{B}$, given by

$$\mathbf{B} = \frac{1}{4\pi} \int\limits_{\substack{\text{all} \\ \text{sources} \\ \text{of } \mathbf{A}}} a\nabla \left(\frac{1}{R}\right) dV \tag{8-24}$$

Continuing,

$$\nabla \times \mathbf{A} = \nabla \times \mathbf{B} + \nabla \times \mathbf{C}$$
$$= \nabla \times \mathbf{C}$$

or

$$\nabla \times \mathbf{C} = \mathbf{b}$$

Hence the solenoidal part of $\mathbf{A}$ must have the same vortices as $\mathbf{A}$. There is one and only one such vector $\mathbf{C}$, given by

$$\mathbf{C} = \frac{1}{4\pi} \int_{\substack{\text{all} \\ \text{vortices} \\ \text{of } \mathbf{A}}} \mathbf{b} \times \nabla\left(\frac{1}{R}\right) dV$$

Hence there is at most one resolution of $\mathbf{A}$ into the sum of an irrotational vector with a solenoidal vector.

Now write $\mathbf{A}$ as the sum

$$\mathbf{A} = \mathbf{B} + \mathbf{C}' \tag{8-25}$$

where $\mathbf{B}$ is given by (8-24). Equation (8-25) expresses $\mathbf{A}$ as the sum of an irrotational vector $\mathbf{B}$ plus another vector $\mathbf{C}'$ which at the moment is determined solely by the fact that it is the difference between $\mathbf{A}$ and $\mathbf{B}$. But, taking divergences on both sides of (8-25),

$$\nabla \cdot \mathbf{A} = \nabla \cdot \mathbf{B} + \nabla \cdot \mathbf{C}'$$
$$a = a + \nabla \cdot \mathbf{C}'$$
$$\nabla \cdot \mathbf{C}' = 0$$

Hence there is at least one resolution of $\mathbf{A}$ into the sum of an irrotational vector with a solenoidal vector.

One concludes that there is one and only one resolution of the given vector field $\mathbf{A}$ into an irrotational and a solenoidal part. Specifically,

$$\mathbf{A}(P') = \frac{1}{4\pi} \int_{\substack{\text{all} \\ \text{sources} \\ \text{of } \mathbf{A}}} a\nabla\left(\frac{1}{R}\right) dV + \frac{1}{4\pi} \int_{\substack{\text{all} \\ \text{vortices} \\ \text{of } \mathbf{A}}} \mathbf{b} \times \nabla\left(\frac{1}{R}\right) dV$$

$$\mathbf{A}(P') = \nabla'\left[\frac{-1}{4\pi} \int_{\substack{\text{all} \\ \text{sources} \\ \text{of } \mathbf{A}}} \frac{a}{R} dV\right] + \nabla' \times \left[\frac{1}{4\pi} \int_{\substack{\text{all} \\ \text{vortices} \\ \text{of } \mathbf{A}}} \frac{\mathbf{b}}{R} dV\right]$$

EXERCISE

Let $\mathbf{A}$ and $\mathbf{B}$ be $O\left(\dfrac{1}{r^2}\right)$ at ∞. Suppose that $\mathbf{A}$ is irrotational everywhere, and that $\mathbf{B}$ is solenoidal everywhere. Prove that

$$\int_{\substack{\text{all} \\ \text{space}}} \mathbf{A} \cdot \mathbf{B}\, dV = 0$$

(*Hint:* Let ϕ be the scalar potential of **A** which is regular at ∞. Let S be the surface of a sphere about the origin. Apply Gauss' theorem to

$$\oint_S \phi \mathbf{B} \cdot d\mathbf{S}$$

and then let S recede to ∞.)

8-7. Behavior of Potential and Gradient Field at Large Distances from the Generating Sources

The preceding sections dealt with vector fields and potentials generated by sources and vortices which were continuous. In many practical problems, however, it is far simpler and adequate to consider discontinuous sources, such as point charges, mass particles, or surface distributions of charge.

The concept of a point source, for example, arises quite naturally when the irrotational field to which a continuous distribution of sources gives rise is observed at great distances from the sources. Let V be a region containing all the sources, and let P' be a point far removed from V. Consider the corresponding potential $\phi(P')$:

$$\phi(P') = -\frac{1}{4\pi} \int_V \frac{a}{R} \, dV$$

where R is the distance PP' from the variable point P of integration to the field point P'. Within V pick an origin O as shown in Fig. 8-2,

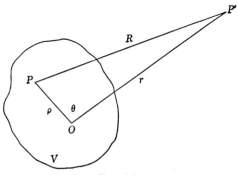

Fig. 8-2.

and let r and ρ denote OP' and OP respectively. Let θ be the angle $P'OP$. Using the law of cosines one can rewrite the expression for ϕ as follows:

$$\phi(P') = -\frac{1}{4\pi} \int_V a[r^2 + \rho^2 - 2r\rho \cos \theta]^{-\frac{1}{2}} \, dV$$

$$= -\frac{1}{4\pi} \int_V \frac{a}{r} \left[1 + \left(\frac{\rho^2}{r^2} - 2\frac{\rho}{r} \cos \theta \right) \right]^{-\frac{1}{2}} dV$$

$$= -\frac{1}{4\pi} \int_V \frac{a}{r} \left[1 - \frac{1}{2} \left(\frac{\rho^2}{r^2} - 2\frac{\rho}{r} \cos \theta \right) + \frac{3}{8} \left(\frac{\rho^2}{r^2} - 2\frac{\rho}{r} \cos \theta \right)^2 \right.$$
$$\left. + \cdots \right] dV$$

$$= -\frac{1}{4\pi} \int_V \frac{a}{r} \left[1 + \frac{\rho}{r} \cos \theta + \frac{1}{2} \frac{\rho^2}{r^2} (3 \cos^2 \theta - 1) + \cdots \right] dV$$

The expansion is valid and term by term integration permissible, if

$$\left| \frac{\rho^2}{r^2} - 2\frac{\rho}{r} \cos \theta \right| < 1$$

which is certainly true for r large. Also r is a constant with respect to the integration. Thus, finally,

$$\phi(P') = -\frac{1}{4\pi r} \int_V a \, dV - \frac{1}{4\pi r^2} \int_V a\rho \cos \theta \, dV$$
$$- \frac{1}{8\pi r^3} \int_V a\rho^2 (3 \cos^2 \theta - 1) \, dV - \cdots \quad (8\text{-}26)$$

The behavior of the vector field $\nabla \phi$ can be deduced from (8-26) which expresses ϕ as an infinite series of potentials $\phi_1, \phi_2, \ldots, \phi_n, \ldots,$ where ϕ_n is $O(1/r^n)$ at ∞. Thus, to first order approximation $\phi(P')$ is given by ϕ_1 where

$$\phi_1(P') = -\frac{q}{4\pi r} \qquad q = \int_V a \, dV \qquad (8\text{-}27)$$

The corresponding contribution to the vector field is

$$\nabla' \phi_1 = \frac{q}{4\pi r^2} \mathbf{r}^0$$

where $\mathbf{r}^0$ is the unit vector directed from O toward P'. One can readily verify that (8-27) satisfies Laplace's equation everywhere except at the origin, at which point potential and gradient field both become infinite.

Should the sum q of all the sources vanish, then the potential ϕ_2 becomes the dominant part of ϕ, where

$$\phi_2(P') = -\frac{1}{4\pi r^2} \int_V a\rho \cos \theta \, dV \qquad (8\text{-}28)$$

The nature of ϕ_2 can be understood a little better by transforming the integral on the right of (8-28) as follows.   Set

$$a\rho \cos \theta = a\rho\varrho^0 \cdot \mathbf{r}^0$$

where ϱ^0 is the unit vector from O toward P.   One has, then:

$$\int_V a\rho \cos \theta \, dV = \int_V a\rho\varrho^0 \cdot \mathbf{r}^0 \, dV$$
$$= \mathbf{r}^0 \cdot \int_V a\rho\varrho^0 \, dV$$

The vector $\mathbf{r}^0$ can be withdrawn from under the integral sign since it is independent of the variable point P of integration.   But once this is done, the integral becomes a vector $\mathbf{m}$ which is independent of P'. Hence (8-28) takes the form

$$\phi_2 = -\frac{\mathbf{m} \cdot \mathbf{r}^0}{4\pi r^2} \tag{8-29}$$

Let (r, θ, Φ) be spherical polar coordinates, the θ axis of which lies in the direction of $\mathbf{m}$.   Then

$$\phi_2(P') = -\frac{m \cos \theta}{4\pi r^2} \tag{8-30}$$

This is the potential due to what is called a dipole source of which m is said to be the dipole moment.   The corresponding dipole vector field is given by $\nabla' \phi_2$, and is analogous to that which would be generated by two equal sources of opposite sign located very close to each other relative to the distance of P' from the sources.   It can be shown that ϕ_2 satisfies Laplace's equation except at the origin, where both potential and gradient field are discontinuous.

One can continue in similar fashion to examine individually the various potentials ϕ_3, ϕ_4, . . . in the expansion of ϕ.   Each ϕ_n will be found to satisfy Laplace's equation except at the origin.   Also it can be shown that the corresponding gradient field possesses a characteristic geometry and can be approximated to by the field generated by finitely many point sources arranged in an appropriate array and all close to each other relative to the distance to P'.   Further consideration of these higher-order multipole sources, as they are called, is left to the interested reader.

EXERCISES

1. For the expansion (8-26) obtain the term in $\frac{1}{r^4}$.

2. Show that ϕ_2 in (8-30) satisfies Laplace's equation everywhere except at the origin.

3. Calculate $\nabla' \phi_2$, where ϕ_2 is given in (8-30).

4. Determine the field lines of the vector field $\nabla' \phi_2$, where ϕ_2 is given in (8-30).

5. Let a source $-q$ be located at the origin of a system of spherical polar coordinates. Let a second source q be located on the half-line $\theta = 0$ at a distance l from the origin. Suppose that each of the sources generates a potential of the type (8-27). Obtain the potential for the point source created by letting $l \to 0$ while q increases simultaneously in such a way that ql remains constant. By comparing your answer with (8-30), show that the above procedure gives rise to a point dipole source.

6. Let a point dipole source of vector moment $-\mathbf{m}$ be located at the origin. Let a second dipole source, of moment $\mathbf{m}$, be located on the half-line $\theta = 0$ at a distance l from the origin. Suppose that the direction of $\mathbf{m}$ coincides with that of the ray $\theta = 0$. Now let l vanish while at the same time m increases in such a way that lm remains constant. The point source so generated is called an axial quadrupole. Obtain the potential and gradient field of an axial quadrupole.

7. Show that the potential of an axial quadrupole satisfies Laplace's equation except at the source point itself.

8. Rework Exercise 6 for the case in which the direction of $\mathbf{m}$ differs from that of the half-line $\theta = 0$.

8-8. Potential of a Gradient Field Due to Discontinuous Sources†

If an intense concentration of gradient field sources exists in a small volume, it is often convenient to replace the actual distribution by a single point source, such as one of those described in the preceding section. When n such concentrations are involved, they may be replaced by n point sources of potentials $\phi_1, \ldots, \phi_n$. Their combined effect is to generate a potential ϕ given by

$$\phi = \sum_{\nu=1}^{n} \phi_\nu$$

Often the intense concentration is spread out in a very thin layer over some surface, as, for example, electric charge on the surface of a conductor. In such a case it is convenient to introduce the concept of a surface distribution of sources. This can be done as follows. Let S be the surface in question, and let P' be a point not on S. Let V be a thin volume enclosing S, consisting of very thin layers on opposite sides of S. Take V thin enough to exclude the point P'. Suppose sources a to be distributed continuously throughout V. The potential at P' due to these

† Henceforth all potentials will be assumed regular at ∞.

sources is

$$\phi(P') = -\frac{1}{4\pi} \int_V \frac{a}{R} \, dV$$

where as usual R is the distance from P' to the point P of integration. If h is the thickness of V measured normally to S, the volume integral can be written as the surface integral:

$$\phi(P') = -\frac{1}{4\pi} \int_S \frac{\bar{a}h}{R} \, dS$$

where $\bar{a}$ is a suitable mean value of a. Let $h \to 0$ and suppose that $\bar{a}$ simultaneously increases in such a way that

$$\lim \bar{a}h = \omega$$

In this way one is led from a very thin volume distribution of sources to a surface distribution. The corresponding potential becomes

$$\phi(P') = -\frac{1}{4\pi} \int_S \frac{\omega}{R} \, dS \tag{8-31}$$

The surface distribution ω in (8-31) comprises what may be called a simple layer of sources. Sometimes the concept of a double layer is useful. Such a layer of dipole sources can be generated as follows.

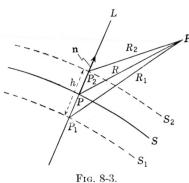

FIG. 8-3.

Let the surface S be given, and let P' be a point not on S. As in Fig. 8-3, let S_1 and S_2 be two surfaces very close to but on opposite sides of S. Take S_1 and S_2 sufficiently close together that P' does not lie between them. Let P denote the general point on S. Through P imagine the line L normal to S and intersecting S_1 and S_2 in P_1 and P_2 respectively. Suppose that on S_1 and S_2 there are simple layers of sources ω, such that

$$\omega(P_1) = -\omega(P_2) \tag{8-32}$$

The potential at P' due to these two simple layers is given by

$$\phi(P') = -\frac{1}{4\pi} \int_{S_2} \frac{\omega(P_2)}{R_2} \, dS - \frac{1}{4\pi} \int_{S_1} \frac{\omega(P_1)}{R_1} \, dS$$

where $R_1 = P'P_1$ and $R_2 = P'P_2$. Because of (8-32) and the relationship between P, P_1, and P_2, the two integrals can be combined into a single integral over S:

$$\phi(P') = -\frac{1}{4\pi} \int_S \omega \left[\frac{1}{R_2} - \frac{1}{R_1} \right] dS$$

Let $\mathbf{n}$ be the unit normal to S in the direction from S_1 to S_2. Denote the distance P_1P_2 by h, and the distance $P'P$ by R. Then

$$\frac{1}{R_2} - \frac{1}{R_1} = \nabla \left(\frac{1}{R} \right) \cdot \mathbf{n}h$$

where the differentiation is with respect to the coordinates of P. Thus, setting $\mathbf{n}\, dS = d\mathbf{S}$,

$$\phi(P') = -\frac{1}{4\pi} \int_S \omega h \nabla \left(\frac{1}{R} \right) \cdot d\mathbf{S}$$

Let $h \to 0$, and suppose that simultaneously ω increases in such a way that

$$\lim \omega h = \tau$$

One is led by this process to a double layer distribution over S, of moment τ. The corresponding potential at P' is

$$\phi(P') = -\frac{1}{4\pi} \int_S \tau \nabla \left(\frac{1}{R} \right) \cdot d\mathbf{S}$$

The foregoing discussion can now be summarized in a single result as follows. Suppose that an irrotational field has continuous sources a contained within a finite volume V; a finite number of point sources of potentials $\phi_1, \ldots, \phi_n$; simple layer distributions of sources ω on a collection S_1 of finite surfaces; and double layer distributions of sources of moments τ on a collection S_2 of finite surfaces. Let P' be a point not on any of the surfaces S_1 or S_2, and not coinciding with any of the point sources. Then the potential at P' of the given field is

$$\phi(P') = -\frac{1}{4\pi} \int_V \frac{a}{R} dV + \sum_{\nu=1}^{n} \phi_\nu - \frac{1}{4\pi} \int_{S_1} \frac{\omega}{R} dS - \frac{1}{4\pi} \int_{S_2} \tau \nabla \left(\frac{1}{R} \right) \cdot d\mathbf{S}$$

EXERCISES

1. Let S be some surface in space, and let P' be a given point. Consider the bundle of lines $P'P$ where P ranges over all points of S. This bundle cuts an area Ω out of the surface of the sphere of unit radius about P' as center. The area Ω, divided by unit area to render it non-dimensional, is said to be the solid angle subtended at P' by S.

Assign a positive and a negative side to S. Let $\mathbf{n}$ be the unit normal to S at P, directed from the negative to the positive side of S. Let R be the distance $P'P$, and let $\mathbf{R}^0$ be the unit vector from P' toward P. Then the solid angle $d\Omega$ of an element dS of S is said to be positive or negative according as the corresponding value of $\mathbf{R}^0 \cdot \mathbf{n}$ is positive or negative.

Prove that

$$\Omega = -\int_S \nabla \left(\frac{1}{R}\right) \cdot d\mathbf{S}$$

where $d\mathbf{S} = \mathbf{n}\, dS$, and where the differentiation in ∇ is with respect to the coordinates of P.

2. Consider a simple closed surface S, and let the interior surface of S be designated as the negative side. Prove that S subtends a solid angle 4π or 0 at a point P' according as P' is interior or exterior to the volume bounded by S.

3. Using the results of Exercise 1, prove that the potential of a double layer on a surface S is

$$\phi(P') = \frac{1}{4\pi} \int_S \tau \, d\Omega$$

where $d\Omega$ is the solid angle subtended at P' by $d\mathbf{S}$, and where the positive side of S is taken to coincide with the positive side of the double layer. In particular, if τ is uniform,

$$\phi(P') = \frac{\tau \Omega}{4\pi}$$

where Ω is the solid angle subtended at P' by S.

4. Let S be a simple closed surface covered with a uniform double layer of moment τ. Suppose the negative side of the layer and of S are both toward the interior of the volume bounded by S. Prove that $\phi(P')$ equals τ or 0 according as P' is interior or exterior to the volume bounded by S.

8-9. Discontinuities in Potential and Gradient Field Due to Discontinuous Sources

It has already been pointed out that both the potential and gradient field of a point source are discontinuous at the source point itself. Consider now the question of their behavior when a simple or double layer is crossed. First take the case of a simple layer of density ω on the surface S.

Let P be a point of S, and let L be a line normal to S at P. Let P' be a point on L. The potential at P' due to the simple layer on S is given by

$$\phi(P') = -\frac{1}{4\pi} \int_S \frac{\omega}{R} \, dS$$

where, as usual, R denotes the distance from P' to the variable point of integration.

Imagine a small circular disk, centered on P, cut from S. Let ϕ be divided into two parts ϕ_1 and ϕ_2, where ϕ_1 is the contribution of the disk, while ϕ_2 is the contribution from the remainder of S. As P' moves along L from one side of S to the other, $\phi_2(P')$ varies continuously, since P' is always at a positive distance from the nearest point on the part of S generating ϕ_2. Consider then the behavior of $\phi_1(P')$.

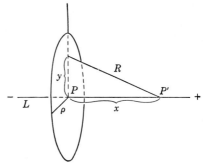

Fig. 8-4.

Let Fig. 8-4 depict the disk generating $\phi_1(P')$. Pick a set of coordinates x on L, as shown. Now suppose the radius ρ of the disk to be so small that the curvature of S may be disregarded, and ω may be considered as constant over the face of the disk. On some line normal to L at P, choose coordinates y. Then

$$\phi_1(P') = -\frac{1}{4\pi} \int_{\text{disk}} \frac{\omega}{R} \, dS$$

$$= -\frac{\omega}{4\pi} \int_0^\rho \frac{2\pi y \, dy}{\sqrt{x^2 + y^2}}$$

$$\phi_1(P') = -\frac{\omega}{2} [\sqrt{x^2 + \rho^2} - \sqrt{x^2}] \tag{8-33}$$

From (8-33) it is clear that ϕ_1 varies continuously along the line L from one side of S to the other. Hence so does ϕ.

Consider now the variation of $\nabla'\phi(P')$ as P' moves along L. Using the same notation as before, $\nabla'\phi_2$ varies continuously from one side of S to the other. It remains, then, to examine $\nabla'\phi_1$, given by

$$\nabla'\phi_1 = -\frac{\omega}{2} \frac{\partial}{\partial x} [\sqrt{x^2 + \rho^2} - \sqrt{x^2}] \, \mathbf{i}$$

where $\mathbf{i}$ is the unit vector in the positive x direction. Thus

$$\nabla'\phi_1 = -\frac{\omega}{2} \left[\frac{x}{\sqrt{x^2 + \rho^2}} - \frac{x}{\sqrt{x^2}} \right] \mathbf{i}$$

From this it is seen that $\nabla' \phi_1$ points in the direction of $\mathbf{i}$ for x positive, and in the direction of $-\mathbf{i}$ for x negative. Also

$$\lim_{x \to 0^+} \nabla' \phi_1 = \frac{\omega}{2} \mathbf{i}$$

$$\lim_{x \to 0^-} \nabla' \phi_1 = -\frac{\omega}{2} \mathbf{i}$$

Hence $\nabla' \phi_1$ has a discontinuity of amount $\omega \mathbf{i}$ as P' passes through P. The same is true of $\nabla' \phi$.

The final conclusion is that a gradient field in crossing a surface S bearing a simple layer of sources of density ω, experiences a discontinuity of amount ω in the component normal to S.

The case of a double layer of sources can be handled similarly. It is left to the reader to show that in passing through a double layer of moment τ a gradient field varies continuously, whereas its potential changes suddenly by an amount τ.

EXERCISES

1. Let S be a surface bearing a double layer of sources of moment τ. Prove that in crossing S, the potential due to the double layer changes by an amount τ.

2. Let S be the surface of Exercise 1. Prove that in crossing S the gradient field generated by the double layer varies continuously from one side to the other.

REFERENCES

Abraham, M. and R. Becker: "The Classical Theory of Electricity and Magnetism," translated by J. Dougall, Hafner Publishing Company, New York, 1932.

Joos, G.: "Theoretical Physics," translated by I. M. Freeman, G. E. Stechert & Company, New York, 1934.

Phillips, H. B.: "Vector Analysis," John Wiley & Sons, Inc., New York, 1933.

Sternberg, W. J., and T. L. Smith: "The Theory of Potential and Spherical Harmonics," University of Toronto Press, Toronto, 1944.

PART II

APPLICATIONS

CHAPTER 9

MISCELLANEOUS APPLICATIONS

9-1. Forces

Forces are vector quantities, and vector techniques are applicable to the solution of force problems. Since the physical effect of a force depends upon the point of application of the force as well as upon its magnitude and direction, one usually has to handle forces as vectors localized in space.

Suppose a rigid system of bodies is at rest. Then the vector sum of all forces acting on the system is zero.

Let $\mathbf{F}$ be one of the forces applied to the system at rest, and let P be any point. Let $\mathbf{r}$ be the vector from P to the point of application of $\mathbf{F}$. Then $\mathbf{r} \times \mathbf{F}$ is a measure of the tendency of $\mathbf{F}$ to turn the system about the point P. It is called the moment of $\mathbf{F}$ with respect to P. That the system be at rest requires that the vector sum of the moments relative to any chosen point of all applied forces vanish.

To specify completely the resultant of a set of forces, one must give not only the vector sum of the forces, but also the line of action. This line of action is that which makes the moment of the vector sum about any point equal to the sum of the separate moments about that point.

EXERCISES

1. Let a rigid body at rest be acted upon by a set of forces. Prove that the sum of the components in any direction of the applied forces vanishes together with the sum of their moments about any point.

2. A boom of uniform cross section is 10 ft long and weighs 50 lb. It is fastened at one end to a vertical post, and supported at the other end by a line running back to a pulley on the post. When the boom is horizontal the line makes an angle of 30° with the boom. At this time what is the tension in the line, and what force does the boom exert on its fastening to the wall?

3. A gate 4 ft high and 3 ft wide is supported on hinges, one 6 in. from the top, the other 1 ft from the bottom. What forces does the gate exert on the fastenings?

4. Let **A** and **B** be two nonparallel forces applied to a rigid body, but not necessarily at the same point. Show how to determine the resultant of **A** and **B**.

5. Rework Exercise 4 for the case in which **A** and **B** are parallel and similarly directed.

6. What is the effect of applying two noncollinear, equal, parallel, but opposite forces to a rigid body? Such a pair of forces is called a couple.

7. A charge Q is distributed uniformly along a rod l centimeters long located in a vacuum. Obtain formulas for the magnitude and direction of the force exerted by the rod upon another charge q, s cm from the rod on a line normal to the rod at one of its ends. (*Hint:* Divide the rod into elemental pieces dx, of total charge $Q\,dx/l$. Then use Coulomb's law (Exercise 17, Sec. 1-4) to calculate the elemental force $d\mathbf{F}$ exerted by this element of charge on q. Finally, obtain the total force **F** by integration, facilitating the calculation by getting separately the components parallel to and normal to the rod.)

9-2. Velocities

As an illustration of problems involving the composition of independent velocities into a resultant velocity, consider the motion of an aircraft in flight. Suppose that the air through which the plane is flying is in motion as a steady wind **W**. At the same time, due to the action of its power plant, the plane moves through the surrounding air mass with a velocity **V** which is entirely independent of the wind. Its motion over the ground is given by the velocity **G**, where

$$\mathbf{G} = \mathbf{V} + \mathbf{W} \tag{9-1}$$

Elementary applications of (9-1) have already been taken up in some of the exercises of Chap. 1. A further application is illustrated in the following example. Suppose an aircraft to have just 6 hr of flying time at a true air speed of 200 knots. Its destination is an airbase A, 1,000 nautical miles S 35° E from the point of origin O. At flight altitude the wind is from the northeast at 40 knots. It appears that the weather may close in at A, so an alternate base B, 300 nautical miles due north of A is chosen to use in case landing at A proves impossible. Determine:

1. The heading to be flown in going directly from O to A, and the corresponding ground speed.
2. The farthest point P from O toward A to which the plane can proceed and still make the alternate airport.
3. The heading and course from P to B, and the corresponding ground speed.

A graphical solution appears in Fig. 9-1.

First the wind triangle is drawn to obtain the heading to be followed in flying from O to A. At the same time the ground speed along the track OA is determined.

Next the line OR is drawn in the direction of the heading for flight from O to A, and of length corresponding to the true air speed times the available flight time. Thus OR is $6 \times 200 = 1,200$ units long. This represents the total path length through the air which the plane can fly. This total path length is independent of the direction of flight.

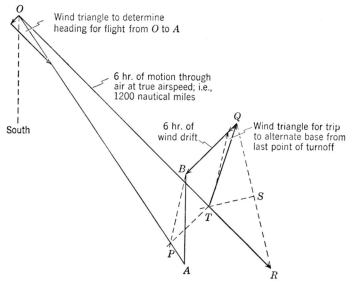

FIG. 9-1. Solution of an alternate airport problem.

Next the arrow BQ is drawn back from B with tail into the direction from which the wind blows. Its length is made equal to the total flying time times the wind velocity; that is, 6×40 or 240 units. Thus QB represents the total drift of the plane during 6 hr of flight.

Draw QR. Erect ST perpendicular to QR at its mid-point S. Let T be the intersection of ST with OR. Draw TQ. Through T draw a line TP parallel to the wind direction and intersecting OA in point P. The point P is the last possible turning-off point for the plane. The direction of PB will be the course to the alternate base; and the direction of TQ will be the required heading. By means of the wind triangle drawn in along QB and TQ as shown, the ground speed along PB can be determined.

It is left to the reader to fill in the details needed to prove that the given construction actually gives the desired solution.

EXERCISES

1. Complete the discussion of the alternate airport problem of the text, proving that the given construction does determine the last point P at which the plane can turn off to the alternate base and still arrive there within the prescribed flying time. Prove also that the solution obtained is the only one there is.

2. Carry through the graphical solution to the alternate airport problem of the text, obtaining the required heading for the flight from O to A, and the corresponding ground speed; the distance from O to P, the last possible point of turnoff; and the required heading, course, and ground speed from P to B. What is the maximum length of time the plane can fly toward A and still make it to the alternate base B?

3. Consider again the alternate airport problem of the text, and refer to the drawing of Fig. 9-2. On a suitable scale draw in the wind vector OW, as shown. Draw lines L_1 and L_2 in the directions from O toward A and from O toward B. With W as center, and on the same scale as OW, strike a circle C of radius corresponding to the 200-knot air speed of the plane. Denote the intersection of C with L_1 by H. The direction of WH is the heading of the plane for the flight from O to A, and the length of OH gives the corresponding ground speed.

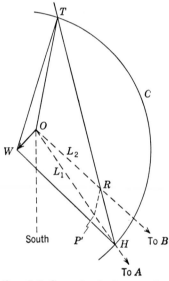

FIG. 9-2. Second solution to alternate airport problem.

On L_2 mark the point R such that length OR represents one-sixth of the distance OB; that is, the distance to the alternate base divided by the total flight time. Draw HR and extend it until it intersects the circle C in a second point T.

Prove that the direction of WT is the required heading of the plane for its flight to B from the last possible turnoff point P on OA. Prove also that OT represents the ground speed and course for the flight from P to B.

Draw the line RP' through R parallel to OT, intersecting OH in P'. Show that OP'/OH times the total flight time gives the time of flight between O and the last possible turnoff point P; or equivalently that OP' times the total flight time gives the distance OP.

(*Hint:* Begin by proving that exactly one hour is consumed in flying OP' at ground speed OH followed by $P'R$ at ground speed OT.)

4. An aircraft carrier is steaming at a fixed rate on a given course. One of its planes with a given total flying time and cruising speed is to make a reconnaissance flight along a straight track having a specified bearing from the position of the carrier at takeoff. The wind aloft is steady. Show how to use the method of Exercise 3 to determine the maximum distance the plane can fly on its reconnaissance run before having to return to the carrier.

5. An aircraft carrier is steaming due west at 15 knots. The wind aloft is from the north at 25 knots. A plane with a total flying time of 4 hr and cruising air speed of 130 knots takes off to make a reconnaissance flight along a track running S 30° W from the point of origin. Find the heading and ground speed for the reconnaissance leg; the maximum time and distance over the ground which the plane can fly on the outward leg and still make it back to the carrier; and the heading, track, and ground speed back to the carrier. What will be the maximum distance between plane and carrier?

9-3. Accelerations

As in the cases of forces and velocities it is not intended to go into any exhaustive treatment of the subject of accelerations but rather to put before the student a few illustrative exercises. Fundamental to many acceleration problems is Newton's law:

$$m\mathbf{a} = \mathbf{F} \tag{9-2}$$

where m is the mass of a particle, $\mathbf{F}$ is a force acting on m, and $\mathbf{a}$ is the acceleration which the force imparts to m. If the force happens to be that due to gravity, then $\mathbf{F}$ is referred to as the weight $\mathbf{W}$ of the mass m, while the acceleration is commonly denoted by $\mathbf{g}$ instead of $\mathbf{a}$.

Picking an origin of coordinates, the displacement of the particle m from the origin can be denoted by the vector $\mathbf{r}$. Then the particle's velocity $\mathbf{v}$ is given by

$$\mathbf{v} = \dot{\mathbf{r}}$$

and its acceleration by

$$\mathbf{a} = \dot{\mathbf{v}} = \ddot{\mathbf{r}}$$

These relations can be used in conjunction with (9-2) to determine the position of m as a function of time.

EXERCISES

1. A rocket weighs 10,000 lb at takeoff, of which 7,500 lb is propellant material. The motor thrust acts along the axis of the rocket and is constant at 20,000 lb throughout powered flight. If the rocket heading is always at 10° to the vertical, what is the inclination to the vertical of the path of flight (a) at takeoff, and (b) at the time when the propellants are just being exhausted?

2. A rocket weighs 10,000 lb at takeoff, and its motor has a rated thrust of 20,000 lb acting along the axis of the rocket. The buildup from zero to full thrust, however, is essentially linear and takes 1 sec after the starting switch is thrown. Suppose the rocket launching stand is tilted so that before takeoff the rocket leans at 5° from the vertical, and that then the internal controls are set so as to maintain this heading for all of the powered flight. At what time after the firing switch is thrown will the rocket leave the launching stand? What will be the path of the rocket from the time of takeoff to the time of full thrust?

3. An electron is 4 cm from a 6-cm rod on a line normal to the rod at its center. The rod bears a positive charge of 1 esu distributed uniformly along the rod. The electron is free to move, and starts from rest. After traveling one centimeter, how fast is the electron moving? Use $e/m = 5.3 \times 10^{17}$ esu/g.

4. Let a particle of mass m be attracted toward the origin by a force which is purely a function of distance r from the origin. Show that the particle moves so that:

a. its radius vector from the origin sweeps out area at a constant rate; and,

b. its path lies entirely in one plane.

(*Hint:* The equation of motion is of the form

$$m\ddot{\mathbf{r}} = f(r)\mathbf{r} \qquad (9\text{-}3)$$

Take the vector product of both sides with $\mathbf{r}$, and integrate.)

5. If the force of attraction in Exercise 4 varies inversely as the square of the distance from the origin, obtain an expression for the speed v of the particle in terms of the distance r from the origin and the initial values r_0, v_0 of r and v. (*Hint:* In (9-3) put the proper expression for $f(r)$; take the scalar product of both sides with $\mathbf{r}$; use the fact that

$$\mathbf{r} \cdot d\mathbf{r} = r\, dr$$

and integrate.)

9-4. Transformations of Coordinates

Sometimes in the treatment of a problem it becomes convenient to change from one coordinate system to another. Often such a shift of coordinates simplifies greatly the algebra required in the solution of the problem. One important class of transformations can be visualized by thinking of the coordinate axes as being moved rigidly in space, while the points of space remain fixed. In general the coordinates of a given point are changed by the relocation of the axes.

Suppose, for example, that the axes are translated without changing their orientation in space. Let **r** and **R** be the positional vectors of a point P relative to the first and the second positions of the coordinate axes. Let **a** be the vector from the initial position of the origin of coordinates to its new position. Then clearly

$$\mathbf{R} = \mathbf{r} - \mathbf{a} \qquad (9\text{-}4)$$

Let (x,y,z) and (X,Y,Z) be the old and the new coordinates respectively. The same base vectors **i**, **j**, **k** can be used in both cases. Equation (9-4) becomes

$$X\mathbf{i} + Y\mathbf{j} + Z\mathbf{k} = (x - a_1)\mathbf{i} + (y - a_2)\mathbf{j} + (z - a_3)\mathbf{k}$$

$$\begin{aligned} X &= x - a_1 \\ Y &= y - a_2 \\ Z &= z - a_3 \end{aligned} \qquad (9\text{-}5)$$

As a second case, suppose that the orientation of the axes is changed, but that the origin remains fixed. Again let (x,y,z) and (X,Y,Z) denote the old and the new coordinates. In this case, because of the change in orientation, one set **i**, **j**, **k** of base vectors must be used for the old coordinates and a different set **I**, **J**, **K** for the new. Let **r** and **R** denote the positional vector of a given point P relative to the old and the new coordinates respectively. Then

$$\mathbf{R} = \mathbf{r}$$

or

$$X\mathbf{I} + Y\mathbf{J} + Z\mathbf{K} = x\mathbf{i} + y\mathbf{j} + z\mathbf{k} \qquad (9\text{-}6)$$

Take the scalar product of both sides with **I**, then with **J**, and finally with **K**:

$$\begin{aligned} X &= (\mathbf{i} \cdot \mathbf{I})x + (\mathbf{j} \cdot \mathbf{I})y + (\mathbf{k} \cdot \mathbf{I})z \\ Y &= (\mathbf{i} \cdot \mathbf{J})x + (\mathbf{j} \cdot \mathbf{J})y + (\mathbf{k} \cdot \mathbf{J})z \\ Z &= (\mathbf{i} \cdot \mathbf{K})x + (\mathbf{j} \cdot \mathbf{K})y + (\mathbf{k} \cdot \mathbf{K})z \end{aligned} \qquad (9\text{-}7)$$

Thus the new coordinates are related to the old ones by a linear transformation in which the coefficients are the cosines of the angles between the old and the new axes. The inverse transformation can be obtained either by solving (9-7) for x, y, z, or by taking the scalar product of both sides of (9-6) with **i**, **j**, and **k** respectively. The result is again a linear transformation:

$$x = (\mathbf{I} \cdot \mathbf{i})X + (\mathbf{J} \cdot \mathbf{i})Y + (\mathbf{K} \cdot \mathbf{i})Z$$
$$y = (\mathbf{I} \cdot \mathbf{j})X + (\mathbf{J} \cdot \mathbf{j})Y + (\mathbf{K} \cdot \mathbf{j})Z \qquad (9\text{-}8)$$
$$z = (\mathbf{I} \cdot \mathbf{k})X + (\mathbf{J} \cdot \mathbf{k})Y + (\mathbf{K} \cdot \mathbf{k})Z$$

Note that the determinant of the coefficients in (9-8) can be obtained from the determinant of (9-7) simply by interchanging rows and columns. It can be shown that both determinants are equal to unity. The proof is left to the reader.

The change in orientation of a set of axes, the origin of which remains fixed, can be thought of as brought about by rotating the system about some fixed line. This can be shown with the help of (9-7). For, if there is such a line, it must pass through the origin, and the new coordinates (X,Y,Z) of every point on the line must be the same as the old coordinates (x,y,z). Thus, the equations

$$x = (\mathbf{i} \cdot \mathbf{I})x + (\mathbf{j} \cdot \mathbf{I})y + (\mathbf{k} \cdot \mathbf{I})z$$
$$y = (\mathbf{i} \cdot \mathbf{J})x + (\mathbf{j} \cdot \mathbf{J})y + (\mathbf{k} \cdot \mathbf{J})z$$
$$z = (\mathbf{i} \cdot \mathbf{K})x + (\mathbf{j} \cdot \mathbf{K})y + (\mathbf{k} \cdot \mathbf{K})z$$

or

$$[(\mathbf{i} \cdot \mathbf{I}) - 1]x + (\mathbf{j} \cdot \mathbf{I})y + (\mathbf{k} \cdot \mathbf{I})z = 0$$
$$(\mathbf{i} \cdot \mathbf{J})x + [(\mathbf{j} \cdot \mathbf{J}) - 1]y + (\mathbf{k} \cdot \mathbf{J})z = 0 \qquad (9\text{-}9)$$
$$(\mathbf{i} \cdot \mathbf{K})x + (\mathbf{j} \cdot \mathbf{K})y + [(\mathbf{k} \cdot \mathbf{K}) - 1]z = 0$$

must have a solution other than $(0,0,0)$. Conversely, if there is a point P not the origin, the coordinates of which satisfy (9-9), then the shift of coordinate axes can be brought about by rotating them about OP.

But the equations (9-9) have a solution for (x,y,z) other than $(0,0,0)$, if and only if the determinant Δ' of its coefficients vanishes. It can readily be shown that Δ' is zero. This then establishes that a change in the orientation, but not the origin, of a set of coordinate axes is equivalent to a rotation of the axes about some line through the origin.

The most general change of coordinates due to a rigid movement of the reference axes can be obtained by translating the axes so as to bring the origin to its new position, and then rotating the axes about a line through the new origin. The corresponding transformation of coordinates can be obtained by combining (9-5) and (9-7).

The foregoing discussion presented transformations of coordinates brought about by moving the coordinate axes rigidly. The points of space were visualized as remaining fixed while the axes moved to a new position. But one can just as well think of the axes as remaining fixed while the points of space move. The coordinate transformations are still given by (9-5) and (9-7), except that now the capital letters refer to the original coordinates, while the small letters represent the new ones.

In particular, one can conclude that a rigid motion of space which leaves one point fixed is equivalent to a rotation of the points of space about some line through the fixed point. This is known as Euler's theorem.

EXERCISES

1. Let **i**, **j**, **k** and **I**, **J**, **K** be two right-handed sets of mutually orthogonal unit vectors. Prove that

$$(\mathbf{i} \cdot \mathbf{I})^2 + (\mathbf{j} \cdot \mathbf{I})^2 + (\mathbf{k} \cdot \mathbf{I})^2 = 1$$
$$(\mathbf{i} \cdot \mathbf{I})(\mathbf{i} \cdot \mathbf{J}) + (\mathbf{j} \cdot \mathbf{I})(\mathbf{j} \cdot \mathbf{J}) + (\mathbf{k} \cdot \mathbf{I})(\mathbf{k} \cdot \mathbf{J}) = 0$$

What is the geometric significance of these relations? Write out 10 other similar relations, and prove them.

2. Let Δ be the determinant of the coefficients of (9-7). Prove that $\Delta = 1$. (*Hint:* Show first that Δ must be positive. Then compute Δ^2 by the usual rule for multiplying determinants, and using the results of Exercise 1.)

3. Let Δ' be the determinant of the equations (9-9). Prove that $\Delta' = 0$. (*Hint:* Form the product $\Delta'\Delta$, where Δ is the determinant of Exercise 2.)

4. Write in both vector and cartesian coordinate form, the translation which carries the point $\mathbf{i} + \mathbf{j} + \mathbf{k}$ into the point $\mathbf{i} - \mathbf{j}$.

5. Given the transformation

$$\sqrt{2}\, X = \quad -y - z$$
$$\sqrt{2}\, Y = \quad\quad y - z$$
$$Z = x$$

Show that the origin remains fixed. Find the direction angles of the axis of the equivalent rotation, and determine the angle of rotation.

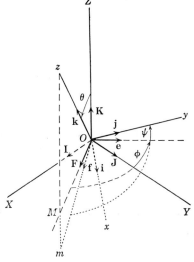

Fig. 9-3. Eulerian angles.

9-5. Eulerian Angles

For many problems involving angular motion of bodies in space, a set of parameters known as Eulerian angles is very useful. As in Fig. 9-3 let O be the common origin of two sets of rectangular coordinate axes $O\text{-}XYZ$ and $O\text{-}xyz$. Suppose the axes $O\text{-}XYZ$ to be fixed in space, and let **I**, **J**, **K** be unit vectors in the directions of OX, OY, and OZ respectively. Let **i**, **j** and **k** be unit vectors along Ox, Oy, and Oz respectively.

Let **e** be the unit vector in the direction of **K** × **k**. Then the Eulerian angles θ, ϕ, ψ are as follows:

θ is the angle from **K** to **k**

ϕ is the angle from **J** to **e**

ψ is the angle from **e** to **j**

Let the plane ZOz intersect plane XOY in OM, and plane xOy in Om. Let **F** and **f** be the unit vectors at the origin in the directions OM and Om respectively. Then **K**, **k**, **F**, and **f** all lie in the plane ZOz; **I**, **J**, **F**, and **e** all lie in XOY; and **i**, **j**, **e**, and **f** all lie in xOy. As a consequence,

$$\mathbf{i} = \cos \psi \mathbf{f} + \sin \psi \mathbf{e}$$
$$\mathbf{e} = -\sin \phi \mathbf{I} + \cos \phi \mathbf{J}$$
$$\mathbf{f} = \cos \theta \mathbf{F} - \sin \theta \mathbf{K}$$
$$\mathbf{F} = \cos \phi \mathbf{I} + \sin \phi \mathbf{J}$$

Hence

$$\mathbf{i} = \cos \psi [\cos \theta (\cos \phi \mathbf{I} + \sin \phi \mathbf{J}) - \sin \theta \mathbf{K}] + \sin \psi [-\sin \phi \mathbf{I} + \cos \phi \mathbf{J}]$$
$$\mathbf{i} = [\cos \theta \cos \phi \cos \psi - \sin \phi \sin \psi]\mathbf{I}$$
$$+ [\cos \theta \sin \phi \cos \psi + \cos \phi \sin \psi]\mathbf{J} - \sin \theta \cos \psi \mathbf{K} \quad (9\text{-}10)$$

From (9-10) the direction cosines of Ox relative to the axes $O\text{-}XYZ$ are found to be as in the top line of the table below:

	X	Y	Z
x	$\cos \theta \cos \phi \cos \psi - \sin \phi \sin \psi$	$\cos \theta \sin \phi \cos \psi + \cos \phi \sin \psi$	$-\sin \theta \cos \psi$
y	$-\cos \theta \cos \phi \sin \psi - \sin \phi \cos \psi$	$-\cos \theta \sin \phi \sin \psi + \cos \phi \cos \psi$	$\sin \theta \sin \psi$
z	$\sin \theta \cos \phi$	$\sin \theta \sin \phi$	$\cos \theta$

The remainder of the table is derived in similar fashion by expressing both **j** and **k** in terms of **I**, **J**, **K**, θ, ϕ, ψ. By reading in columns instead of rows, one gets from the table the direction cosines of OX, OY, and OZ relative to the axes $O\text{-}xyz$.

EXERCISES

1. Verify that the Eulerian angles correspond to what are commonly called pitch, yaw, and roll.

2. Complete the derivation of the table of direction cosines given in the text.

3. Using the notation of the text, express **I**, **J**, **K** in terms of **i**, **j**, **k**, θ, ϕ, ψ.

REFERENCES

Dickson, L. E.: "New First Course in the Theory of Equations," John Wiley & Sons, Inc., New York, 1939.

Whittaker, E. T.: "A Treatise on the Analytical Dynamics of Particles and Rigid Bodies," Cambridge University Press, New York, 1937.

CHAPTER 10

MOTIONS IN SPACE

10-1. Rigid Motions in Space

Rotation of physical bodies is fundamental to many engineering applications and scientific phenomena. Yet quite often such rotational motions are not clearly understood, apparently due largely to difficulty experienced in attempting to visualize mentally what takes place physically. The material in the present chapter is intended to provide a basic set of concepts and facts in terms of which the general motions of bodies and particles in space can be understood.

For the discussion to follow it will be necessary to visualize a reference space, thought of as fixed, with respect to which the motions under study are considered. In any physical case, such a space would be defined in terms of some physical objects. Most commonly such a framework of reference consists of the walls and floor of a room, and for many practical problems this is entirely adequate in spite of the fact that the reference frame is itself rotating, being attached to the earth. For great fixity the stars can be used as a reference, although even in this case relative motions of the earth, sun, and stars cause the reference frame to rotate. The rotation is so exceedingly small, however, that in virtually every practical case it can be ignored. Leaving aside the problem of how actually to find one, in the discussion to follow the existence of a fixed frame of reference, or fixed space, will be assumed. Henceforth, the term "space" will be used to mean "the fixed reference space."

Customarily the motion of a physical body is thought of entirely as a motion of the material comprising the body. For the sake of generality, however, it will be convenient to visualize a second space rigidly attached to the body, moving and rotating as the body does. In a more general sense, then, the term "body" will mean "the space attached to the body." On this basis a "line in the body" may not actually pass through the material body itself but might be simply a "line in the space attached to the body," that is, a line which remains fixed relative to the body. Similarly, a point in the space of the body will be referred to as a point of the body.

Certain elementary facts are fundamental to the understanding of motion in space. Some are listed below. They should be understood clearly and fixed firmly in mind.

1. The position of a rigid body in space is specified uniquely when the positions in space of three noncollinear points of the body are specified.

2. A body is said to be translated when all points of the body are moved an equal distance in the same direction.

The analytic representation of a translation of a body is analogous to (9-4) for the rigid translation of a set of coordinate axes. Relative to a fixed origin in space the general point of the body before translation can be represented by a vector $\mathbf{r}$, and after translation by a different vector $\mathbf{R}$. For each point of the body, the difference $\mathbf{R} - \mathbf{r}$ between the new and the old positional vectors must be just the constant vector $\mathbf{a}$, the magnitude and direction of which are the magnitude and direction of the translation. Thus, the analytic transformation which represents the physical translation is simply

$$\mathbf{R} = \mathbf{r} + \mathbf{a} \qquad (10\text{-}1)$$

3. A motion of a rigid body which leaves every point of a line-in-the-body fixed in space is a simple rotation of every point of the body through a common angle about the fixed line.

The fixed line is called the axis of rotation. Statement 3 serves to define what is meant by a simple rotation. As long as the axis remains fixed in space, the points of the body are constrained to move in arcs of circles orthogonal to and centered on the axis. Plainly all points of the body sweep out arcs of the same number of degrees. The central angle corresponding to these arcs is called the angle of the rotation.

By their wording, statements 2 and 3 lead one to think of actual physical motions. In the former case one thinks of the points of the body as moving at a common rate in a common fixed direction, while in the latter case one imagines the points as sliding along circular paths and turning at a common angular rate about the axis. Often, however, the paths by which the points of the body come to their final positions are immaterial, only the relationship between the original and final locations being of interest. This latter relationship, in fact, is all that the analytic expression (10-1) for a translation provides. Thus, the actual motions of the body in passing from the original to the final positions may have been very complicated, but if the relation (10-1) holds, the end result could have been accomplished by a simple translation of the body. This fact is expressed by saying that the translation is equivalent to the motion which actually occurred. The equivalence, of course, refers solely to the sameness of the end result. On this basis it will be shown in the course of the present discussion that the most general transportation of a rigid body is equivalent to a simple translation combined with a simple rotation.

4. *Any transportation of a rigid body which leaves a point-of-the-body fixed in space is equivalent to a simple rotation of the body about some line through that point.*

Statement 4 is known as Euler's theorem. It implies that in a rigid motion for which there is a fixed point in space there is also necessarily a line of fixed points in space. Here especially it is important to observe that Euler's theorem expresses a relationship between initial and final positions of the body. During the actual physical motion every line and point may have moved. But if any one point finally returned to its original position, then all the points of at least one line also returned to their original positions. The proof of Euler's theorem was given in Sec. 9-4.

Consider the motion M of a body in which a line L of the body retains its original direction in space. Then a simple translation T will bring the points of L back to their original positions. Hence the combination of M followed by T is equivalent to a simple rotation of the body through some angle θ about a fixed axis in space. Since no rotation occurs during the translation T, it is customary to say that in the motion M the body was rotated about L through the angle θ. This convention permits speaking of rotation about a line-in-the-body even though the line changes in position, but not in direction. The following statements are now easy to verify:

5. *If a rigid body is rotated through an angle about a line-in-the-body, the direction of the line, but not necessarily its position, in space remaining fixed, the body is at the same time rotated through an equal angle about every other line-in-the-body parallel to the first line.*

6. *The rotation of a rigid body about any line-in-the-body fixed in space is equivalent to an equal rotation about any parallel line-in-the-body fixed in space followed or preceded by a translation perpendicular to the axis of rotation.*

Conversely, a rotation about a line-in-the-body fixed in space followed or preceded by a translation perpendicular to the axis of rotation is equivalent to an equal rotation alone about some parallel line-in-the-body fixed in space.

EXERCISES

1. Prove statement 5 of the text.
2. Prove statement 6 of the text.

10-2. The Most General Motion of a Rigid Body

The most general motion of a rigid body can be accomplished by a translation followed by a simple rotation about some line fixed in space. This is done simply by translating the body so that a specified point moves to its new position in space; after which the remainder of the motion leaves that point fixed in its new position and can accordingly, by Euler's theorem, be a simple rotation about some line through that point. The direction of the axis and the amount of rotation are independent of the translation, as will become apparent from the discussion in the next paragraph.

Any of the translations used above may be separated into two components, one parallel and the other perpendicular to the axis of rotation. The perpendicular component plus the rotation may then be replaced by a simple rotation of equal amount about some parallel axis. It follows that the most general motion of a rigid body can be accomplished by a translation followed by a rotation about an axis parallel to the direction of translation. It is plain that for a motion which is not purely a translation there can be only one such axis, that the amount of translation is unique and the amount of rotation unique except for addition of multiples of 2π radians, that the motion leaves the axis fixed in space except for the sliding of its points along the axis, and that the translation may precede, follow, or accompany the rotation. Such a motion is called a screw. The most general motion of a rigid body is, therefore, a screw.

EXERCISE

Prove that the axis of a given screw is unique, and that the angle of rotation is unique except for additive multiples of 2π radians.

10-3. Analytic Representation of a Screw

It is a simple matter to represent a screw motion analytically. Suppose that the line L of Fig. 10-1 is the axis of the screw. Let **e** be the unit vector along L in the direction of the translational component of the screw. Let **a** be the point on L nearest the origin of coordinates. Let D be the amount of translational motion, and let η be the angle of rotation about L. Let **R** be the point into which an arbitrary point **r** of the body is carried by the screw, and let **A** be the point into which **r** is carried by the translation alone. Let **C** be the common foot of the perpendiculars from **A** and **R** onto L. Let **B** be the foot of the perpendicular from **R** onto **A** − **C**.

$$\mathbf{A} = \mathbf{r} + D\mathbf{e}$$

Also

$$C = a + (r - a) \cdot ee + De$$
$$B = A + (C - A)(1 - \cos \eta)$$

Note that $R - B$ is normal to both $A - a$ and e, and that

$$|R - B| = |A - C| \, |\sin \eta|$$

But, from the figure,

$$|e \times (A - a)| = |A - C|$$

Hence

$$R - B = e \times (A - a) \sin \eta$$

Thus

$$R = A + (C - A)(1 - \cos \eta) + e \times (A - a) \sin \eta$$
$$= r + De + [a + (r - a) \cdot ee + De - r - De](1 - \cos \eta)$$
$$+ e \times (r + De - a) \sin \eta$$

$$R = r + De + e \times (r - a) \sin \eta$$
$$+ [(r - a) \cdot ee - (r - a)](1 - \cos \eta) \quad (10\text{-}2)$$

Relation (10-2) connects the coordinates of any point of the body in its initial position with those of the same point of the body in its final position following the application of the screw.

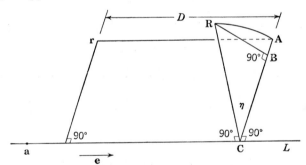

FIG. 10-1. Analysis of a screw motion.

EXERCISES

1. Write in cartesian coordinate form the transformation which equation (10-2) expresses in vector form.

2. Rewrite (10-2) so as to represent the motion consisting solely of a rotation of angle η about a line through the origin.

3. To what does the equation obtained in Exercise 2 reduce if the angle of rotation is the infinitesimal $\Delta\eta$ and higher-order terms are neglected?

4. Use the result of Exercise 3 to show that infinitesimal rotations are vector quantities.

10-4. Continuous Motion of a Rigid Body

Suppose that a rigid body is moving in any fashion whatever. Then from the discussion of Sec. 10-2 it is plain that at each instant of time when the motion is not purely translational, there is a unique line-fixed-in-space about which the body is rotating and along which it is sliding. That is, there is a unique line-in-the-body which is momentarily fixed-in-space except for motion along the line itself. The fixed line is called the instantaneous axis of rotation.

Relative to a point fixed in the body, the motion appears to be simply a rotation identical with that about the instantaneous axis. For this reason it is convenient to express the motion of a rigid body as a combination of the motion through space of a point fixed in the body, together with the rotations of the body relative to the moving point.

Pick any point in the moving body and let $\mathbf{R}_0(t)$ be its positional vector relative to some fixed origin O. Let $\mathbf{r}(t)$ and $\mathbf{R}(t)$ be the positional vectors of any arbitrary point of the body referred to $\mathbf{R}_0$ and O respectively. As indicated, all these vectors are functions of time t. First

$$\mathbf{R} = \mathbf{R}_0 + \mathbf{r}$$

from which, using a dot to denote differentiation with respect to time:

$$\dot{\mathbf{R}} = \dot{\mathbf{R}}_0 + \dot{\mathbf{r}}$$

Since the points $\mathbf{R}_0$ and $\mathbf{r}$ are fixed in the body and since $\mathbf{r}$ is referred to $\mathbf{R}_0$, the only variation in the vector $\mathbf{r}$ will be that due to rotation.

Suppose that at time t the direction of the instantaneous axis of rotation is that of the unit vector $\mathbf{e}$. Let $\Delta\theta$ be the angle through which the body rotates about the instantaneous axis in the interval from t to $t + \Delta t$. Since $\mathbf{e}$ is momentarily fixed, one can use (10-2) with D and $\mathbf{a}$ equal to zero and η replaced by $\Delta\theta$, to give $\mathbf{r}(t + \Delta t)$ in terms of $\mathbf{r}(t)$. Dropping terms of higher order, one has

$$\mathbf{r}(t + \Delta t) - \mathbf{r}(t) = \mathbf{e} \times \mathbf{r}(t) \sin \Delta\theta$$
$$\frac{\mathbf{r}(t + \Delta t) - \mathbf{r}(t)}{\Delta t} = \mathbf{e} \times \mathbf{r}(t) \frac{\sin \Delta\theta}{\Delta t}$$

Letting $\Delta t \to 0$,

$$\dot{\mathbf{r}}(t) = \mathbf{e}(t)\dot{\theta} \times \mathbf{r}(t)$$

or

$$\dot{\mathbf{r}} = \boldsymbol{\omega} \times \mathbf{r} \tag{10-3}$$

where $\boldsymbol{\omega}$ is the vector $\mathbf{e}\dot{\theta}$.

The vector ω is called the instantaneous angular velocity of the moving body. It is plainly just the instantaneous rate of rotation of the body about the instantaneous axis of rotation.

One has, finally,

$$\dot{R} = \dot{R}_0 + \omega \times r \tag{10-4}$$

The total motion $\dot{R}$ of a point in the body is separated by (10-4) into the translational motion $\dot{R}_0$ through space of a reference point R_0 fixed in the body plus the rotational motion $\omega \times r$ of the point in the body relative to the reference point R_0.

EXERCISES

1. How fast is a floor in the District of Columbia turning about the vertical direction?

2. Describe qualitatively and quantitatively how the vertical direction in the District of Columbia is changing in space with time.

10-5. Time Variation of a Vector Referred to Moving Axes

It is now a simple matter to obtain the absolute time variation of a vector A in terms of its apparent time variation relative to a moving system of axes. For if

$$A = a_1 e_1 + a_2 e_2 + a_3 e_3$$

where the e_ν are the instantaneous unit vectors along the three axes of the moving system, then

$$\dot{A} = \dot{a}_1 e_1 + \dot{a}_2 e_2 + \dot{a}_3 e_3 + a_1 \dot{e}_1 + a_2 \dot{e}_2 + a_3 \dot{e}_3$$

But relation (10-3) above clearly applies to the vectors e_ν, so that

$$\dot{A} = \dot{a}_1 e_1 + \dot{a}_2 e_2 + \dot{a}_3 e_3 + a_1 \omega \times e_1 + a_2 \omega \times e_2 + a_3 \omega \times e_3$$

where ω is the instantaneous angular velocity of the moving axes. Thus

$$\dot{A} = \dot{a}_1 e_1 + \dot{a}_2 e_2 + \dot{a}_3 e_3 + \omega \times (a_1 e_1 + a_2 e_2 + a_3 e_3) = \dot{a}_1 e_1 + \dot{a}_2 e_2 + \dot{a}_3 e_3 + \omega \times A$$

But the expression

$$\dot{a}_1 e_1 + \dot{a}_2 e_2 + \dot{a}_3 e_3$$

gives the apparent rate of change of A as seen by an observer who moves with the moving axes but who ignores the motion of those axes. If this apparent rate of change be denoted by $d'A/dt$, one has

$$\dot{A} = \frac{d'A}{dt} + \omega \times A$$

This relation is intuitively evident from the fact that the rate of change of $\mathbf{A}$ should be that which would occur if $\mathbf{A}$ were fixed in the moving system, namely $\boldsymbol{\omega} \times \mathbf{A}$, plus the apparent rate of change of $\mathbf{A}$ within the system, namely $d'\mathbf{A}/dt$.

Symbolically for any vector *referred to the moving system of axes*, one has

$$\frac{d}{dt} = \frac{d'}{dt} + \boldsymbol{\omega} \times \qquad (10\text{-}5)$$

As a check, one may observe that (10-5) applied to the positional vector $\mathbf{r}$ of a point fixed in the moving system, for which

$$\frac{d'\mathbf{r}}{dt} = 0$$

gives

$$\dot{\mathbf{r}} = \boldsymbol{\omega} \times \mathbf{r}$$

as it should.

It is also of interest to observe that the time variation of the angular velocity of a moving system is given by

$$\dot{\boldsymbol{\omega}} = \frac{d'\boldsymbol{\omega}}{dt} + \boldsymbol{\omega} \times \boldsymbol{\omega}$$

or

$$\dot{\boldsymbol{\omega}} = \frac{d'\boldsymbol{\omega}}{dt}$$

Thus the absolute time variation of $\boldsymbol{\omega}$ and the apparent time variation of $\boldsymbol{\omega}$ are identical. This is an immediate consequence of the fact that in both cases directions are referred to fixed space. Moreover, it is plain that the rotational motion alone should have no effect upon vectors parallel to the axis of rotation, and $\boldsymbol{\omega}$ is always parallel to the axis. The quantity

$$\dot{\boldsymbol{\omega}} = \frac{d'\boldsymbol{\omega}}{dt}$$

is called the angular acceleration of the moving system.

EXERCISE

A particle of mass m slides at a constant rate v along a radius of a turntable whirling at a constant angular rate ω. What is the momentum in space of the particle? Use two methods to obtain your result.

10-6. Motion of a Particle Referred to a Moving System

Let $\mathbf{R}$ be the positional vector of a moving particle referred to a fixed system of coordinates, and let $\mathbf{r}$ be its position vector relative to a moving set of axes. Then

$$\mathbf{R} = \mathbf{R}_0 + \mathbf{r}$$

where $\mathbf{R}_0$ is the origin of the moving axes referred to the fixed system. The absolute velocity $\dot{\mathbf{R}}$ is given by

$$\dot{\mathbf{R}} = \dot{\mathbf{R}}_0 + \dot{\mathbf{r}}$$
$$= \dot{\mathbf{R}}_0 + \frac{d'\mathbf{r}}{dt} + \boldsymbol{\omega} \times \mathbf{r}$$

From this the apparent velocity in the moving system becomes

$$\frac{d'\mathbf{r}}{dt} = \dot{\mathbf{R}} - \dot{\mathbf{R}}_0 - \boldsymbol{\omega} \times \mathbf{r}$$

To obtain the apparent velocity of a particle referred to moving coordinates, one must correct the absolute velocity $\dot{\mathbf{R}}$ for velocity $\dot{\mathbf{R}}_0$ of the moving origin and for rotation $\boldsymbol{\omega}$ of the moving coordinate axes.

Continuing, one gets

$$\ddot{\mathbf{R}} = \ddot{\mathbf{R}}_0 + \left(\frac{d'}{dt} + \boldsymbol{\omega} \times\right)\left(\frac{d'\mathbf{r}}{dt} + \boldsymbol{\omega} \times \mathbf{r}\right)$$
$$= \ddot{\mathbf{R}}_0 + \frac{d'^2\mathbf{r}}{dt^2} + \boldsymbol{\omega} \times (\boldsymbol{\omega} \times \mathbf{r}) + 2\boldsymbol{\omega} \times \frac{d'\mathbf{r}}{dt} + \dot{\boldsymbol{\omega}} \times \mathbf{r}$$

Hence the apparent acceleration of the particle in the moving system is given by

$$\frac{d'^2\mathbf{r}}{dt^2} = \ddot{\mathbf{R}} - \ddot{\mathbf{R}}_0 - \boldsymbol{\omega} \times (\boldsymbol{\omega} \times \mathbf{r}) - 2\boldsymbol{\omega} \times \frac{d'\mathbf{r}}{dt} - \dot{\boldsymbol{\omega}} \times \mathbf{r} \qquad (10\text{-}6)$$

To obtain the apparent acceleration $d'^2\mathbf{r}/dt^2$ one must correct the absolute acceleration $\ddot{\mathbf{R}}$ with an acceleration $-\ddot{\mathbf{R}}_0$ due to motion of the origin, with a centrifugal acceleration $-\boldsymbol{\omega} \times (\boldsymbol{\omega} \times \mathbf{r})$ due to rotation of axes, with a Coriolis acceleration $-2\boldsymbol{\omega} \times (d'\mathbf{r}/dt)$ due to apparent motion within the moving axes, and with an acceleration $-\dot{\boldsymbol{\omega}} \times \mathbf{r}$ induced by changes in the angular velocity of the moving axes.

If m is the mass of the particle, Newton's equations of motion become

$$m\frac{d'^2\mathbf{r}}{dt^2} = \mathbf{F} - m\ddot{\mathbf{R}}_0 - m\boldsymbol{\omega} \times (\boldsymbol{\omega} \times \mathbf{r}) - 2m\boldsymbol{\omega} \times \frac{d'\mathbf{r}}{dt} - m\dot{\boldsymbol{\omega}} \times \mathbf{r}$$

where $m\ddot{\mathbf{R}}$ has been replaced by the force acting on the particle. The quantity $-m\ddot{\mathbf{R}}_0$ is an apparent force introduced by motion of the origin of coordinates; if the origin is unaccelerated this term drops out. The expression $-m\boldsymbol{\omega} \times (\boldsymbol{\omega} \times \mathbf{r})$ is the centrifugal force with which one is familiar in connection with rotating systems; it operates normally to and away from the line through the origin parallel to ω and is equal in magnitude to $mp\omega^2$ where p is the distance of the particle from that line. Whenever the particle has an apparent motion in the moving system a Coriolis force $-2m\omega \times d'\mathbf{r}/dt$ arises, operating normally to both ω and the apparent particle velocity. For a nonzero apparent velocity $d'\mathbf{r}/dt$, the magnitude of the Coriolis force is greatest when the motion is normal to ω and vanishes when $d'\mathbf{r}/dt$ is parallel to ω. The last quantity $-m\dot{\omega} \times \mathbf{r}$ enters only if the angular velocity of the moving axes is variable.

EXERCISES

1. Prove that the centrifugal force "felt" by a person at rest in a rotating system operates normally to and away from the axis of rotation, and is equal in magnitude to $mp\omega^2$, where m is the mass of the person, ω is the angular velocity of the system, and p is the distance of the person from the axis of rotation.

2. By how much is the weight of an object in the District of Columbia changed in magnitude and direction by the earth's rotation?

3. A stone is dropped from a height of 100 km above a point on the earth at latitude 40° N. Where will the stone land relative to the point on the ground directly below the release point? (*Hint:* Set up a coordinate system with origin at the point on the ground directly below the release point, and with axes vertical, east, and north. Use (10-6) neglecting the centrifugal acceleration term and that in $\dot{\omega}$. Set up the differential equations of motion. Then drop higher-order terms and integrate.)

10-7. Kinematics of a Moving Particle

Velocity and Acceleration. Let the path of a moving particle be given by

$$\mathbf{r} = \mathbf{r}(s(t))$$

where t is time and s is arc length along the path measured from a suitable point. The particle's velocity is given by

$$\mathbf{v} = \dot{\mathbf{r}} = \frac{d\mathbf{r}}{ds}\dot{s}$$

or

$$\mathbf{v} = \dot{s}\boldsymbol{\tau} \qquad \boldsymbol{\tau} = \frac{d\mathbf{r}}{ds}$$

The vector $\boldsymbol{\tau}$ is the unit vector tangent to the path and directed in the sense of increasing s. Hence the sign of $\dot{s}$ tells the sense in which the particle traverses the path.   The speed of the particle is given by

$$v = |\dot{s}|$$

The acceleration **a** of the particle is obtained from

$$\mathbf{a} = \ddot{\mathbf{r}}$$

$$= \ddot{s}\boldsymbol{\tau} + \dot{s}^2 \frac{d\boldsymbol{\tau}}{ds}$$

Hence the acceleration consists of a component $\ddot{s}$ along the tangent to the path plus another component in the direction of the vector $d\boldsymbol{\tau}/ds$.

Since $\boldsymbol{\tau}$ is a unit vector, $d\boldsymbol{\tau}/ds$ must be normal to $\boldsymbol{\tau}$.   The drawing in Fig. 10-2 shows the vector $\boldsymbol{\tau}$ at point A of the particle's path, and $\boldsymbol{\tau} + \Delta\boldsymbol{\tau}$

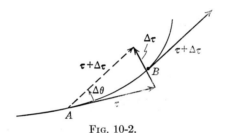

FIG. 10-2.

at a neighboring point B.   By sliding the tail of $\boldsymbol{\tau} + \Delta\boldsymbol{\tau}$ to the point A one can draw in $\Delta\boldsymbol{\tau}$ as shown.   Since both $\boldsymbol{\tau}$ and $\boldsymbol{\tau} + \Delta\boldsymbol{\tau}$ are unit vectors, one has

$$|\Delta\boldsymbol{\tau}| \cong |\Delta\theta|$$

where $\Delta\theta$ is the angle between $\boldsymbol{\tau}$ and $\boldsymbol{\tau} + \Delta\boldsymbol{\tau}$.   Thus

$$\lim_{\Delta s \to 0} \left|\frac{\Delta\boldsymbol{\tau}}{\Delta s}\right| = \lim_{\Delta s \to 0} \left|\frac{\Delta\theta}{\Delta s}\right|$$

But the limit on the right of this relation is known as the curvature K of the path, the reciprocal of which is the radius of curvature ρ.   Hence the magnitude of $d\boldsymbol{\tau}/ds$ is $1/\rho$.

Let **n** be the unit vector in the direction of $d\boldsymbol{\tau}/ds$.   Then

$$\frac{d\boldsymbol{\tau}}{ds} = \frac{\mathbf{n}}{\rho}$$

$$\mathbf{a} = \ddot{s}\boldsymbol{\tau} + \frac{\dot{s}^2}{\rho}\mathbf{n}$$

In addition to the component $\ddot{s}$ along the tangent, the acceleration has a component $\dot{s}^2/\rho$ normal to the tangent in the direction of **n** which is called the principal normal to the curve.

The acceleration of the particle lies entirely in the plane of $\boldsymbol{\tau}$ and $\mathbf{n}$ which is known as the osculating plane. It can be shown that of all the planes containing $\boldsymbol{\tau}$ the osculating plane has closest contact with the path.

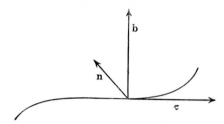

FIG. 10-3. Fundamental trihedral for a space curve.

Torsion. Let $\mathbf{b}$ be the unit vector $\boldsymbol{\tau} \times \mathbf{n}$. The vector $\mathbf{b}$, shown in Fig. 10-3, is called the binormal to the curve. Since

$$\mathbf{b} \cdot \boldsymbol{\tau} = 0$$

$$\frac{d\mathbf{b}}{ds} \cdot \boldsymbol{\tau} + \mathbf{b} \cdot \frac{d\boldsymbol{\tau}}{ds} = 0$$

$$\frac{d\mathbf{b}}{ds} \cdot \boldsymbol{\tau} + \mathbf{b} \cdot \frac{\mathbf{n}}{\rho} = 0$$

$$\frac{d\mathbf{b}}{ds} \cdot \boldsymbol{\tau} = 0$$

Thus $d\mathbf{b}/ds$ is normal to $\boldsymbol{\tau}$. But $d\mathbf{b}/ds$ is also normal to $\mathbf{b}$. It follows that $d\mathbf{b}/ds$ is parallel to $\mathbf{n}$.

Set

$$\frac{d\mathbf{b}}{ds} = \frac{1}{T} \mathbf{n}$$

The quantity $1/T$ is called the torsion of the curve. It is a simple matter to attach a meaning to $1/T$. Let $\Delta\mathbf{b}$ be the change in $\mathbf{b}$ due to a small increment Δs in s. Let $\Delta\psi$ be the angle between $\mathbf{b}$ and $\mathbf{b} + \Delta\mathbf{b}$. Then

$$|\Delta\mathbf{b}| = |\Delta\psi|$$

whence,

$$\left|\frac{d\mathbf{b}}{ds}\right| = \left|\frac{d\psi}{ds}\right|$$

or

$$\left|\frac{1}{T}\right| = \left|\frac{d\psi}{ds}\right|$$

The magnitude of the torsion is the rate of turning of $\mathbf{b}$ about the tangent $\boldsymbol{\tau}$ as s varies.

Since the rate of turning of $\mathbf{b}$ about $\boldsymbol{\tau}$ is the same as the rate of turning of the osculating plane about $\boldsymbol{\tau}$, and since the osculating plane has closest contact with the path, it is plain that $1/T$ furnishes a measure of the twisting of the path. The sign of $1/T$ determines the direction of twisting relative to τ and $\mathbf{n}$.

The Frenet-Serret formulas. Since

$$\mathbf{n} = \mathbf{b} \times \tau$$

$$\frac{d\mathbf{n}}{ds} = \frac{1}{T}\mathbf{n} \times \tau + \mathbf{b} \times \frac{\mathbf{n}}{\rho}$$

$$\frac{d\mathbf{n}}{ds} = -\frac{1}{\rho}\tau - \frac{1}{T}\mathbf{b}$$

This, together with other relations obtained above constitute the Frenet-Serret formulas for a curve in space:

$$\frac{d\tau}{ds} = \frac{1}{\rho}\mathbf{n}$$

$$\frac{d\mathbf{n}}{ds} = -\frac{1}{\rho}\tau - \frac{1}{T}\mathbf{b} \qquad (10\text{-}7)$$

$$\frac{d\mathbf{b}}{ds} = \frac{1}{T}\mathbf{n}$$

The moving trihedral. The vectors τ, $\mathbf{n}$, $\mathbf{b}$ together form what is called the fundamental trihedral for the path of the particle. As the particle moves, the trihedral does also, and one obtains from (10-7)

$$\dot{\tau} = \frac{\dot{s}}{\rho}\mathbf{n}$$

$$\dot{\mathbf{n}} = -\frac{\dot{s}}{\rho}\tau - \frac{\dot{s}}{T}\mathbf{b}$$

$$\dot{\mathbf{b}} = \frac{\dot{s}}{T}\mathbf{n}$$

If $\boldsymbol{\omega}$ be the angular velocity of the trihedral, one can show that

$$\boldsymbol{\omega} = -\frac{\dot{s}}{T}\tau + \frac{\dot{s}}{\rho}\mathbf{b} \qquad (10\text{-}8)$$

Thus there is no rotation about the principal normal.

EXERCISES

1. A bead slides under the action of gravity on a perfectly smooth parabolic wire of the form

$$z^2 = y$$

where the y axis is horizontal and the z axis is vertical. If the bead is moving at 2 cm/sec at the point $(1,1)$, what is its total acceleration there?

2. Show how to calculate $\frac{1}{\rho}$ and $\frac{1}{T}$ from (10-7).

3. Let $\mathbf{r}(s) = \dfrac{1}{\sqrt{2}} (\cos s\mathbf{i} + \sin s\mathbf{j} + s\mathbf{k})$, where s is arc length along the path. Identify the curve, and determine the curvature and torsion at an arbitrary point on the path.

4. Establish (10-8).

5. Let $\mathbf{r} = \mathbf{r}(u)$ be a differentiable curve in space. Show how to calculate arc length s along the curve in terms of u. (*Hint:* $\mathbf{r}' = \boldsymbol{\tau} \dfrac{ds}{du}$, where the prime denotes differentiation with respect to u.)

6. Let $\mathbf{r} = \mathbf{r}(u)$ be a differentiable curve in space. What condition must $\mathbf{r}'(u)$ satisfy in order that u be arc length along the curve?

7. Let $\mathbf{r} = \mathbf{r}(u)$ be a path in space, for which $\mathbf{r}'$ and $\mathbf{r}''$ exist. Show how to calculate $\boldsymbol{\tau}$, $\mathbf{n}$, $\mathbf{b}$, $\dfrac{1}{\rho}$, and $\dfrac{1}{T}$. (*Hint:* First note that $\boldsymbol{\tau}$ is parallel to $\mathbf{r}'$. From this fact get $\boldsymbol{\tau}$. Then show that $\mathbf{b}$ must be parallel to $\mathbf{r}' \times \mathbf{r}''$. From this fact get $\mathbf{b}$, etc.)

8. Determine $\boldsymbol{\tau}$, $\mathbf{n}$, $\mathbf{b}$, ρ, and $\dfrac{1}{T}$ for the general point of the curve

$$r = u\mathbf{i} + u^2\mathbf{j} + u^3\mathbf{k}$$

9. Let

$$\mathbf{r} = \mathbf{r}(s)$$

be a differentiable curve in space, where s is arc length along the curve. Expand $\mathbf{r}(s)$ in powers of s about $s = 0$, giving the coefficients of the powers of s (to as far as the third power) in terms of $\boldsymbol{\tau}(0)$, $\mathbf{n}(0)$, $\mathbf{b}(0)$, $\rho(0)$, $\dfrac{1}{T(0)}$.

10. Use the result of Exercise 9 to describe the shape of a differentiable space curve at a general point of the curve.

11. Prove that, of all the planes through a point P_0 on a differentiable space curve the osculating plane at point P_0 has closest contact with the curve. (*Hint:* Consider an arbitrary plane Π through a point P_0 of the curve. Obtain an expression for the distance D of a neighboring point P of the curve from Π in terms of the arc length s from P_0 to P. Then arrange for D to be of highest possible order in s.)

REFERENCES

Graustein, W. C.: "Differential Geometry," The Macmillan Company, New York, 1935.

Joos, G.: "Theoretical Physics," translated by I. M. Freeman, G. E. Stechert & Company, New York, 1934.

Whittaker, E. T.: "A Treatise on the Analytical Dynamics of Particles and Rigid Bodies," Cambridge University Press, New York, 1937.

CHAPTER 11

A SKETCH OF ELECTROMAGNETIC THEORY

11-1. Maxwell's Equations

As a basis for electromagnetic theory one can start with the many experimental facts which have been assembled on the subject, and proceed from them to the formulation of Maxwell's equations. Or one can postulate the validity of Maxwell's equations. In the latter case, one deduces various laws and results from the equations, which deductions are then subject to experimental check. The fact that the laws so deduced can be verified experimentally finally establishes the validity of the equations.

Taking the second approach, let it be assumed that

$$\gamma \nabla \times \mathbf{E} + \frac{\partial \mathbf{B}}{\partial t} = 0 \tag{11-1}$$

$$\gamma \nabla \times \mathbf{H} - \frac{\partial \mathbf{D}}{\partial t} = \beta \mathbf{J} \tag{11-2}$$

where **E** = electric field intensity
     D = electric flux density, or electric displacement
     H = magnetic field intensity
     B = magnetic flux density, or magnetic induction
     J = current density
It is assumed that a systematic set of units will be used. One specifies the particular set to be employed through the choice of numerical values and dimensions for γ and β, and for the quantities ϵ_0 and μ_0 to be introduced below. To keep the choice of units open, γ and β will be carried along in the analyses to follow. The subject of units will be discussed in Sec. 11-21.

11-2. The Maxwellian Field Vectors

Suppose an element of electric charge q to be moving with a velocity **v** in a Maxwellian field. Then it can be shown experimentally that q experiences a force **F** given by

$$\mathbf{F} = q(\mathbf{E} + \mathbf{v} \times \mathbf{B}) \tag{11-3}$$

155

Relation (11-3) furnishes a link between the electromagnetic field vectors and the familiar concept of force. From it one sees that $\mathbf{E}$ has the dimensions of force over charge, while $\mathbf{B}$ has the dimensions of force over charge-times-velocity.

In a given medium $\mathbf{D}$ is some function of $\mathbf{E}$, the functional relationship being characteristic of the medium. Likewise $\mathbf{H}$ depends upon $\mathbf{B}$. Usually

$$\mathbf{D} = \epsilon\mathbf{E} \tag{11-4}$$

where ϵ is a constant called the permittivity of the medium. Similarly, except for ferromagnetic materials,

$$\mathbf{B} = \mu\mathbf{H} \tag{11-5}$$

where μ is a constant called the magnetic inductive capacity of the medium. Throughout the present chapter it will be assumed that (11-4) and (11-5) hold.

Let ϵ_0, μ_0 be the values of ϵ and μ for empty space. Then

$$k_e = \frac{\epsilon}{\epsilon_0}$$

is called the dielectric constant of the medium, while

$$k_m = \frac{\mu}{\mu_0}$$

is called its permeability.

The current density $\mathbf{J}$ is a rate of flow of electric charge. Its dimensions are charge per unit area per unit time. Often the flow of charge in an electric field of intensity $\mathbf{E}$ obeys the law

$$\mathbf{J} = \sigma\mathbf{E} \tag{11-6}$$

where σ is called the conductivity of the medium through which the charge is flowing. In other cases the flow of charge may have to be determined by direct appeal to Newton's laws of motion, using (11-3) for the accelerating force. In the following pages only current flows obeying (11-6) will be considered.

Let ρ denote charge density. Then the total amount of charge in a volume V is given by

$$\int_V \rho \, dV$$

and the rate of loss of charge from V is

$$-\frac{d}{dt}\int_V \rho \, dV = -\int_V \frac{\partial\rho}{\partial t} \, dV$$

assuming V fixed. But since $\mathbf{J}$ is current density, the rate of loss of charge is also given by

$$\oint_{\substack{\text{bdy} \\ \text{of } V}} \mathbf{J} \cdot d\mathbf{S}$$

whence

$$\oint_{\substack{\text{bdy} \\ \text{of } V}} \mathbf{J} \cdot d\mathbf{S} = -\int_V \frac{\partial \rho}{\partial t} dV$$

$$\int_V \left[\nabla \cdot \mathbf{J} + \frac{\partial \rho}{\partial t} \right] dV = 0$$

Since this must hold for all volumes V, one has at every point

$$\nabla \cdot \mathbf{J} + \frac{\partial \rho}{\partial t} = 0 \tag{11-7}$$

This is known as the equation of continuity for charge flow.

Now return to (11-2). Form the divergence of both sides:

$$\gamma \nabla \cdot \nabla \times \mathbf{H} - \nabla \cdot \frac{\partial \mathbf{D}}{\partial t} = \beta \nabla \cdot \mathbf{J}$$

Using (11-7),

$$\frac{\partial}{\partial t} [\nabla \cdot \mathbf{D} - \beta \rho] = 0$$

$$\nabla \cdot \mathbf{D} - \beta \rho = \text{constant}$$

If one assumes that the field was generated at some finite time in the past, the constant must be zero. Experimentally this turns out to be the case:

$$\nabla \cdot \mathbf{D} = \beta \rho \tag{11-8}$$

Integrating over a volume V containing total net charge q, one gets

$$\int_{\substack{\text{bdy} \\ \text{of } V}} \mathbf{D} \cdot d\mathbf{S} = \beta q \tag{11-9}$$

From (11-1)

$$\gamma \nabla \cdot \nabla \times \mathbf{E} + \nabla \cdot \frac{\partial \mathbf{B}}{\partial t} = 0$$

$$\frac{\partial}{\partial t} \nabla \cdot \mathbf{B} = 0$$

$$\nabla \cdot \mathbf{B} = \text{constant}$$

Once again one assumes the constant to be zero, which is in keeping with experiment:

$$\nabla \cdot \mathbf{B} = 0 \qquad (11\text{-}10)$$

This amounts to saying that there are no true magnetic charges. The field $\mathbf{B}$ is solenoidal.

EXERCISES

1. A charge q of mass m moving at velocity $\mathbf{v}_0$, is suddenly subjected to a uniform electric field $\mathbf{E}$. Determine its subsequent motion.

2. A charge q of mass m moving with a velocity $\mathbf{v}_0$, is suddenly subjected to a uniform magnetic field $\mathbf{B}$. Determine its subsequent motion.

3. A uniform electric field $\mathbf{E}$ is at right angles to a uniform magnetic field $\mathbf{B}$. A charge q of mass m is initially at rest in the field. Determine the subsequent motion of the charge.

4. Consider Eqs. (11-1) and (11-8) for the static case; i.e., for the case in which the field vectors are constant with respect to time. Assume ρ continuous and zero everywhere outside of some finite region. Obtain an expression giving $\mathbf{D}$ explicitly in terms of the charge density ρ.

5. Consider Eqs. (11-2) and (11-10) for the static case. Assume $\mathbf{J}$ continuous and confined to some finite region of space. Obtain an expression giving $\mathbf{B}$ explicitly in terms of $\mathbf{J}$.

11-3. Flow of Charge. Displacement Current

In the preceding section it was shown that the flow of charge must obey an equation of continuity, given by (11-7). From it,

$$\nabla \cdot \mathbf{J} = -\frac{\partial \rho}{\partial t} \qquad (11\text{-}11)$$

Thus if charge density builds up at a point, the current density diminishes; and vice versa. A point at which charge is accumulating appears as a sink for $\mathbf{J}$, while one at which charge is disappearing appears as a source for $\mathbf{J}$.

From (11-2) one has

$$\nabla \cdot \mathbf{J} = -\nabla \cdot \left(\frac{1}{\beta} \frac{\partial \mathbf{D}}{\partial t} \right) \qquad (11\text{-}12)$$

This relationship implies that every point which is a sink for $\mathbf{J}$ is simultaneously a source of equal intensity for the quantity $\dfrac{1}{\beta} \dfrac{\partial \mathbf{D}}{\partial t}$. Thus $\dfrac{1}{\beta} \dfrac{\partial \mathbf{D}}{\partial t}$ appears as a sort of current density and is referred to as a displacement current. Every source for $\mathbf{J}$ is a sink for displacement current.

Combining (11-11) with (11-12) yields

$$\nabla \cdot \left(\frac{1}{\beta} \frac{\partial \mathbf{D}}{\partial t} \right) = \frac{\partial \rho}{\partial t}$$

Hence, as charge accumulates in a region, the flux density emanating from that region builds up; and as charge leaves a region, the emanating flux density decreases.

Rewriting (11-12) gives

$$\nabla \cdot \left[\mathbf{J} + \frac{1}{\beta} \frac{\partial \mathbf{D}}{\partial t} \right] = 0 \qquad (11\text{-}13)$$

This is essentially Kirchhoff's second law. From it one concludes that if displacement as well as conduction currents be included, then the algebraic sum of all currents emanating from a given point is zero.

Rewrite (11-7) and (11-8) as

$$\nabla \cdot (\sigma \mathbf{E}) + \frac{\partial \rho}{\partial t} = 0$$

$$\Delta \cdot (\epsilon \mathbf{E}) = \beta \rho$$

and combine them to get

$$\frac{1}{\sigma} \frac{\partial \rho}{\partial t} + \frac{\beta}{\epsilon} \rho = 0$$

$$\frac{\partial \rho}{\partial t} = - \frac{\beta \sigma}{\epsilon} \rho$$

$$\rho = \rho_0 e^{-\frac{\beta \sigma}{\epsilon} t}$$

where ρ_0 is charge density at time $t = 0$. Thus within a conductor charge decays at a rate which is independent of the applied field. If the charge density is initially zero, it is forever so. If not initially zero, it starts at once to disappear, the charge reappearing in equal amount at the surface of the conductor. The time

$$\tau = \frac{\epsilon}{\beta \sigma}$$

is known as the relaxation time for the medium concerned.

EXERCISE

Calculate the relaxation time for copper, water, and glass. (For the mks system of units $\beta = 1$; for the Gaussian system, $\beta = 4\pi$.)

11-4. Potentials for the Maxwellian Field

Since $\mathbf{B}$ is solenoidal, there is a vector potential $\mathbf{A}$ for it such that

$$\mathbf{B} = \nabla \times \mathbf{A}$$

The vector $\mathbf{E}$ can be written as the sum of an irrotational vector $\mathbf{E}_1$ plus a solenoidal vector $\mathbf{E}_2$. One can express $\mathbf{E}_1$ in the form $-\nabla\phi_1$, where the minus sign is introduced for a reason that will appear later in Sec. 11-12. From (11-1)

$$\gamma\nabla \times \mathbf{E} + \frac{\partial \mathbf{B}}{\partial t} = \gamma\nabla \times \mathbf{E}_2 + \frac{\partial}{\partial t}\nabla \times \mathbf{A} = 0$$

$$\nabla \times \left(\mathbf{E}_2 + \frac{1}{\gamma}\frac{\partial \mathbf{A}}{\partial t}\right) = 0$$

This means that

$$\mathbf{E}_2 + \frac{1}{\gamma}\frac{\partial \mathbf{A}}{\partial t}$$

is of the form $-\nabla\phi_2$. Thus

$$\mathbf{E} = -\nabla\phi - \frac{1}{\gamma}\frac{\partial \mathbf{A}}{\partial t}$$

where $\phi = \phi_1 + \phi_2$.

The Maxwellian field has, therefore, potentials ϕ and $\mathbf{A}$ from which the field vectors can be calculated according to the relations

$$\mathbf{E} = -\nabla\phi - \frac{1}{\gamma}\frac{\partial \mathbf{A}}{\partial t} \tag{11-14}$$

$$\mathbf{B} = \nabla \times \mathbf{A} \tag{11-15}$$

11-5. Relation between B and Total Current Distribution

Since $\mathbf{B}$ is solenoidal, one should be able to calculate it in terms of its vortices. According to (11-2) these are

$$\nabla \times \mathbf{B} = \frac{\mu}{\gamma}\left[\frac{\partial \mathbf{D}}{\partial t} + \beta\mathbf{J}\right]$$

Hence one is tempted to use (8-23) and write

$$\mathbf{B}(P') = \frac{\mu}{4\pi\gamma}\int_V \left[\frac{\partial \mathbf{D}}{\partial t} + \beta\mathbf{J}\right] \times \nabla\left(\frac{1}{R}\right) dV \tag{11-16}$$

where R is the distance from P' to the point of integration P; where the differentiation in ∇ is with respect to the coordinates of P; and where V contains all the vortices of $\mathbf{B}$. But, through its derivation from (8-23), (11-16) rests upon the tacit assumption that the effect of changes in

$$\frac{\partial \mathbf{D}}{\partial t} + \beta\mathbf{J} \tag{11-17}$$

are communicated instantaneously to the field at P', which is not true. On the other hand, if distances are small and the variations in (11-17) are slow relative to the propagation of effects in the field, then (11-16) may be used. This is the case in normal circuit theory. The formula is precisely true when (11-17) does not vary at all with time.

Now suppose that the conduction and displacement currents generating **B** all flow in a filament or tube of cross section S. Let the axis of the tube be denoted by Γ. Let s and τ respectively denote arc length and the unit tangent along Γ. One can write

$$dV = S \, ds$$

Use I to represent the current through the cross section S. Then

$$\left[\frac{\partial \mathbf{D}}{\partial t} + \beta \mathbf{J} \right] dV = \frac{\beta I}{S} \, \tau \, dV$$
$$= \beta I \tau \, ds$$

Since the filament contains the total current, I is constant. Hence

$$\mathbf{B} = \frac{\beta \mu I}{4\pi\gamma} \int_{\Gamma} \tau \times \nabla \left(\frac{1}{R} \right) ds \tag{11-18}$$

It is seen that **B** is proportional to the total current I.

EXERCISES

1. A steady current I flows in a very long straight wire. Calculate the field **B** about the wire.

2. A steady current I flows in a circular loop. Calculate **B** at the center of the loop.

3. Rework Exercise 2 to get **B** at any point on the line normal to the plane of the loop at its center.

4. A helical coil is wound on a circular cylinder of length l. The helix has n loops of wire per unit length along the cylinder. A steady current I flows in the wire. What is the field **B** at the center of the helix?

5. A steady current I flows in each of two very long parallel wires, but in opposite directions. Calculate the field **B** about the wires.

11-6. Faraday's Law of Induction

Consider a simple closed loop Γ in space, and pick any simple surface S spanning Γ. From (11-1),

$$\gamma \int_S \nabla \times \mathbf{E} \cdot d\mathbf{S} + \int \frac{\partial \mathbf{B}}{\partial t} \cdot d\mathbf{S} = 0$$
$$\oint_\Gamma \mathbf{E} \cdot d\mathbf{r} = -\frac{1}{\gamma} \int_S \frac{\partial \mathbf{B}}{\partial t} \cdot d\mathbf{S}$$

Keeping Γ and S fixed,

$$\oint_\Gamma \mathbf{E} \cdot d\mathbf{r} = -\frac{1}{\gamma}\frac{d\Phi}{dt} \qquad \Phi = \int \mathbf{B} \cdot d\mathbf{S} \qquad (11\text{-}19)$$

This is Faraday's law of induction for the special case of fixed loops. The quantity Φ is the total flux of $\mathbf{B}$ through S. Because $\mathbf{B}$ is solenoidal, Φ is the same for all simple surfaces spanning Γ. The circulation of $\mathbf{E}$ about Γ, given by the integral on the left of (11-19), is commonly referred to as the electromotive force (emf) generated by the changing flux Φ.

In words, Faraday's law states that a decreasing magnetic flux through a loop generates a positive emf about the loop, while an increasing flux generates a negative, or counter, emf about the loop. In both cases the emf is proportional to the rate of change of flux.

Actually the law of induction embodied in (11-19) is more general than the derivation from Maxwell's equations would indicate. Experimentally it is found that (11-19) holds even if S and Γ are not fixed. For example, if the total flux threading Γ changes because Γ is moving, there is still an emf induced in the loop in accordance with (11-19), and this is so even if the magnetic field itself is static. This in fact points to a way of introducing energy into the Maxwellian field, as is done with electrical generators in which coils are rotated in a magnetic field, thereby converting the mechanical energy causing the rotation into electrical energy.

EXERCISE

Using (11-18), show that

$$\frac{1}{\gamma}\frac{d\Phi}{dt} = L\frac{dI}{dt} \qquad (11\text{-}20)$$

where I is the current flowing in a loop Γ, Φ is the magnetic flux threading Γ, and L is a constant depending on the geometry of the loop and on the medium in which it lies. The quantity L is called the self-inductance of Γ.

11-7. Resistance and Ohm's Law

Consider a flow of charge in keeping with (11-6). Fix attention upon a filament of current flowing between points a and b. Let S be the cross-sectional area of the filament taken normal to the axis of the filament. Use s to denote arc length along the filament, and let τ be the unit vector tangent to its axis. The total current I crossing the area S is given by

$$I = \mathbf{J} \cdot S\tau$$

Hence

$$\frac{I}{\sigma S} ds = \mathbf{E} \cdot \mathbf{\tau} ds$$

$$\int_a^b \frac{I}{\sigma S} ds = \int_a^b \mathbf{E} \cdot d\mathbf{r} \tag{11-21}$$

The cases in which I is constant, as when the filament is composed of flow lines, are of greatest interest usually. In these cases (11-21) is rewritten as

$$\int_a^b \mathbf{E} \cdot d\mathbf{r} = V = IR = I \int_a^b \frac{ds}{\sigma S} \tag{11-22}$$

The quantity V is called the voltage drop between a and b, while R is called the electrical resistance of the filament. Relation (11-22) is simply Ohm's law for current flow in a resistive element.

EXERCISE

Calculate the resistance of 1,000 ft of copper wire 0.1 in. in diameter.

11-8. Condensers

The relation (11-13) says that the current density function

$$\mathbf{J} + \frac{1}{\beta} \frac{\partial \mathbf{D}}{\partial t} \tag{11-23}$$

is solenoidal. This means that the total current flow is constant through every cross section of a tube composed of a bundle of flow lines. Ordinary electrical circuits are designed to direct virtually all the flow along prescribed paths, such as along wires and through condensers. It is assumed that the solenoidal property may be applied with negligible error to the branches and loops of the circuit. This leads at once to Kirchhoff's second law that the algebraic sum of all currents, both conduction and displacement, emanating from a given point in the circuit is zero.

Along the conducting wires of a circuit it is generally assumed that only conduction current flows, although at very high frequencies displacement current effects are often not negligible.

A condenser is constructed by placing two conducting sheets close together, but separated by a nonconductor. No conduction current can flow in the insulating material of the condenser. Thus, because of the solenoidal character of (11-23) an equivalent displacement current passes through the condenser material. As conduction current causes a build up of positive charge on one plate of the condenser, the flux density between the plates builds up, which is to say that a displacement current flows. This displacement current terminates at the other plate, and an equal conduction current flows away causing a negative charge to build up on the second condenser plate equal to the positive charge on the first plate.

Since the flux density in the insulating material of the condenser is proportional to the total charge q on the positive plate, then so is the electric field strength within the condenser. Hence

$$\int \mathbf{E} \cdot d\mathbf{r} = \frac{q}{C} \qquad (11\text{-}24)$$

integrating from one plate to the other. The constant of proportionality C is called the capacitance or capacity of the condenser. Once again calling $\int \mathbf{E} \cdot d\mathbf{r}$ the voltage drop V across the element, one has

$$CV = q$$

Relations (11-24) and (11-9) can be used to compute C. Consider, for example, a condenser of two parallel plates of area A and separation d. Except for a small amount of leakage at the edges, the fields $\mathbf{D}$ and $\mathbf{E}$ are normal to the plates and are uniform. Hence

$$DA = \beta q = \epsilon E A$$

where again q is the charge on the positive plate. But

$$V = Ed = \frac{q}{C}$$

Combining,

$$V = \frac{\beta d q}{\epsilon A}$$

$$C = \frac{\epsilon A}{\beta d}$$

EXERCISES

1. Calculate the capacitance of a condenser the plates of which are coaxial circular cylinders of equal length and coincident centers.

2. Calculate the capacitance of a condenser the plates of which are concentric spheres.

3. In the result of Exercise 2 let the radius of the outer sphere become infinite, and thereby determine the capacitance of the other sphere relative to the space in which it is embedded.

11-9. Series Circuit without EMF

Consider a closed circuit of one or more turns which has a resistance R and a capacitance C in series. On the one hand, one has from (11-22) and (11-24),

$$\oint \mathbf{E} \cdot d\mathbf{r} = RI + \frac{q}{C}$$

where the integration is taken around the circuit, where I is the conduction current, and where q is the charge on the condenser. At the same time, from (11-19):

$$\oint \mathbf{E} \cdot d\mathbf{r} = -\frac{1}{\gamma}\frac{d\Phi}{dt}$$

where Φ is the total magnetic flux threading the circuit. Thus

$$RI + \frac{q}{C} = -\frac{1}{\gamma}\frac{d\Phi}{dt}$$

$$\frac{1}{\gamma}\frac{d\Phi}{dt} + RI + \frac{q}{C} = 0 \tag{11-25}$$

This is Kirchhoff's first law. From it the behavior of the circuit can be determined as a function of time once initial conditions are specified.

EXERCISES

1. Show that q in (11-25) can be written as

$$q = q_0 + \int_0^t I\, dt$$

2. Using (11-20) and the result of Exercise 1, show that (11-25) can be written as

$$L\ddot{q} + R\dot{q} + \frac{q}{C} = 0$$

or as

$$L\ddot{I} + R\dot{I} + \frac{I}{C} = 0$$

11-10. Series Circuit with EMF

The case in which an emf is inserted into a circuit can be handled much as in the derivation of (11-25). The applied emf may be generated by a number of means. It is in effect due to some process which separates charge, thereby setting up an electric field. The process is something outside the realm of Maxwell's equations. It is a means whereby energy is introduced into the Maxwell field. For purposes of discussion its effect may be described in terms of a pseudo-field $\mathbf{E}'$ directed from b to a within the generator, Fig. 11-1, and zero outside the generator. $\mathbf{E}'$ causes charge to separate within the generator, a charge of one sign accumulating at a, and an equal charge of opposite sign accumulating at b. But as the charge separates the usual Maxwellian field $\mathbf{E}$ is set up, continuing to increase until equilibrium is established within the generator, where at that time

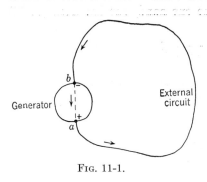

FIG. 11-1.

$$\mathbf{E} + \mathbf{E}' = 0$$

Now integrate around the loop from a to a again. One has

$$\int_{a}^{b} \mathbf{E} \cdot d\mathbf{r} = \oint_{a}^{a} (\mathbf{E} + \mathbf{E}') \cdot d\mathbf{r} = \oint_{a}^{a} \mathbf{E} \cdot d\mathbf{r} + \int_{b}^{a} \mathbf{E}' \cdot d\mathbf{r}$$
$$\text{outside} \qquad\qquad\qquad\qquad\qquad\qquad\qquad \text{inside}$$
$$\text{generator} \qquad\qquad\qquad\qquad\qquad\qquad\qquad \text{generator}$$

The left-hand equality holds because $\mathbf{E} + \mathbf{E}'$ vanishes inside the generator while $\mathbf{E}'$ vanishes outside. The right-hand equality holds because $\mathbf{E}'$ vanishes outside the generator. Using (11-22), (11-24), and (11-19):

$$RI + \frac{q}{C} = -\frac{1}{\gamma}\frac{d\Phi}{dt} + E_g$$

where E_g denotes the generator emf, given by

$$E_g = \int_{b}^{a} \mathbf{E}' \cdot d\mathbf{r}$$
$$\text{inside}$$
$$\text{generator}$$

Hence

$$\frac{1}{\gamma}\frac{d\Phi}{dt} + RI + \frac{q}{C} = E_g$$

Using (11-20) this can be rewritten

$$L\frac{dI}{dt} + RI + \frac{q}{C} = E_g \tag{11-26}$$

where L is the self-inductance of the circuit.

One should note that E_g is not a constant in general but is a function of the current that flows and of the generating process. It is often convenient to express E_g in terms of E_0, the open-circuit voltage, i.e., the emf generated when no external current flows. One has

$$E_g = E_0 - f(I)$$

In general, one can express $f(I)$ in the form

$$f(I) = L_g \frac{dI}{dt} + R_g I + \frac{q_g}{C_g}$$

where L_g, R_g, and C_g are referred to as the self-inductance, resistance, and capacitance of the generator. With these, (11-26) becomes

$$(L + L_g) \frac{dI}{dt} + (R + R_g)I + \frac{q}{C} + \frac{q_g}{C_g} = E_0$$

where E_0 is constant.

EXERCISE

Starting with the discussion of Secs. 11-9 and 11-10, develop the theory of electrical circuits. For the inductive interaction of different loops in a circuit, it will be necessary to introduce the concept of mutual inductance M of two loops, analogous to self-inductance L for a single loop.

11-11. Discontinuities in the Maxwell Field Vectors

Maxwell's equations apply to media the properties of which are continuous. In the case in which two media of different properties adjoin, the field vectors satisfy Maxwell's equations in both media, but vary discontinuously in crossing the interface between the two media. Also the presence of surface charges or surface currents generates discontinuities in the field vectors.

Consider first the case of the vector **B**. Suppose that the passage from one medium to the other occurs through a very thin transition layer in which the properties of the media, charge distributions, and currents vary continuously, though rapidly. Let S be the interface between the two media, and pick a point P on S. Now imagine a small right cylinder centered on P, normal to S, and reaching through the transition layer on both sides of S. Let h be the height of the cylinder, and let ΔS be the area cut out of S by the cylinder. Let **n** be the unit normal to S at P. Integrating over the surface of the cylinder, one has

$$\oint \mathbf{B} \cdot d\mathbf{S} = \int_{\substack{\text{vol. of} \\ \text{cylinder}}} \nabla \cdot \mathbf{B} \, dV = 0$$

Hence

$$\mathbf{n} \cdot (\mathbf{B}_2 - \mathbf{B}_1) \, \Delta S + \text{contributions of sides} = 0$$

where the subscript 2 refers to the medium toward which **n** points, while subscript 1 refers to the other medium, and where an appropriate mean value of $\mathbf{n} \cdot (\mathbf{B}_2 - \mathbf{B}_1)$ is chosen.

Now let the transition layer shrink down to the surface S, and at the same time let $h \to 0$. One gets

$$\mathbf{n} \cdot (\mathbf{B}_2 - \mathbf{B}_1) \, \Delta S = 0$$

or

$$\mathbf{n} \cdot (\mathbf{B}_2 - \mathbf{B}_1) = 0 \qquad (11\text{-}27)$$

at some mean value point in ΔS. But this holds for every ΔS containing P, no matter how small. Hence, letting ΔS vanish, one finds that (11-27) holds at P. Thus the normal component of $\mathbf{B}$ varies continuously through a surface of discontinuity in the medium.

A similar discussion can be given for $\mathbf{D}$, except that in this case one starts with

$$\oint_{\substack{\text{surface} \\ \text{of} \\ \text{cylinder}}} \mathbf{D} \cdot d\mathbf{S} = \beta q$$

where q is the total charge contained in the elemental cylinder. It is assumed that as the transition layer shrinks down to S, and $h \to 0$, the total charge q within the cylinder stays constant, leading thus to a surface charge $q_s = q$, of density ρ_s where

$$q_s = \rho_s \, \Delta S$$

Hence

$$\mathbf{n} \cdot (\mathbf{D}_2 - \mathbf{D}_1) \, \Delta S = \beta \rho_s \, \Delta S$$

Dividing out ΔS, and letting $\Delta S \to 0$, one gets at P

$$\mathbf{n} \cdot (\mathbf{D}_2 - \mathbf{D}_1) = \beta \rho_s \qquad (11\text{-}28)$$

The normal component of $\mathbf{D}$ changes at a surface of discontinuity by an amount proportional to the surface charge density.

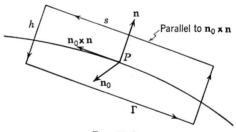

FIG. 11-2.

Consider again the interface S and the thin transition layer of the preceding paragraphs. Choose point P on S. As in Fig. 11-2, let Γ be a small rectangular loop of length s and height h, the plane of which is normal to S and contains P, and let $\mathbf{n}_0$ be the unit normal to the plane of Γ at P. Suppose that the sides s of Γ are parallel to the tangent plane to S at P, and that they lie on opposite sides of the transition layer. Then

$$\oint_\Gamma \mathbf{E} \cdot d\mathbf{r} + \frac{1}{\gamma} \int_\Sigma \frac{\partial \mathbf{B}}{\partial t} \cdot d\mathbf{S} = 0$$

where Σ is the area of the rectangle enclosed by Γ. This can be replaced by

$$\mathbf{n}_0 \times \mathbf{n} \cdot (\mathbf{E}_2 - \mathbf{E}_1)s + \text{contributions from the ends of } \Gamma + \frac{1}{\gamma} \frac{\partial \mathbf{B}}{\partial t} sh = 0$$

where again the subscript 2 refers to the side of S toward which $\mathbf{n}$ points, while subscript 1 refers to the other side. Assuming $\mathbf{E}$, $\mathbf{B}$, and $\dfrac{\partial \mathbf{B}}{\partial t}$ bounded, and letting the transition layer shrink down to S, while $h \to 0$, one gets

$$\mathbf{n}_0 \cdot \mathbf{n} \times (\mathbf{E}_2 - \mathbf{E}_1) = 0$$

for some mean value of $\mathbf{E}_2 - \mathbf{E}_1$ along a line on S through P normal to $\mathbf{n}_0$. Letting $s \to 0$, one gets the same relation at P. Since this must hold for all $\mathbf{n}_0$, one has finally at P

$$\mathbf{n} \times (\mathbf{E}_2 - \mathbf{E}_1) = 0 \qquad (11\text{-}29)$$

This means that either $\mathbf{E}_2 = \mathbf{E}_1$, or else $\mathbf{E}_2 - \mathbf{E}_1$ is parallel to $\mathbf{n}$, which in turn implies that the tangential component of $\mathbf{E}$ varies continuously through the surface of discontinuity.

Using again the loop Γ of the preceding paragraph, one has

$$\oint_\Gamma \mathbf{H} \cdot d\mathbf{r} - \frac{1}{\gamma} \int_\Sigma \frac{\partial \mathbf{D}}{\partial t} \cdot d\mathbf{S} - \frac{\beta}{\gamma} \int_\Sigma \mathbf{J} \cdot d\mathbf{S} = 0$$

Proceeding as before, letting the transition layer shrink down upon S while $h \to 0$, one concludes that at P

$$\mathbf{n} \times (\mathbf{H}_2 - \mathbf{H}_1) = \lim_{h \to 0} \left[\frac{1}{\gamma} \frac{\partial \mathbf{D}}{\partial t} h + \frac{\beta}{\gamma} \mathbf{J}h \right] \qquad (11\text{-}30)$$

If the field vectors and their derivatives are assumed bounded, and the conductivities of the two media are finite, then $\mathbf{J}$ also is bounded, and the right side of (11-30) vanishes. Many important practical problems, however, are handled conveniently by assuming one of the media to be infinitely conducting. This admits of a nonzero limit to $\mathbf{J}h$ as $h \to 0$, leading to the concept of a surface distribution of current of density $\mathbf{J}_s$. In this case

$$\mathbf{n} \times (\mathbf{H}_2 - \mathbf{H}_1) = \frac{\beta}{\gamma} \mathbf{J}_s \qquad (11\text{-}31)$$

1. Discuss the behavior of the normal components of **H** and **E** at a surface of discontinuity.

2. Discuss the behavior of the tangential components of **D** and **B** at a surface of discontinuity.

11-12. Energy in an Electromagnetic Field

So far the discussion has been concerned only with the form of the Maxwellian field. But the fundamental quantities associated with any field are the energy and momentum therein. Consider the question of energy.

Experimentally the vector **E** is found to be a force per unit charge. If one moves a charge q in an electrostatic field, the force exerted on q by the field is $q\mathbf{E}$, and the work W done *on the field* in moving the charge from a point a to a point b is

$$W = -q \int_a^b \mathbf{E} \cdot d\mathbf{r}$$
$$= q \int_a^b \nabla\phi \cdot d\mathbf{r}$$
$$W = q[\phi(b) - \phi(a)]$$

where ϕ is the potential of the field **E**. In keeping with the usual practice, ϕ is taken as regular at infinity. Thus $\phi(\infty)$ is zero, and the work done on the field in bringing the charge from infinity to the point b is

$$W = q\phi(b) \qquad (11\text{-}32)$$

This is the potential energy of the charge in the field. If W is positive, the energy is stored in the field, and may be recovered in removing the charge to infinity. When W is negative, energy was extracted from the field in moving q from infinity to point b and must be restored to the field in removing q to infinity again.

From (11-32), one can proceed to calculate the total energy stored in an electrostatic field caused by a given distribution of charge. The case of a set of point charges is easily handled and is left to the reader. For the present discussion, consider a continuous distribution of charges. The work done to change the charge density by $\delta\rho$ throughout a neighborhood dV of point P is given by

$$\phi(P)\, \delta\rho\, dV$$

Similarly to change a surface charge density ρ_s in a neighborhood dS of point P' requires work

$$\phi(P') \, \delta\rho_s \, dS$$

Summing over the whole field, one gets the following change dW in total energy:

$$dW = \int_V \phi \, \delta\rho \, dV + \int_S \phi \, \delta\rho_s \, dS$$

But this may also be approached from another angle. Modifying the charge distribution changes the potential. Thus one may also calculate dW as

$$d\dot{V} = \int_V \rho \, \delta\phi \, dV + \int_S \rho_s \, \delta\phi \, dS$$

Hence

$$dW = \tfrac{1}{2} \int_V (\phi \, \delta\rho + \rho \, \delta\phi) \, dV + \tfrac{1}{2} \int_S (\phi \, \delta\rho_s + \rho_s \, \delta\phi) \, dS$$

$$= \tfrac{1}{2} \int_V \delta(\phi\rho) \, dV + \tfrac{1}{2} \int_S \delta(\phi\rho_s) \, dS$$

Finally, the total energy W in the field is

$$W = \tfrac{1}{2} \int_V \phi\rho \, dV + \tfrac{1}{2} \int_S \phi\rho_s \, dS \qquad (11\text{-}33)$$

Now recall the first of Green's theorems:

$$\int_V (\phi\nabla^2\psi + \nabla\phi \cdot \nabla\psi) \, dV = \oint_{\substack{\text{bdy} \\ \text{of } V}} \phi\nabla\psi \cdot d\mathbf{S}$$

Let the boundary of V consist of a surface enclosing the entire charge distribution, plus the surfaces of thin volumes just enveloping those surfaces on which there are surface charges. Within the volume V so defined, the field vectors and their potentials are continuous with continuous derivatives; and one can put $\psi = \epsilon\phi$. Thus

$$\int_V (-\phi\nabla \cdot \mathbf{D} + \mathbf{E} \cdot \mathbf{D}) \, dV = - \oint_{\substack{\text{bdy} \\ \text{of } V}} \phi\mathbf{D} \cdot d\mathbf{S}$$

Making the surface containing the whole charge distribution recede to infinity, the corresponding part of the surface integral drops out. For the remaining surfaces of integration, reverse the direction of the normals so that they now point into V; take together surface elements lying opposite each other relative to the charge-bearing surfaces; and then let the thin containing volumes shrink down upon the charged surfaces.

The surface integral becomes

$$\beta \int_S \phi \rho_s \, dS$$

where S is now the totality of charged surfaces. Finally, replacing $\nabla \cdot \mathbf{D}$ by $\beta\rho$,

$$\frac{1}{\beta} \int_{\substack{\text{all} \\ \text{space}}} \mathbf{E} \cdot \mathbf{D} \, dV = \int_{\substack{\text{all} \\ \text{space}}} \phi\rho \, dV + \int_S \phi \rho_s \, dS$$

Comparing this with (11-33), one sees that the potential energy W of the field is given by

$$W = \frac{1}{2\beta} \int_{\substack{\text{all} \\ \text{space}}} \mathbf{E} \cdot \mathbf{D} \, dV \tag{11-34}$$

It is as though energy were distributed with a volume density of

$$\frac{\mathbf{E} \cdot \mathbf{D}}{2\beta} \tag{11-35}$$

Although the result has been derived for the electrostatic case, it is customary to assume it true for electromagnetic fields in general. This assumption appears to be consistent with experiment.

For magnetostatic fields in which $\mathbf{B}$ is a linear function of $\mathbf{H}$, similar considerations show that the energy W due to current distributions is given by

$$W = \frac{1}{2\beta} \int_{\substack{\text{all} \\ \text{space}}} \mathbf{H} \cdot \mathbf{B} \, dV \tag{11-36}$$

One assumes in the general case that energy is stored in the field with a density

$$\frac{\mathbf{H} \cdot \mathbf{B}}{2\beta} \tag{11-37}$$

There appears to be no conflict with experiment in making such an assumption.

EXERCISES

1. Obtain an expression for the potential energy of the field due to a given configuration of n point charges.

2. What is the potential energy of an electron in the field of a proton? Calculate this energy for the case in which the electron is 10^{-8} cm from the proton.

11-13. Flow of Energy. Poynting's Vector

From Maxwell's equations,

$$\gamma \mathbf{H} \cdot \nabla \times \mathbf{E} + \mathbf{H} \cdot \frac{\partial \mathbf{B}}{\partial t} = 0$$

$$\gamma \mathbf{E} \cdot \nabla \times \mathbf{H} - \mathbf{E} \cdot \frac{\partial \mathbf{D}}{\partial t} = \beta \mathbf{E} \cdot \mathbf{J}$$

Combining these,

$$\frac{\gamma}{\beta} \nabla \cdot (\mathbf{E} \times \mathbf{H}) = -\mathbf{E} \cdot \mathbf{J} - \left[\frac{1}{\beta} \mathbf{E} \cdot \frac{\partial \mathbf{D}}{\partial t} + \frac{1}{\beta} \mathbf{H} \cdot \frac{\partial \mathbf{B}}{\partial t} \right] \qquad (11\text{-}38)$$

From the discussion of Sec. 11-12, one interprets the bracketed term on the right side of (11-38) as the net rate at which electric and magnetic energies leave the point in question.   The first term on the right can be shown to represent the net rate at which moving charge carries energy away from the point.   It follows that the left side should be interpreted as the total net rate at which energy flows away from the point in question.

These considerations lead one finally to interpret the vector

$$\frac{\gamma}{\beta} \mathbf{E} \times \mathbf{H}$$

called Poynting's vector, as an energy flow vector. Poynting's vector appears quite generally to give the rate and direction of flow of energy in the electromagnetic field with which it is associated.

11-14. The Wave Equation

From Maxwell's first equation, (11-1), one has

$$\gamma \nabla \times (\nabla \times \mathbf{E}) + \frac{\partial}{\partial t} \nabla \times \mathbf{B} = 0$$

Using (11-2) and (11-5):

$$\gamma [\nabla (\nabla \cdot \mathbf{E}) - \nabla^2 \mathbf{E}] + \mu \frac{\partial}{\partial t} \left[\frac{1}{\gamma} \frac{\partial \mathbf{D}}{\partial t} + \frac{\beta}{\gamma} \mathbf{J} \right] = 0$$

Finally, bringing in (11-4) and (11-6),

$$\nabla^2 \mathbf{E} - \frac{\beta \mu \sigma}{\gamma^2} \frac{\partial \mathbf{E}}{\partial t} - \frac{\mu \epsilon}{\gamma^2} \frac{\partial^2 \mathbf{E}}{\partial t^2} = \nabla (\nabla \cdot \mathbf{E}) = \frac{\beta}{\epsilon} \nabla \rho$$

Similar steps can be taken to show that the other Maxwell field vectors, and the potentials ϕ and $\mathbf{A}$ of (11-14) and (11-15) all satisfy equations similar to the one just derived for $\mathbf{E}$.   In fact, by way of summary, one now has

$$\gamma \nabla \times \mathbf{E} + \frac{\partial \mathbf{B}}{\partial t} = 0 \qquad (11\text{-}39)$$

$$\gamma \nabla \times \mathbf{H} - \frac{\partial \mathbf{D}}{\partial t} = \beta \mathbf{J} \qquad (11\text{-}40)$$

$$\nabla \cdot \mathbf{B} = 0 \qquad (11\text{-}41)$$

$$\nabla \cdot \mathbf{D} = \beta \rho \qquad (11\text{-}42)$$

$$\mathbf{D} = \epsilon \mathbf{E} \qquad (11\text{-}43)$$

$$\mathbf{B} = \mu \mathbf{H} \qquad (11\text{-}44)$$

$$\mathbf{J} = \sigma \mathbf{E} \qquad (11\text{-}45)$$

$$\mathbf{E} = -\nabla\phi - \frac{1}{\gamma}\frac{\partial \mathbf{A}}{\partial t} \qquad (11\text{-}46)$$

$$\mathbf{B} = \nabla \times \mathbf{A} \qquad (11\text{-}47)$$

$$LE = \nabla(\nabla \cdot \mathbf{E}) = \frac{\beta}{\epsilon}\nabla\rho \qquad L \equiv \nabla^2 - \frac{\beta\mu\sigma}{\gamma^2}\frac{\partial}{\partial t} - \frac{\mu\epsilon}{\gamma^2}\frac{\partial^2}{\partial t^2} \qquad (11\text{-}48)$$

$$LD = \nabla(\nabla \cdot \mathbf{D}) = \beta\nabla\rho \qquad (11\text{-}49)$$

$$LH = \nabla(\nabla \cdot \mathbf{H}) = 0 \qquad (11\text{-}50)$$

$$LB = \nabla(\nabla \cdot \mathbf{B}) = 0 \qquad (11\text{-}51)$$

$$LA = \nabla\left[\nabla \cdot \mathbf{A} + \frac{\beta\mu\sigma}{\gamma}\phi + \frac{\mu\epsilon}{\gamma}\frac{\partial\phi}{\partial t}\right] \qquad (11\text{-}52)$$

$$L\phi = -\frac{\beta\rho}{\epsilon} - \frac{1}{\gamma}\frac{\partial}{\partial t}\left[\nabla \cdot \mathbf{A} + \frac{\beta\mu\sigma}{\gamma}\phi + \frac{\mu\epsilon}{\gamma}\frac{\partial\phi}{\partial t}\right] \qquad (11\text{-}53)$$

A solution to a Maxwell field problem must satisfy relations (11-39) to (11-42) and whatever boundary conditions are imposed. The various vectors comprising such a solution are further related in a manner characteristic of the physical medium in which the field exists. For this text, these "constitutive relations," as they are sometimes called, are assumed to be (11-43) to (11-45).

In solving a given problem, one can start directly with the Maxwell equations themselves, and by various manipulations come out with an answer. Or one can make use of the fact that the field vectors satisfy relations (11-48) to (11-51). Hence one can start by solving these equations. It must be emphasized, however, that one cannot group solutions of (11-48) to (11-51) arbitrarily and come up with a solution of Maxwell's equations. A given solution of (11-48) must be paired with the appropriate solution of (11-50) in order to satisfy (11-39) to (11-45).

Finally, one can proceed to calculate the potentials ϕ and $\mathbf{A}$ of (11-46) and (11-47) by solving (11-52) and (11-53). From these, then, the Maxwell field can be computed. In this approach one can, for example, set

$$\nabla \cdot \mathbf{A} + \frac{\beta\mu\sigma}{\gamma}\phi + \frac{\mu\epsilon}{\gamma}\frac{\partial\phi}{\partial t} = 0 \qquad (11\text{-}54)$$

thereby simplifying (11-52) and (11-53) to

$$LA = 0 \tag{11-55}$$

$$L\phi = -\frac{\beta\rho}{\epsilon} \tag{11-56}$$

A solution of (11-55) with a solution of (11-56), which together satisfy (11-54), can be used in (11-46) and (11-47) to give **E** and **B**.

It will be found that the Maxwell equations have an infinite variety of solutions. There are numerous ways of determining particular solutions. In an actual problem one uses a promising technique to obtain a collection of particular solutions of Maxwell's equations. Then one attempts to combine these in such a way as to satisfy the boundary conditions of the problem. Since Maxwell's equations are linear, the various solutions can be combined linearly in attempting to meet the boundary conditions.

One cannot help but be struck by the fact that the left sides of (11-48) to (11-53) are identical in form. In fact, when the right sides vanish, the equations all reduce to the form

$$\nabla^2 f - b \frac{\partial f}{\partial t} - \frac{1}{v^2} \frac{\partial^2 f}{\partial t^2} = 0 \tag{11-57}$$

This is called a wave equation since solutions of it represent traveling waves. This can be seen most clearly by considering the case in which $b = 0$. Then

$$\nabla^2 f = \frac{1}{v^2} \frac{\partial^2 f}{\partial t^2} \tag{11-58}$$

Let $f(u)$ be any differentiable function of the variable u. Then $f(x - vt)$ is a solution of (11-58), as may be verified by direct substitution. The expression $f(x - vt)$ represents the propagation of a wave of shape $f(u)$, in the direction of the positive x axis, with a speed v. For, the value of x corresponding to a given fixed value of u, hence of $f(u)$, must satisfy the relation

$$x - vt = u = \text{constant}$$

Since time t increases steadily, so must x in order to keep u constant; and in fact one must have

$$\frac{dx}{dt} - v = 0$$

or

$$\frac{dx}{dt} = v$$

The second term in (11-57) is referred to as the damping term. When $b \neq 0$, the amplitude of the wave is modified as the wave progresses.

EXERCISES

1. Let E_1, D_1, H_1, B_1, J_1, and E_2, D_2, H_2, B_2, J_2 be two sets of vectors satisfying Maxwell's equations. Show that $E_1 + E_2$, $D_1 + D_2$, ..., $J_1 + J_2$ also satisfy Maxwell's equations.

2. Let $E_1 + iE_2$, $D_1 + iD_2$, ..., $J_1 + iJ_2$ satisfy Maxwell's equations, where $i = \sqrt{-1}$, and where E_1, E_2, D_1, ..., J_2 are all real. Using the fact that γ and β are real, prove that E_1, D_1, ..., J_1 satisfy Maxwell's equations. Prove the same for E_2, D_2, ..., J_2.

3. Derive relations (11-49) to (11-51).

4. Derive (11-52) and (11-53).

5. Discuss (11-39) to (11-53) for the static case, i.e., the case in which vectors and potentials do not vary with time.

6. In (11-58) suppose that f depends only on x and t, and can be written in the form

$$f(x,t) = X(x)T(t) \tag{11-59}$$

Substituting in (11-58),

$$\frac{1}{X}\frac{\partial^2 X}{\partial x^2} = \frac{1}{v^2 T}\frac{\partial^2 T}{\partial t^2}$$

The left side depends only on x, the right side only on t. Since x and t are completely independent variables both sides must be constant, equal to $-k^2$, say. Complete the solution for $f(x,t)$, and show that it represents a wave propagated with a phase speed v.

7. Apply the technique of Exercise 6 to solve (11-57) when f is of the form (11-59). Show that a nonvanishing b gives rise to an attenuation of the propagating wave.

8. Consider (11-48) in a charge-free nonconducting region. Using the technique of Exercise 6, solve for E, assuming E to depend only on x and t. Determine the velocity of phase propagation.

9. Repeat Exercise 8 for the case of a conducting region.

11-15. Solution of Maxwell's Equations

It was pointed out in Exercise 2 of Sec. 11-14, that either the real part or the imaginary part of a complex solution to Maxwell's equations is itself a solution. For the answer to a practical problem one wants a real solution. But in the algebraic manipulations involved in determining a solution to Maxwell's equations, it is often far easier to use complex quantities. It is common, therefore, to obtain complex solutions to

Maxwell's equations, and then at the end to take either the real or the imaginary part for constructing the practical answer to the problem at hand. This approach is particularly useful in handling problems in which the field vectors vary sinusoidally with time. By handling complex solutions to the field equations, one can use the simple exponential $e^{i\omega t}$ to represent the time variations, instead of the cumbersome quantities $\sin \omega t$ and $\cos \omega t$.

An ever-present problem in the solving of Maxwell's equations is that of obtaining solutions with enough arbitrary constants to use as parameters in fitting required boundary conditions. A particularly useful solution can be obtained by writing $\mathbf{E}$ in the form

$$\mathbf{E} = \mathbf{E}_0 e^{i(\omega t - \mathbf{K} \cdot \mathbf{r})} \tag{11-60}$$

The quantity $\mathbf{K}$ is known as the propagation constant. As usual, $\mathbf{r}$ denotes the radius vector from the origin. The frequency of the signal represented by (11-60) is $\omega/2\pi$. From (11-60) one has

$$\nabla^2 \mathbf{E} = -\mathbf{K} \cdot \mathbf{K} \mathbf{E}$$

$$\frac{\partial \mathbf{E}}{\partial t} = i\omega \mathbf{E}$$

$$\frac{\partial^2 \mathbf{E}}{\partial t^2} = -\omega^2 \mathbf{E}$$

Now consider a conducting, but neutral, region, so that $\rho \equiv 0$. Relation (11-48) yields

$$\left[-\mathbf{K} \cdot \mathbf{K} - \frac{\beta\mu\sigma}{\gamma^2} i\omega + \frac{\mu\epsilon}{\gamma^2} \omega^2 \right] \mathbf{E} = 0$$

or

$$\mathbf{K} \cdot \mathbf{K} = \frac{\mu\epsilon\omega^2}{\gamma^2} - i \frac{\beta\mu\sigma\omega}{\gamma^2} \tag{11-61}$$

Thus $\mathbf{K}$ must be complex:

$$\mathbf{K} = \mathbf{K}_1 + i\mathbf{K}_2$$

Hence

$$K_1^2 - K_2^2 + i2\mathbf{K}_1 \cdot \mathbf{K}_2 = \frac{\mu\epsilon\omega^2}{\gamma^2} - i \frac{\beta\mu\sigma\omega}{\gamma^2}$$

$$K_1^2 - K_2^2 = \frac{\mu\epsilon\omega^2}{\gamma^2} \tag{11-62}$$

$$K_1 K_2 = - \frac{\beta\mu\sigma\omega}{2\gamma^2 \cos \theta} \tag{11-63}$$

where θ is the angle between $\mathbf{K}_1$ and $\mathbf{K}_2$. It is assumed that $\cos \theta$ does not vanish. In the case in which $\cos \theta$ does vanish, $\mathbf{K}_1$ and $\mathbf{K}_2$ are perpendicular, σ vanishes, and one of K_1 and K_2 is fixed in terms of the other through (11-62).

Solving (11-62) and (11-63) gives:

$$K_1 = \frac{\omega}{\gamma}\sqrt{\frac{\mu\epsilon}{2}}\left[\sqrt{1 + \frac{\beta^2\sigma^2}{\epsilon^2\omega^2\cos^2\theta}} + 1\right]^{\frac{1}{2}} \qquad (11\text{-}64)$$

$$K_2 = \frac{\omega}{\gamma}\sqrt{\frac{\mu\epsilon}{2}}\left[\sqrt{1 + \frac{\beta^2\sigma^2}{\epsilon^2\omega^2\cos^2\theta}} - 1\right]^{\frac{1}{2}} \qquad (11\text{-}65)$$

With K_1 and K_2 given by (11-64) and (11-65), the vector $\mathbf{E}$ in (11-60) solves the wave equation (11-48). One has

$$\mathbf{E} = \mathbf{E}_0 e^{\mathbf{K}_2 \cdot \mathbf{r}} e^{i(\omega t - \mathbf{K}_1 \cdot \mathbf{r})} \qquad (11\text{-}66)$$

From this it is seen that $\mathbf{K}_1$ determines the velocity of propagation of a given phase of the electric vector. Hence $\mathbf{K}_1$ is called the phase propagation constant. The value of $\mathbf{K}_2$ determines the manner in which the electric vector is attenuated as it propagates. It is called the attenuation constant. Since K_1 and K_2 are nonnegative, it follows from (11-63) that θ lies between $\frac{\pi}{2}$ and π.

Now that $\mathbf{E}$ has been determined it remains to calculate $\mathbf{H}$, say, so that $\mathbf{E}, \mathbf{H}, \mathbf{D} \,(= \epsilon\mathbf{E})$, $\mathbf{B} \,(= \mu\mathbf{H})$, and $\mathbf{J} \,(= \sigma\mathbf{E})$ satisfy (11-39) to (11-42). To this end, note first that since Maxwell's equations are linear, all the vectors must have the same exponential factors. Hence $\mathbf{H}$ has the form

$$\mathbf{H} = \mathbf{H}_0 e^{\mathbf{K}_2 \cdot \mathbf{r}} e^{i(\omega t - \mathbf{K}_1 \cdot \mathbf{r})} \qquad (11\text{-}67)$$

Secondly, observe that with $\rho \equiv 0$ as assumed, and with $\mathbf{E}$ and $\mathbf{H}$ of the form (11-66) and (11-67), (11-39) to (11-42) can be written as

$$\mathbf{K} \times \mathbf{E} = \frac{\mu\omega}{\gamma}\mathbf{H} \qquad (11\text{-}68)$$

$$\mathbf{K} \times \mathbf{H} = \frac{-\epsilon\omega + i\beta\sigma}{\gamma}\mathbf{E} \qquad (11\text{-}69)$$

$$\mathbf{K} \cdot \mathbf{E} = 0 \qquad (11\text{-}70)$$

$$\mathbf{K} \cdot \mathbf{H} = 0 \qquad (11\text{-}71)$$

where $\mathbf{K} = \mathbf{K}_1 + i\mathbf{K}_2$. Since $\mathbf{E}$ and $\mathbf{H}$ have the same exponential factors, (11-68) to (11-71) hold also with $\mathbf{E}$ and $\mathbf{H}$ replaced by $\mathbf{E}_0$ and $\mathbf{H}_0$. The relations furnish the means for determining $\mathbf{H}$ in terms of $\mathbf{E}$.

As an example, consider the case in which $\mathbf{E}_0$ is real, and $\theta = \pi$. Take the positive z axis in the direction of $\mathbf{K}_1$. Then

$$\mathbf{E} = \mathbf{E}_0 e^{-K_2 z} e^{i(\omega t - K_1 z)}$$

$$\mathbf{H} = (\mathbf{H}_{01} + i\mathbf{H}_{02}) e^{-K_2 z} e^{i(\omega t - K_1 z)}$$

From (11-68), canceling the exponentials,

$$\mathbf{H}_{01} + i\mathbf{H}_{02} = \frac{\gamma}{\mu\omega} (\mathbf{K}_1 + i\mathbf{K}_2) \times \mathbf{E}_0$$

Hence

$$\mathbf{H} = \frac{\gamma}{\mu\omega} (\mathbf{K}_1 + i\mathbf{K}_2) \times \mathbf{E}_0 e^{-K_{2}z} e^{i(\omega t - K_1 z)}$$

$$= \frac{\gamma}{\mu\omega} \{[\mathbf{K}_1 \times \mathbf{E}_0 \cos(\omega t - K_1 z) - \mathbf{K}_2 \times \mathbf{E}_0 \sin(\omega t - K_1 z)]$$

$$+ i[\mathbf{K}_2 \times \mathbf{E}_0 \cos(\omega t - K_1 z) + \mathbf{K}_1 \times \mathbf{E}_0 \sin(\omega t - K_1 z)]\} e^{-K_{2}z}$$

Thus, a real solution is

$$\mathbf{E}_1 = \mathbf{E}_0 e^{-K_{2}z} \cos(\omega t - K_1 z)$$

$$\mathbf{H}_1 = \frac{\gamma}{\mu\omega} e^{-K_{2}z}[\mathbf{K}_1 \times \mathbf{E}_0 \cos(\omega t - K_1 z) - \mathbf{K}_2 \times \mathbf{E}_0 \sin(\omega t - K_1 z)]$$

From (11-70) $\mathbf{E}$ is normal to the direction of propagation. Take the positive x axis in the direction of $\mathbf{E}$. Then, using subscripts x, y, and z to denote x, y, and z components,

$$E_{1x} = E_0 e^{-K_{2}z} \cos(\omega t - K_1 z)$$
$$E_{1y} = E_{1z} = 0$$
$$H_{1x} = H_{1z} = 0 \qquad\qquad (11\text{-}72)$$
$$H_{1y} = \frac{\gamma}{\mu\omega} E_0 e^{-K_{2}z}[K_1 \cos(\omega t - K_1 z) + K_2 \sin(\omega t - K_1 z)]$$

The solution (11-72) of Maxwell's equations represents a transverse, plane, electromagnetic wave. Since the constant-phase surfaces are all planes normal to the z axis, the wave is said to be a plane wave. Since $\mathbf{E}$ and $\mathbf{H}$ are both normal to the direction of phase propagation, the wave is said to be transverse. Note also that $\mathbf{H}$ is perpendicular to $\mathbf{E}$.

The wave propagates in the positive direction along the z axis at a speed v given by

$$v = \frac{\omega}{K_1} \qquad\qquad (11\text{-}73)$$

It is attenuated in the same direction by the factor $e^{-K_{2}z}$. Thus the nature of $\mathbf{K}_1$ as a phase constant and that of $\mathbf{K}_2$ as an attenuation constant are readily apparent in (11-72).

The value of the phase propagation speed for free space is commonly denoted by c, and is the speed of light in a vacuum. In terms of c, v is often expressed as

$$v = \frac{c}{n} \qquad\qquad (11\text{-}74)$$

where n is called the index of refraction of the medium in which the wave is traveling. Comparing (11-74) with (11-73), and using (11-64), one gets

$$n = \sqrt{k_m k_e} \left[\tfrac{1}{2} \left(\sqrt{1 + \frac{\beta^2 \sigma^2}{\epsilon^2 \omega^2 \cos^2 \theta}} + 1 \right) \right]^{\frac{1}{2}} \qquad (11\text{-}75)$$

$$n = \frac{K_1 c}{\omega} \qquad (11\text{-}76)$$

$$c = \frac{\gamma}{\sqrt{\mu_0 \epsilon_0}} \qquad (11\text{-}77)$$

EXERCISES

1. Solve (11-62) with (11-63) to obtain (11-64) and (11-65).

2. Determine the instantaneous rate of flow of energy in the wave represented by (11-72).

3. Using the result of Exercise 2 and integrating with respect to time over a complete cycle, calculate the average rate of flow of energy in the wave of (11-72).

4. By using the imaginary parts of the complex solution obtained in the text for Maxwell's equations, give a second real solution to Maxwell's equations. Use the form of (11-72) to present the answer.

11-16. Refraction and Reflection of Plane Waves—Basic Theory

Consider the propagation of a plane electromagnetic wave through two media which adjoin along a plane interface. Let the interface be the plane $z = 0$. Suppose a wave comes up from below $z = 0$. In general, upon striking the boundary of the two media, part of the wave will be reflected, and part transmitted. In the notation to follow, no-primes, primes, and double-primes will be used consistently to denote the incoming, the transmitted, and the reflected waves respectively. For the phase and attenuation constants $\mathbf{K}_1$ and $\mathbf{K}_2$, the Greek letters α, β, γ with appropriate subscripts and primes will be used to denote the direction angles relative to the x, y, and z axes respectively. Thus

$$\mathbf{K}_2' = K_2'(\cos \alpha_2' \mathbf{i} + \cos \beta_2' \mathbf{j} + \cos \gamma_2' \mathbf{k})$$

Also, subscripts 1 and 2 will be used to denote real and imaginary parts of a quantity, while subscripts x, y, and z will be used to denote components relative to the x, y, and z axes. For example:

$$\begin{aligned}
\mathbf{E}_0 &= \mathbf{E}_{01} + i\mathbf{E}_{02} \\
&= (E_{01x} + iE_{02x})\mathbf{i} + (E_{01y} + iE_{02y})\mathbf{j} + (E_{01z} + iE_{02z})\mathbf{k}
\end{aligned}$$

Assume both media to possess finite conductivities and to be neutral. Assume also that there is no accumulation of charge on the boundary surface between the media. The incoming, transmitted, and reflected waves must all be solutions of Maxwell's equations. Also, from the discussion of Sec. 11-11, it is seen that the tangential component of the composite wave in the first medium, consisting of the incoming and reflected waves, must match identically along the plane $z = 0$ with the tangential component of the transmitted wave in the second medium. To meet these boundary conditions, one must have at $z = 0$

$$\begin{aligned} E_x + E_x'' &= E_x' \\ E_y + E_y'' &= E_y' \\ H_x + H_x'' &= H_x' \\ H_y + H_y'' &= H_y' \end{aligned} \tag{11-78}$$

It turns out to be possible to meet these boundary conditions using solutions of Maxwell's equations in which the field vectors have the form (11-66), and for which, accordingly, Maxwell's equations take the form (11-68) to (11-71). With such solutions, it is plain that (11-78) will be satisfied only if all the exponentials agree. For this to happen the components in the xy plane of $\mathbf{K}_1$, $\mathbf{K}_1'$, and $\mathbf{K}_1''$ must be identical. Thus the directions of propagation of all the waves must lie in a common plane through the z axis. Take this plane as the xz plane. Then one can write

$$\begin{aligned} \mathbf{K}_1 &= K_1(\sin \gamma_1 \mathbf{i} + \cos \gamma_1 \mathbf{k}) \\ \mathbf{K}_1' &= K_1'(\sin \gamma_1' \mathbf{i} + \cos \gamma_1' \mathbf{k}) \\ \mathbf{K}_1'' &= K_1''(\sin \gamma_1'' \mathbf{i} + \cos \gamma_1'' \mathbf{k}) \end{aligned}$$

But, from the above remarks,

$$K_1 \sin \gamma_1 = K_1' \sin \gamma_1' \tag{11-79}$$

Using (11-76), this leads to Snell's law of refraction:

$$n_1 \sin \gamma_1 = n_1' \sin \gamma_1' \tag{11-80}$$

For the incoming and reflected waves,

$$K_1 \sin \gamma_1 = K_1'' \sin \gamma_1''$$

But since both are in the same medium, $K_1 = K_1''$ and

$$\sin \gamma_1 = \sin \gamma_1''$$

Hence either $\gamma_1'' = \gamma_1$ or $\gamma_1'' = \pi - \gamma_1$. For the case of reflection, the latter holds. This says that the angle of reflection equals the angle of incidence.

With these results one has

$$\begin{aligned}
\mathbf{K}_1 &= K_1(\sin \gamma_1 \mathbf{i} + \cos \gamma_1 \mathbf{k}) \\
\mathbf{K}_1' &= K_1 \sin \gamma_1 \mathbf{i} + K_1' \cos \gamma_1' \mathbf{k} \\
\mathbf{K}_1'' &= K_1(\sin \gamma_1 \mathbf{i} - \cos \gamma_1 \mathbf{k})
\end{aligned} \tag{11-81}$$

By similar reasoning, one concludes that the components of $\mathbf{K}_2$, $\mathbf{K}_2'$, and $\mathbf{K}_2''$ normal to the z axis are all identical, hence that these three vectors also lie in a common plane through the z axis. One can write

$$\begin{aligned}
\mathbf{K}_2 &= K_2(\cos \alpha_2 \mathbf{i} + \cos \beta_2 \mathbf{j} + \cos \gamma_2 \mathbf{k}) \\
\mathbf{K}_2' &= K_2(\cos \alpha_2 \mathbf{i} + \cos \beta_2 \mathbf{j}) + K_2' \cos \gamma_2' \mathbf{k} \\
\mathbf{K}_2'' &= K_2(\cos \alpha_2 \mathbf{i} + \cos \beta_2 \mathbf{j} - \cos \gamma_2 \mathbf{k})
\end{aligned} \tag{11-82}$$

With the $\mathbf{K}$'s given in (11-81) and (11-82), the exponential parts of the vectors $\mathbf{E}$, $\mathbf{E}'$, . . . , $\mathbf{H}''$ cancel out of (11-78), leaving only the constant factors $\mathbf{E}_0$, $\mathbf{E}_0'$, . . . , $\mathbf{H}_0''$. These equations together with Maxwell's equations (11-68) to (11-71), which hold separately for the incoming, the transmitted, and the reflected waves, can now be used to determine the constant factors. Eliminating the magnetic vectors, and writing the results out in component form, one has

$$E'_{01x} - E''_{01x} = E_{01x} \tag{11-83}$$

$$E'_{01y} - E''_{01y} = E_{01y} \tag{11-84}$$

$$E'_{02x} - E''_{02x} = E_{02x} \tag{11-85}$$

$$E'_{02y} - E''_{02y} = E_{02y} \tag{11-86}$$

$$-\frac{K'_1 \cos \gamma'_1}{\mu'} E'_{01y} - \frac{K_2 \cos \beta_2}{\mu'} E'_{02z} + \frac{K'_2 \cos \gamma'_2}{\mu'} E'_{02y}$$

$$-\frac{K_1 \cos \gamma_1}{\mu} E''_{01y} + \frac{K_2 \cos \beta_2}{\mu} E''_{02z} - \frac{K_2 \cos \gamma_2}{\mu} E''_{02y}$$

$$= -\frac{K_1 \cos \gamma_1}{\mu} E_{01y} - \frac{K_2 \cos \beta_2}{\mu} E_{02z} + \frac{K_2 \cos \gamma_2}{\mu} E_{02y} \tag{11-87}$$

$$\frac{K'_1 \cos \gamma'_1}{\mu'} E'_{01x} - \frac{K_1 \sin \gamma_1}{\mu'} E'_{01z} - \frac{K'_2 \cos \gamma'_2}{\mu'} E'_{02x} + \frac{K_2 \cos \alpha_2}{\mu'} E'_{02z}$$

$$+\frac{K_1 \cos \gamma_1}{\mu} E''_{01x} + \frac{K_1 \sin \gamma_1}{\mu} E''_{01z} - \frac{K_2 \cos \gamma_2}{\mu} E''_{02x}$$

$$-\frac{K_2 \cos \alpha_2}{\mu} E''_{02z} = \frac{K_1 \cos \gamma_1}{\mu} E_{01x} - \frac{K_1 \sin \gamma_1}{\mu} E_{01z} - \frac{K_2 \cos \gamma_2}{\mu} E_{02x}$$

$$+\frac{K_2 \cos \alpha_2}{\mu} E_{02z} \tag{11-88}$$

$$\frac{K_2 \cos \beta_2}{\mu'} E'_{01z} - \frac{K'_2 \cos \gamma'_2}{\mu'} E'_{01y} - \frac{K'_1 \cos \gamma'_1}{\mu'} E'_{02y}$$

$$- \frac{K_2 \cos \beta_2}{\mu} E''_{01z} - \frac{K_2 \cos \gamma_2}{\mu} E''_{01y} - \frac{K_1 \cos \gamma_1}{\mu} E''_{02y}$$

$$= \frac{K_2 \cos \beta_2}{\mu} E_{01z} - \frac{K_2 \cos \gamma_2}{\mu} E_{01y} - \frac{K_1 \cos \gamma_1}{\mu} E_{02y} \quad (11\text{-}89)$$

$$\frac{K'_2 \cos \gamma'_2}{\mu'} E'_{01x} - \frac{K_2 \cos \alpha_2}{\mu'} E'_{01z} + \frac{K'_1 \cos \gamma'_1}{\mu'} E'_{02x} - \frac{K_1 \sin \gamma_1}{\mu'} E'_{02z}$$

$$+ \frac{K_2 \cos \gamma_2}{\mu} E''_{01x} + \frac{K_2 \cos \alpha_2}{\mu} E''_{01z} + \frac{K_1 \cos \gamma_1}{\mu} E''_{02x}$$

$$+ \frac{K_1 \sin \gamma_1}{\mu} E''_{02z} = \frac{K_2 \cos \gamma_2}{\mu} E_{01x} - \frac{K_2 \cos \alpha_2}{\mu} E_{01z} + \frac{K_1 \cos \gamma_1}{\mu} E_{02x}$$

$$- \frac{K_1 \sin \gamma_1}{\mu} E_{02z} \quad (11\text{-}90)$$

$$K_1 \sin \gamma_1 E''_{01x} - K_1 \cos \gamma_1 E''_{01z} - K_2 \cos \alpha_2 E''_{02x} - K_2 \cos \beta_2 E''_{02y}$$
$$+ K_2 \cos \gamma_2 E''_{02z} = 0 \quad (11\text{-}91)$$

$$K_2 \cos \alpha_2 E''_{01x} + K_2 \cos \beta_2 E''_{01y} - K_2 \cos \gamma_2 E''_{01z} + K_1 \sin \gamma_1 E''_{02x}$$
$$- K_1 \cos \gamma_1 E''_{02z} = 0 \quad (11\text{-}92)$$

$$K_1 \sin \gamma_1 E'_{01x} + K'_1 \cos \gamma'_1 E'_{01z} - K_2 \cos \alpha_2 E'_{02x} - K_2 \cos \beta_2 E'_{02y}$$
$$- K'_2 \cos \gamma'_2 E'_{02z} = 0 \quad (11\text{-}93)$$

$$K_2 \cos \alpha_2 E'_{01x} + K_2 \cos \beta_2 E'_{01y} - K'_2 \cos \gamma'_2 E'_{01z} + K_1 \sin \gamma_1 E'_{02x}$$
$$+ K'_1 \cos \gamma' E'_{02z} = 0 \quad (11\text{-}94)$$

EXERCISE

Derive Eqs. (11-83) to (11-94).

11-17. Refraction and Reflection of Plane Waves—Normal Incidence

Continuing the discussion of Sec. 11-16, suppose the two media to be nonconducting so that $K_2 = K_2' = 0$. Also, suppose the incoming wave to be incident normally upon $z = 0$ so that $\gamma_1 = 0$. Finally, take $\mathbf{E}_0$ as real, so that $E_{2x} = E_{2y} = E_{2z} = 0$.

There is no loss of generality in taking $E_{1y} = 0$, which will be done Since $\gamma_1 = 0$, then $\gamma_1' = 0$ also. One has

$$\mathbf{K}_1 = K_1\mathbf{k} \qquad \mathbf{K}_1'' = -K_1\mathbf{k} \qquad \mathbf{K}_1' = K_1'\mathbf{k}$$

From (11-70), one has

$$\mathbf{K} \cdot \mathbf{E} = \mathbf{K}_1 \cdot \mathbf{E} = K_1 E_{1z} = 0$$

Hence $E_{1z} = 0$.

Equations (11-83) to (11-94) now become

(a) $$E'_{01x} - E''_{01x} = E_{01x}$$

(b) $$E'_{01y} - E''_{01y} = 0$$

(c) $$E'_{02x} - E''_{02x} = 0$$

(d) $$E'_{02y} - E''_{02y} = 0$$

(e) $$-\frac{K'_1}{\mu'} E'_{01y} - \frac{K_1}{\mu} E''_{01y} = 0$$

(f) $$\frac{K'_1}{\mu'} E'_{01x} + \frac{K_1}{\mu} E''_{01x} = \frac{K_1}{\mu} E_{01x}$$

(g) $$-\frac{K'_1}{\mu'} E'_{02y} - \frac{K_1}{\mu} E''_{02y} = 0$$

(h) $$\frac{K'_1}{\mu'} E'_{02x} + \frac{K_1}{\mu} E''_{02x} = 0$$

(i) $$-K_1 E''_{01z} = 0$$

(j) $$-K_1 E''_{02z} = 0$$

(k) $$K'_1 E'_{01z} = 0$$

(l) $$K'_1 E'_{02z} = 0$$

From (i) to (l): $E''_{01z} = E''_{02z} = E'_{01z} = E'_{02z} = 0$

From (c) and (h): $E'_{02x} = E''_{02x} = 0$

From (d) and (g): $E'_{02y} = E''_{02y} = 0$

From (b) and (f): $E'_{01y} = E''_{01y} = 0$

There remain

$$E'_{01x} \quad - E''_{01x} \quad = E_{01x}$$

$$\frac{K'_1}{\mu'} E'_{01x} + \frac{K_1}{\mu} E''_{01x} = \frac{K_1}{\mu} E_{01x}$$

Solving these, introducing indices of refraction from (11-76), and calculating the **H**'s by means of (11-68), one gets, finally,

$$E_x = E_{01x} e^{i\omega\left(t - \frac{n}{c}z\right)}$$
$$E_y = E_z = 0$$
$$H_x = H_z = 0 \tag{11-95}$$
$$H_y = \frac{\gamma n}{c\mu} E_{01x} e^{i\omega\left(t - \frac{n}{c}z\right)}$$

$$E_x' = R' E_{01x} e^{i\omega\left(t - \frac{n'}{c}z\right)}$$
$$E_y' = E_z' = 0$$
$$H_x' = H_z' = 0 \tag{11-96}$$
$$H_y' = \frac{\gamma n'}{c\mu'} R' E_{01x} e^{i\omega\left(t - \frac{n'}{c}z\right)}$$

$$R' = \frac{2n/\mu}{n/\mu + n'/\mu'}$$

$$E_x'' = R''E_{01x}e^{i\omega\left(t+\frac{n}{c}z\right)}$$
$$E_y'' = E_z'' = 0$$
$$H_x'' = H_z'' = 0 \tag{11-97}$$
$$H_y'' = -\frac{\gamma n}{c\mu}R''E_{01x}e^{i\omega\left(t+\frac{n}{c}z\right)}$$
$$R'' = \frac{n/\mu - n'/\mu'}{n/\mu + n'/\mu'}$$

Comparing (11-97) with (11-95), one sees that the quantity R'' plays the role of a reflection coefficient. In the case of nonmagnetic media, $\mu = \mu' = 1$, and R'' becomes

$$\frac{n - n'}{n + n'}$$

It can be shown that R''^2 is the reflection coefficient for power.

EXERCISES

1. Fill in the details of the derivation of (11-95) to (11-97).

2. From (11-95) to (11-97), write out a real solution to the problem considered in the text.

3. Let a plane electromagnetic wave be normally incident upon a plane surface separating two nonconducting media. Show that the average power reflected is R''^2 times the average power incident upon the reflecting surface, where R'' is given in (11-97).

11-18. Refraction and Reflection of Plane Waves—Oblique Incidence

Extending the discussion of the last two sections, suppose again that $K_2 = K_2' = 0$. This time let the incoming wave fall obliquely upon the plane $z = 0$. Take $\mathbf{E}_0$ real, and let $\beta_1 = 90°$. Then

$$\mathbf{K} \cdot \mathbf{E} = 0$$

reduces to

$$\mathbf{K}_1 \cdot \mathbf{E}_1 = 0$$

which implies $\mathbf{E}_1$ is normal to $\mathbf{K}_1$. The various possibilities are intermediate between two extremes, namely, the case in which $E_{1x} = E_{1z} = 0$ and that in which $E_{1y} = 0$. In the former case the wave is said to be horizontally polarized relative to the reflecting surface; in the latter case, vertically polarized.

Case 1. *Horizontal polarization.* In this case Eqs. (11-83) to (11-94) become:

(a) $$E'_{01x} - E''_{01x} = 0$$

(b) $$E'_{01y} - E''_{01y} = E_{01y}$$

(c) $$E'_{02x} - E''_{02x} = 0$$

(d) $$E'_{02y} - E''_{02y} = 0$$

(e) $$-\frac{K'_1 \cos \gamma'_1}{\mu'} E'_{01y} - \frac{K_1 \cos \gamma_1}{\mu} E''_{01y} = -\frac{K_1 \cos \gamma_1}{\mu} E_{01y}$$

(f) $$\frac{K'_1 \cos \gamma'_1}{\mu'} E'_{01x} - \frac{K_1 \sin \gamma_1}{\mu'} E'_{01z} + \frac{K_1 \cos \gamma_1}{\mu} E''_{01x}$$
$$+ \frac{K_1 \sin \gamma_1}{\mu} E''_{01z} = 0$$

(g) $$-\frac{K'_1 \cos \gamma'_1}{\mu'} E'_{02y} - \frac{K_1 \cos \gamma_1}{\mu} E''_{02y} = 0$$

(h) $$\frac{K'_1 \cos \gamma'_1}{\mu'} E'_{02x} - \frac{K_1 \sin \gamma_1}{\mu'} E'_{02z} + \frac{K_1 \cos \gamma_1}{\mu} E''_{02x}$$
$$+ \frac{K_1 \sin \gamma_1}{\mu} E''_{02z} = 0$$

(i) $$K_1 \sin \gamma_1 E''_{01x} - K_1 \cos \gamma_1 E''_{01z} = 0$$

(j) $$K_1 \sin \gamma_1 E''_{02x} - K_1 \cos \gamma_1 F''_{02z} = 0$$

(k) $$K_1 \sin \gamma_1 E'_{01x} + K'_1 \cos \gamma'_1 F'_{01z} = 0$$

(l) $$K_1 \sin \gamma_1 E'_{02x} + K'_1 \cos \gamma'_1 E'_{02z} = 0$$

From (d) and (g): $E'_{02y} = E''_{02y} = 0$. The determinant of Eqs. (c), (h), (j), and (l) is

$$\begin{vmatrix} 1 & 0 & -1 & 0 \\ \dfrac{K_1' \cos \gamma_1'}{\mu'} & -\dfrac{K_1 \sin \gamma_1}{\mu'} & \dfrac{K_1 \cos \gamma_1}{\mu} & \dfrac{K_1 \sin \gamma_1}{\mu} \\ 0 & 0 & K_1 \sin \gamma_1 & -K_1 \cos \gamma_1 \\ K_1 \sin \gamma_1 & K_1' \cos \gamma_1' & 0 & 0 \end{vmatrix}$$

which does not vanish. Hence $E'_{02x} = E'_{02z} = E''_{02x} = E''_{02z} = 0$. Similarly, from (a), (f), (i), and (k): $E'_{01x} = E'_{01z} = E''_{01x} = E''_{01z} = 0$. There remain

$$E'_{01y} \quad - \quad E''_{01y} \quad = \quad E_{01y}$$
$$\frac{K'_1 \cos \gamma'_1}{\mu'} E'_{01y} + \frac{K_1 \cos \gamma_1}{\mu} E''_{01y} = \frac{K_1 \cos \gamma_1}{\mu} E_{01y}$$

Solving, introducing indices of refraction, and calculating the **H**'s, one has

$$E_x = E_z = 0$$

$$E_y = E_{01y} \exp\left\{ i\omega \left[t - \frac{n}{c} (x \sin \gamma_1 + z \cos \gamma_1) \right] \right\}$$

$$H_x = -\frac{\gamma n}{c\mu} \cos \gamma_1 E_{01y} \exp\left\{ i\omega \left[t - \frac{n}{c} (x \sin \gamma_1 + z \cos \gamma_1) \right] \right\} \quad (11\text{-}98)$$

$$H_y = 0$$

$$H_z = \frac{\gamma n}{c\mu} \sin \gamma_1 E_{01y} \exp \left\{ i\omega \left[t - \frac{n}{c} (x \sin \gamma_1 + z \cos \gamma_1) \right] \right\}$$

$$E_x' = E_z' = 0$$

$$E_y' = R' E_{01y} \exp \left\{ i\omega \left[t - \frac{n'}{c} (x \sin \gamma_1' + z \cos \gamma_1') \right] \right\}$$

$$H_x' = -\frac{\gamma n'}{c\mu'} \cos \gamma_1' R' E_{01y} \exp \left\{ i\omega \left[t - \frac{n'}{c} (x \sin \gamma_1' + z \cos \gamma_1') \right] \right\}$$

$$H_y' = 0 \tag{11-99}$$

$$H_z' = \frac{\gamma n'}{c\mu'} \sin \gamma_1' R' E_{01y} \exp \left\{ i\omega \left[t - \frac{n'}{c} (x \sin \gamma_1' + z \cos \gamma_1') \right] \right\}$$

$$R' = \frac{2 \dfrac{n}{\mu} \cos \gamma_1}{\dfrac{n}{\mu} \cos \gamma_1 + \dfrac{n'}{\mu'} \cos \gamma_1'}$$

$$E_x'' = E_z'' = 0$$

$$E_y'' = R'' E_{01y} \exp \left\{ i\omega \left[t - \frac{n}{c} (x \sin \gamma_1 - z \cos \gamma_1) \right] \right\}$$

$$H_x'' = \frac{\gamma n}{c\mu} \cos \gamma_1 R'' E_{01y} \exp \left\{ i\omega \left[t - \frac{n}{c} (x \sin \gamma_1 - z \cos \gamma_1) \right] \right\}$$

$$H_y'' = 0 \tag{11-100}$$

$$H_z'' = \frac{\gamma n}{c\mu} \sin \gamma_1 R'' E_{01y} \exp \left\{ i\omega \left[t - \frac{n}{c} (x \sin \gamma_1 - z \cos \gamma_1) \right] \right\}$$

$$R'' = \frac{\dfrac{n}{\mu} \cos \gamma_1 - \dfrac{n'}{\mu'} \cos \gamma_1'}{\dfrac{n}{\mu} \cos \gamma_1 + \dfrac{n'}{\mu'} \cos \gamma_1'}$$

Case 2. Vertical Polarization. In this case both E_x and E_z are different from zero. The analysis is a little more complicated than in the case of horizontal polarization, but basically the same. One gets:

$$E_x = E_{01x} \exp \left\{ i\omega \left[t - \frac{n}{c} (x \sin \gamma_1 + z \cos \gamma_1) \right] \right\}$$

$$E_y = 0$$

$$E_z = -E_{01x} \tan \gamma_1 \exp \left\{ i\omega \left[t - \frac{n}{c} (x \sin \gamma_1 + z \cos \gamma_1) \right] \right\} \tag{11-101}$$

$$H_x = H_z = 0$$

$$H_y = -\frac{\gamma n}{c\mu} \sec \gamma_1 E_{01x} \exp \left\{ i\omega \left[t - \frac{n}{c} (x \sin \gamma_1 + z \cos \gamma_1) \right] \right\}$$

$$E_x' = R' \cos \gamma_1' E_{01x} \exp\left\{i\omega\left[t - \frac{n'}{c}(x \sin \gamma_1' + z \cos \gamma_1')\right]\right\}$$

$$E_y' = 0$$

$$E_z' = -R' \sin \gamma_1' E_{01x} \exp\left\{i\omega\left[t - \frac{n'}{c}(x \sin \gamma_1' + z \cos \gamma_1')\right]\right\}$$

$$H_x' = H_z' = 0$$

$$H_y' = -\frac{\gamma n'}{c\mu'} R' E_{01x} \exp\left\{i\omega\left[t - \frac{n'}{c}(x \sin \gamma_1' + z \cos \gamma_1')\right]\right\}$$

(11-102)

$$R' = \frac{2\dfrac{n}{\mu}}{\dfrac{n'}{\mu'}\cos \gamma_1 + \dfrac{n}{\mu}\cos \gamma_1'}$$

$$E_x'' = -R'' E_{01x} \exp\left\{i\omega\left[t - \frac{n}{c}(x \sin \gamma_1 - z \cos \gamma_1)\right]\right\}$$

$$E_y'' = 0$$

$$E_z'' = -R'' \tan \gamma_1 E_{01x} \exp\left\{i\omega\left[t - \frac{n}{c}(x \sin \gamma_1 - z \cos \gamma_1)\right]\right\}$$

$$H_x'' = H_z'' = 0$$

$$H_y'' = \frac{\gamma n}{c\mu} R'' \sec \gamma_1 E_{01x} \exp\left\{i\omega\left[t - \frac{n}{c}(x \sin \gamma_1 - z \cos \gamma_1)\right]\right\}$$

(11-103)

$$R'' = \frac{\dfrac{n'}{\mu'}\cos \gamma_1 - \dfrac{n}{\mu}\cos \gamma_1'}{\dfrac{n'}{\mu'}\cos \gamma_1 + \dfrac{n}{\mu}\cos \gamma_1'}$$

Polarizing angle. There is an interesting difference between the reflection of a vertically polarized wave and the reflection of one which is horizontally polarized. Consider, for example, the case in which $n' > n$. Then

$$\sin \gamma_1' = \frac{n}{n'} \sin \gamma_1 < \sin \gamma_1$$

As γ_1 goes from 0 to $\frac{\pi}{2}$, γ_1' goes from 0 to some value less than $\frac{\pi}{2}$. Hence the reflection coefficient R'' goes from

$$\frac{n/\mu - n'/\mu'}{n/\mu + n'/\mu'}$$

to -1 for the case of horizontal polarization; and from

$$\frac{n'/\mu' - n/\mu}{n'/\mu' + n/\mu}$$

to -1 for the case of vertical polarization. Thus, one or the other reflection coefficient goes from a positive value to a negative value, hence passes through zero. At the angle for which this occurs, nothing is reflected. This angle is, then, a "polarizing angle," and is so called. From a beam containing both polarizations, the one is reflected, the other not. In the case of nonmagnetic media, $\mu = \mu' = 1$, and with $n' > n$ as assumed above, it is the vertically polarized wave for which the reflection coefficient vanishes at the polarizing angle. It can be shown that the polarizing angle γ_{1p} is given by

$$\tan \gamma_{1p} = \frac{n'}{n} \qquad (11\text{-}104)$$

EXERCISES

1. Show that for the case of nonmagnetic media, $\mu = \mu' = 1$, the reflection coefficient R'' of (11-100) can be put in the form

$$R'' = \frac{\sin (\gamma_1' - \gamma_1)}{\sin (\gamma_1' + \gamma_1)} \qquad \text{(Fresnel)}$$

2. Show that for the case of grazing incidence and nonmagnetic media, the reflection coefficient R'' of (11-100) becomes -1.

3. Derive the relations (11-101) to (11-103).

4. Show that for nonmagnetic media, the reflection coefficient R'' of (11-103) can be put in the form

$$R'' = \frac{\tan (\gamma_1 - \gamma_1')}{\tan (\gamma_1 + \gamma_1')} \qquad \text{(Fresnel)}$$

5. Using the result of Exercise 4, establish (11-104).

11-19. Total Reflection

Continue the study of the reflection and refraction of an electromagnetic wave striking the plane interface between two media. Using the notation of the preceding sections, suppose that $K_1 > K_1'$. From

$$\sin \gamma_1' = \frac{K_1}{K_1'} \sin \gamma_1$$

it is seen that for $\arcsin (K_1'/K_1) < \gamma_1 \leq \pi/2$, $\sin \gamma_1'$ is real but greater than 1. It follows that γ_1' no longer represents the angle between $\mathbf{K}_1'$ and $\mathbf{k}$, but is imaginary. It can easily be shown that $\gamma_1' = \pi/2 + i\zeta$, where $0 < \zeta \leq \cosh^{-1} (K_1/K_1')$.

The analytic arguments of continuity in Sec. 11-16 matching up incident, reflected, and transmitted waves at the interface between the two media are still valid even when γ_1' is imaginary. Thus one continues to take $K_1' \sin \gamma_1'$ equal to $K_1 \sin \gamma_1$. It remains then, simply to examine what form the solutions obtained previously take for the present case. One gets

$$\cos \gamma_1' = -i \sqrt{\frac{K_1{}^2}{K_1{}'^2} \sin^2 \gamma_1 - 1} = -i \sqrt{\frac{n^2}{n'^2} \sin^2 \gamma_1 - 1}$$

Consider the effect upon (11-98) to (11-100), for example. Equations (11-98) are unchanged. In Eqs. (11-100), the exponentials are unchanged, but the reflection coefficient R'' becomes

$$R'' = \frac{\dfrac{n}{\mu} \cos \gamma_1 + i\dfrac{n'}{\mu'} \sqrt{\dfrac{n^2}{n'^2} \sin^2 \gamma_1 - 1}}{\dfrac{n}{\mu} \cos \gamma_1 - i\dfrac{n'}{\mu'} \sqrt{\dfrac{n^2}{n'^2} \sin^2 \gamma_1 - 1}}$$

As γ_1 varies from arcsin (n'/n) to $\pi/2$, R'' goes from 1 along the unit circle in the complex plane, through quadrants I and II in succession, to -1. Thus, when $\gamma_1 = $ arcsin (n'/n), the electric vector of the reflected wave shows no phase shift relative to the incident wave. But as γ_1 increases, the reflected wave exhibits a greater and greater advancement in phase, until for $\gamma_1 = \pi/2$, the electric vector of the reflected wave is π radians out of phase with that of the incident wave. It can be shown that on the average as much energy is carried away from the plane $z = 0$ by the reflected wave as is brought to it by the incident wave. For this reason the phenomenon is called total reflection.

Finally, examine the transmitted wave (11-99). Here both the transmission coefficient R' and the exponential are altered. The latter is of greater interest, and for it one gets

$$\exp\left\{i\omega\left[t - \frac{n'}{c} x \sin \gamma_1' + i\frac{z}{c} \sqrt{n^2 \sin^2 \gamma_1 - n'^2}\right]\right\}$$
$$= \exp\left(-\frac{\omega z}{c} \sqrt{n^2 \sin^2 \gamma_1 - n'^2}\right) \exp\left[i\omega\left(t - \frac{n'}{c} x \sin \gamma_1'\right)\right]$$

Hence the disturbance above the plane $z = 0$ is damped out as the distance from $z = 0$ increases. The phase surfaces are propagated in the x direction at a phase velocity less than that shown for the ordinary reflection case. For $\gamma_1 = $ arcsin (n'/n) the damping factor is zero. Maximum attenuation occurs for $\gamma_1 = \pi/2$, for which the damping factor is

$$\exp\left(-\frac{\omega z}{c}\sqrt{n^2 - n'^2}\right).$$

A similar discussion applies to a vertically polarized wave.

EXERCISE

Show that, in the case of total reflection discussed in the text, the *average power* at $z = 0$ in the reflected wave is the same as that in the incident wave.

11-20. Refraction and Reflection of Plane Waves—Conducting Media

A wave propagating through a conducting medium is attenuated in the direction of propagation, energy being lost in heating of the medium. It is not necessarily true, however, that the maximum rate of attenuation occurs in the direction of phase propagation. For example, consider the case of a wave impinging obliquely from a nonconducting medium upon a conducting one. Again let $z = 0$ be the interface between the media, and let the incident wave come up from below. Use the notation adopted in the preceding sections.

One has $K_2 = 0$, $K_2' \neq 0$. By the requirements of continuity, then

$$\mathbf{K}_2' = -K_2'\mathbf{k}$$

Hence the maximum attenuation is in the direction normal to the interface. The vector $\mathbf{K}_1'$, on the other hand, has the same horizontal component as $\mathbf{K}_1$; hence the direction of phase propagation in the conducting medium is not normal to $z = 0$.

In the present case it will be found that the reflection coefficient is a complex number. Hence the incident wave electric vector experiences a phase shift upon reflection.

11-21. Units and Dimensions

The preceding discussion of electromagnetic theory was given without reference to any special system of units. To keep the question of units open, the parameters γ and β were introduced into Maxwell's equations at the very start, and were carried along as the theory developed. When practical applications of the theory are to be made, however, and quantitative answers are required, some workable system of units must be introduced. It is in terms of the chosen units that experimental data and the results of theoretical calculations are expressed.

$c \cong 3 \cdot 10^{10}$(cm/sec)		Meter-kilogram-second system (mks)					Centimeter-Gram-		
		The Giorgi system		The electromagnetic system (emu)			The electrostatic system (esu)		
Physical entity	Symbol	$\beta = 1$ $\mu_0 = 4\pi \cdot 10^{-7}$ $\gamma = 1$ $\epsilon_0 = \dfrac{10^7}{4\pi c^2}$ (sec/m)^2		$\beta = 4\pi$ $\mu_0 = 1$ $\gamma = 1$ $\epsilon_0 = \dfrac{1}{c^2}$ (sec/cm)^2			$\beta = 4\pi$ $\mu_0 = \dfrac{1}{c^2}$ (sec/cm)^2 $\gamma = 1$ $\epsilon_0 = 1$		
		Name	Dimensions	Measure of the mks unit in emu	Name	Dimensions	Measure of the mks unit in esu	Name	Dimensions
Length	l	meter	L	10^2	centimeter	L	10^2	centimeter	L
Mass	m	kilogram	M	10^3	gram	M	10^3	gram	M
Time	t	second	T	1	second	T	1	second	T
Velocity	v	meter/sec	$\dfrac{L}{T}$	10^2	cm/sec	$\dfrac{L}{T}$	10^2	cm/sec	$\dfrac{L}{T}$
Acceleration	a	meter/sec^2	$\dfrac{L}{T^2}$	10^2	cm/sec^2	$\dfrac{L}{T^2}$	10^2	cm/sec^2	$\dfrac{L}{T^2}$
Force	f	newton	$\dfrac{ML}{T^2}$	10^5	dyne	$\dfrac{ML}{T^2}$	10^5	dyne	$\dfrac{ML}{T^2}$
Work or energy	W	joule = newton-m = watt-sec	$\dfrac{ML^2}{T^2}$	10^7	erg	$\dfrac{ML^2}{T^2}$	10^7	erg	$\dfrac{ML^2}{T^2}$
Power	P	joule/sec = watt	$\dfrac{ML^2}{T^3}$	10^7	erg/sec = abwatt	$\dfrac{ML^2}{T^3}$	10^7	erg/sec	$\dfrac{ML^2}{T^3}$
Charge	q	coulomb	$M^{\frac12}L^{\frac12}$	10^{-1}	abcoulomb	$M^{\frac12}L^{\frac12}$	$10^{-1}c$	statcoulomb	$\dfrac{M^{\frac12}L^{\frac32}}{T}$
Current	I	ampere	$\dfrac{M^{\frac12}L^{\frac12}}{T}$	10^{-1}	abampere	$\dfrac{M^{\frac12}L^{\frac12}}{T}$	$10^{-1}c$	statampere	$\dfrac{M^{\frac12}L^{\frac32}}{T^2}$
Current density	J	ampere/sq m	$\dfrac{M^{\frac12}}{TL^{\frac32}}$	10^{-5}	abamp/sq cm	$\dfrac{M^{\frac12}}{TL^{\frac32}}$	$10^{-5}c$	statamp/sq cm	$\dfrac{M^{\frac12}}{L^{\frac12}T^2}$
Electric intensity	E	newton/coulomb or volt/meter	$\dfrac{M^{\frac12}L^{\frac12}}{T^2}$	10^6	abvolt/cm = dyne/abcoul.	$\dfrac{M^{\frac12}L^{\frac12}}{T^2}$	$\dfrac{10^6}{c}$	dyne/statcoul = statvolt/cm	$\dfrac{M^{\frac12}}{L^{\frac12}T}$
Electric displacement or electric flux density	D	coulomb/sq m	$\dfrac{M^{\frac12}}{L^{\frac32}}$	$4\pi \cdot 10^{-5}$	abcoulomb/sq cm	$\dfrac{M^{\frac12}}{L^{\frac32}}$	$4\pi \cdot 10^{-5}c$	statcoul/sq cm	$\dfrac{M^{\frac12}}{L^{\frac12}T}$
Electromotive force or electric potential	V	volt = joule/coulomb	$\dfrac{M^{\frac12}L^{\frac32}}{T^2}$	10^8	abvolt	$\dfrac{M^{\frac12}L^{\frac32}}{T^2}$	$\dfrac{10^8}{c}$	statvolt	$\dfrac{M^{\frac12}L^{\frac12}}{T}$

OF UNITS

Second Systems (cgs)

The Gaussian system			The Heaviside-Lorentz system			Defining Relation	
$\beta = 4\pi \qquad \mu_0 = 1$			$\beta = 1 \qquad \mu_0 = 1$				
$\gamma = c(\text{cm/sec}) \quad \epsilon_0 = 1$			$\gamma = c(\text{cm/sec}) \quad \epsilon_0 = 1$				
Measure of the mks unit in Gaussian units	Name	Dimensions	Measure of the mks unit in H-L units	Name	Dimensions		
10^2	centimeter	L	10^2	centimeter	L		Fundamental units. Dimensional symbols: L, M, T
10^3	gram	M	10^3	gram	M		
1	second	T	1	second	T		
10^2	cm/sec	$\dfrac{L}{T}$	10^2	cm/sec	$\dfrac{L}{T}$	$\mathbf{v} = \dfrac{d\mathbf{r}}{dt}$	
10^2	cm/sec²	$\dfrac{L}{T^2}$	10^2	cm/sec²	$\dfrac{L}{T^2}$	$\mathbf{a} = \dfrac{d^2\mathbf{r}}{dt^2}$	
10^5	dyne	$\dfrac{ML}{T^2}$	10^5	dyne	$\dfrac{ML}{T^2}$	$\mathbf{f} = m\mathbf{a}$	Mechanical quantities
10^7	erg	$\dfrac{ML^2}{T^2}$	10^7	erg	$\dfrac{ML^2}{T^2}$	$W = \displaystyle\int_a^b \mathbf{f} \cdot d\mathbf{r}$	
10^7	abwatt	$\dfrac{ML^2}{T^3}$	10^7	abwatt	$\dfrac{ML^2}{T^3}$	$P = \dfrac{dW}{dt}$	
$10^{-1}c$	statcoulomb	$\dfrac{M^{\frac12}L^{\frac32}}{T}$	$\sqrt{4\pi} \cdot 10^{-1}c$		$\dfrac{M^{\frac12}L^{\frac32}}{T}$	$\mathbf{f} = \dfrac{\beta}{4\pi\epsilon_0}\dfrac{q_1 q_2}{r^2}\mathbf{r}^0$	
$10^{-1}c$	statampere	$\dfrac{M^{\frac12}L^{\frac32}}{T^2}$	$\sqrt{4\pi} \cdot 10^{-1}c$		$\dfrac{M^{\frac12}L^{\frac32}}{T^2}$	$I = \dfrac{dq}{dt}$	
$10^{-5}c$	statamp/sq cm	$\dfrac{M^{\frac12}}{L^{\frac12}T^2}$	$\sqrt{4\pi}\,10^{-5}c$		$\dfrac{M^{\frac12}}{L^{\frac12}T^2}$	$\displaystyle\int_s\!\!\int \mathbf{J} \cdot d\mathbf{S} = I$	
$\dfrac{10^6}{c}$	statvolt/cm = dyne/statcoul	$\dfrac{M^{\frac12}}{L^{\frac12}T}$	$10^6/\sqrt{4\pi c}$		$\dfrac{M^{\frac12}}{L^{\frac12}T}$	$\mathbf{E} = \dfrac{\beta}{4\pi\epsilon_0}\dfrac{q}{r^2}\mathbf{r}^0,\ \mathbf{f} = q\mathbf{E}$	Electrical quantities
$4\pi \cdot 10^{-5}c$	statcoul/sq cm	$\dfrac{M^{\frac12}}{L^{\frac12}T}$	$\sqrt{4\pi}\,10^{-5}c$		$\dfrac{M^{\frac12}}{L^{\frac12}T}$	$\displaystyle\int_s\!\!\int \mathbf{D} \cdot d\mathbf{S} = \beta q \text{ or } \mathbf{D} = \epsilon_0 \mathbf{E}$	
$\dfrac{10^8}{c}$	statvolt	$\dfrac{M^{\frac12}L^{\frac12}}{T}$	$10^8/\sqrt{4\pi c}$		$\dfrac{M^{\frac12}L^{\frac12}}{T}$	$\displaystyle\int_a^b \mathbf{E} \cdot d\mathbf{r} = V_a - V_b$	

$c \cong 3 \cdot 10^{10}$ (cm/sec)		Meter-kilogram-second system (mks)					Centimeter-Gram-		
		The Giorgi system		The electromagnetic system (emu)			The electrostatic system (esu)		
Physical entity	S y m b o l	$\beta = 1$ $\mu_0 = 4\pi \cdot 10^{-7}$ $\gamma = 1$ $\epsilon_0 = \dfrac{10^7}{4\pi c^2}$ (sec/m)²		$\beta = 4\pi \quad \mu_0 = 1$ $\gamma = 1 \quad \epsilon_0 = \dfrac{1}{c^2}$ (sec/cm)²			$\beta = 4\pi \quad \mu_0 = \dfrac{1}{c^2}$ (sec/cm)² $\gamma = 1 \quad \epsilon_0 = 1$		
		Name	Dimensions	Measure of the mks unit in emu	Name	Dimensions	Measure of the mks unit in esu	Name	Dimensions
Conductivity	σ	mho/meter	$\dfrac{T}{L^2}$	10^{-11}		$\dfrac{T}{L^2}$			
Resistance	R	ohm	$\dfrac{L}{T}$	10^9	abohm	$\dfrac{L}{T}$	$\dfrac{10^9}{c^2}$	statohm	$\dfrac{T}{L}$
Capacitance	C	farad	$\dfrac{T^2}{L}$	10^{-9}	abfarad	$\dfrac{T^2}{L}$	$10^{-9}c^2$	statfarad	L
Inductance	L	henry	L	10^9	abhenry	L	$\dfrac{10^9}{c^2}$	stathenry	$\dfrac{T^2}{L}$
Magnetic flux	Φ	weber = volt-sec	$\dfrac{M^{\frac12}L^{\frac32}}{T}$	10^8	maxwell = abvolt-sec	$\dfrac{M^{\frac12}L^{\frac32}}{T}$	$\dfrac{10^8}{c}$	statvolt-sec = statweber	$M^{\frac12}L^{\frac12}$
Magnetic flux density	B	weber/sq m	$\dfrac{M^{\frac12}}{L^{\frac12}T}$	10^4	gauss	$\dfrac{M^{\frac12}}{L^{\frac12}T}$	$\dfrac{10^4}{c}$		$\dfrac{M^{\frac12}}{L^{\frac32}}$
Magnetic intensity	H	amp turn/m	$\dfrac{M^{\frac12}}{L^{\frac12}T}$	$4\pi \cdot 10^{-3}$	oersted = gilbert/cm	$\dfrac{M^{\frac12}}{L^{\frac12}T}$	$4\pi \cdot 10^{-3}c$	statoersted	$\dfrac{M^{\frac12}L^{\frac12}}{T^2}$
Magnetic pole-strength	q^*				maxwell	$\dfrac{M^{\frac12}L^{\frac32}}{T}$			$M^{\frac12}L^{\frac12}$
Magnetomotive force or magnetic potential	mmf	amp turn	$\dfrac{M^{\frac12}L^{\frac12}}{T}$	$4\pi \cdot 10^{-1}$	gilbert	$\dfrac{M^{\frac12}L^{\frac12}}{T}$	$4\pi \cdot 10^{-1}c$		$\dfrac{M^{\frac12}L^{\frac32}}{T^2}$
Magnetic reluctance	$\Re$	amp turn/weber	$\dfrac{1}{L}$	$4\pi \cdot 10^{-9}$		$\dfrac{1}{L}$	$4\pi \cdot 10^{-9}c^2$		$\dfrac{L}{T^2}$

The table is read as shown in the following examples:

$$10^8 \text{ abvolts} = 1 \text{ volt};$$

and

$$\frac{10^8}{c} \text{ statvolts} = 10^8 \text{ abvolts}$$

or

$$1 \text{ statvolt} = c \text{ abvolts}$$

OF UNITS (*Continued*)

Second Systems (cgs)							
The Gaussian system			The Heaviside-Lorentz system				
$\beta = 4\pi$ $\mu_0 = 1$ $\gamma = c$(cm/sec) $\epsilon_0 = 1$			$\beta = 1$ $\mu_0 = 1$ $\gamma = c$(cm/sec) $\epsilon_0 = 1$			Defining Relation	
Measure of the mks unit in Gaussian units	Name	Dimensions	Measure of the mks unit in H-L units	Name	Dimensions		
						$\mathbf{J} = \sigma\mathbf{E}$	
$\dfrac{10^9}{c^2}$	statohm	$\dfrac{T}{L}$	$10^9/4\pi c^2$		$\dfrac{T}{L}$	$V = IR$ or $R = \dfrac{l}{\sigma s}$ s = cross-sectional area of conductor	Electrical quantities
$10^{-9}c^2$	statfarad	L	$4\pi 10^{-9}c^2$		L	$q = CV$	
$\dfrac{10^9}{c^2}$		$\dfrac{T^2}{L}$	$10^9/4\pi c^2$		$\dfrac{T^2}{L}$	$L\dfrac{dI}{dt} = V$	
10^8	maxwell	$\dfrac{M^{\frac12}L^{\frac32}}{T}$	$10^8/\sqrt{4\pi}$		$\dfrac{M^{\frac12}L^{\frac32}}{T}$	$\Phi = \displaystyle\int_s\!\!\int \mathbf{B}\cdot d\mathbf{S}$ and $\dfrac{d\Phi}{dt} = -\gamma\oint_c \mathbf{E}\cdot d\mathbf{r}$	
10^4	gauss	$\dfrac{M^{\frac12}}{L^{\frac12}T}$	$10^4/\sqrt{4\pi}$		$\dfrac{M^{\frac12}}{L^{\frac12}T}$		
$4\pi\cdot 10^{-3}$	oersted = gilbert/cm	$\dfrac{M^{\frac12}}{L^{\frac32}T}$	$\sqrt{4\pi}\cdot 10^{-3}$		$\dfrac{M^{\frac12}}{L^{\frac32}T}$	$\mathbf{H} = \dfrac{1}{\mu}\mathbf{B}$	Magnetic quantities
		$\dfrac{M^{\frac12}L^{\frac32}}{T}$				$f = q^*H$	
$4\pi\cdot 10^{-1}$	gilbert	$\dfrac{M^{\frac12}L^{\frac12}}{T}$	$\sqrt{4\pi}\cdot 10^{-1}$		$\dfrac{M^{\frac12}L^{\frac12}}{T}$	$\text{mmf} = \displaystyle\int_a^b \mathbf{H}\cdot d\mathbf{r}$	
		$\dfrac{1}{L}$			$\dfrac{1}{L}$	$\mathcal{R} = \dfrac{\text{mmf}}{\Phi}$	

It so happens, as every student of physics and engineering soon learns to his dismay, that there are many different systems in use. Moreover, to pick one system as a favorite, and to adhere only to that, is not practicable, since all the systems are met with in the literature. The student who would save himself continuing confusion on the subject ought very early in his career to tackle the problem of organizing the different systems in his own mind. The accompanying table of units can be used as a guide. To derive maximum benefit from it, the reader should rederive every entry in it for himself.

To begin, length, mass, and time are selected as fundamental quantities in terms of which all other quantities are to be expressed. Having picked mass as one of the basic quantities, the systems to be set up become what are called "inertial systems" of units. This is in contrast to "gravitational systems" also in use, in which weight replaces mass as one of the fundamental quantities.

After choosing the basic quantities, one then must specify the units in terms of which they are to be measured. In the Giorgi system, these are the meter, the kilogram, and the second. For all the other systems listed they are the centimeter, the gram, and the second.

One then proceeds to define other quantities and their units of measurement in a systematic step-by-step fashion, using experimental laws to relate each new quantity and unit to quantities and units previously defined. The sequence of relations used in the table of the text is given in the next to the last column on the right. The treatment of mechanical quantities is straightforward and presents no difficulties. The numerical factors connecting the meter-kilogram-second (mks) units with the centimeter-gram-second (cgs) units are easily obtained.

The electric and magnetic quantities and units in the various systems can be defined systematically in the order given by making Maxwell's equations (11-39) to (11-42) the starting point. From these one gets (11-50) for example, which in free space reduces to

$$\nabla^2 \mathbf{H} - \frac{\epsilon_0 \mu_0}{\gamma^2} \frac{\partial^2 \mathbf{H}}{\partial t^2} = 0$$

One concludes that the quantity $\gamma/\sqrt{\epsilon_0\mu_0}$ has the dimensions of a velocity. By experiment

$$\frac{\gamma}{\sqrt{\epsilon_0\mu_0}} = c \cong 3.10^{10} \text{ cm-sec}^{-1}$$

The assignment of values and dimensions to the parameters γ, ϵ_0, μ_0 in accordance with this relation can be done in various ways, resulting in differing systems of units, as indicated at the top of the table.

If one wishes to introduce the concept of a magnetic pole strength q^*, then the experimental result can be used that $q^*\mathbf{H}$ is a force.

The parameter β is a pure number. When $\beta = 4\pi$, the resulting system of units is "unrationalized." Thus the electromagnetic, the electrostatic, and Gaussian systems are unrationalized. A "rationalized" system arises when β is taken as unity. The Giorgi system is a rationalized mks system. The Heaviside-Lorentz system is simply a rationalized Gaussian system.

Having derived the table of units, the problem arises as to how to remember it. This turns out to be fairly simple as a study of the entries will show. In the first place it suffices to memorize the conversion from the Giorgi to the electromagnetic system. This is obvious in the case of the mechanical quantities, since all the cgs systems coincide here. For electric and magnetic quantities note that in general if the measure of the mks unit in emu involves a positive power of 10, then the measure of the electromagnetic unit in electrostatic units is c^{-1}; whereas if the measure of the mks unit in emu involves a negative power of 10, then the measure of the electromagnetic unit in electrostatic units is c. The exceptions are resistance, conductivity, capacitance, inductance, and reluctance; and even here the rule applies with c^{-1} and c replaced by c^{-2} and c^2.

The Gaussian system is simply a cgs system using electrostatic units for electric quantities, and electromagnetic units for magnetic quantities.

It is left to the reader to devise a mnemonic for the Heaviside-Lorentz system of units.

EXERCISES

1. Derive the table of units given in the text.
2. Memorize the table of units derived in Exercise 1.

REFERENCES

Abraham, M., and R. Becker: "The Classical Theory of Electricity and Magnetism," translated by J. Dougall, Hafner Publishing Company, New York, 1932.

Joos, G.: "Theoretical Physics," translated by I. M. Freeman, G. E. Stechert & Company, New York, 1934.

Slater, J. C.: "Microwave Transmission," McGraw-Hill Book Company, Inc., New York, 1942.

Slater, J. C., and N. H. Frank: "Electromagnetism," McGraw-Hill Book Company, Inc., New York, 1947.

Stratton, J. A.: "Electromagnetic Theory," McGraw-Hill Book Company, Inc., New York, 1941.

ANSWERS TO EXERCISES IN PART I

Answers are given to all Exercises except those of a discussion type and those which contain the answer in their statement.

Sec. 1-1

4. Ellipsoids   6. 238°K   7. $p = p_0 \exp \left(- \dfrac{g_0 M}{RT} \dfrac{3963h}{3963 + h} \right)$

8. $\Delta T / T = h/3963 = .018$

Sec. 1-2

2. Consider a 180° rotation about the z axis followed by a 180° rotation about the y axis.

Sec. 1-4

1. $(-3/\sqrt{2}, 3/\sqrt{2})$ 2. ± 2 3. 5, arccos $(\frac{3}{5})$ 4. 13, arccos $(\frac{4}{13})$
5. y component $= \pm 12$; angle with positive x axis $=$ arccos $(-\frac{5}{13})$
6. $\pm 1/\sqrt{2}$ 7. $(2,6)$ 8. $((\sqrt{3} - 1)/2, (\sqrt{3} + 1)/2)$ 9. $(1,-7)$
10. $(\frac{5}{2},\frac{5}{2})$ 11. 158 knots, N 24° E   12. 18.6 knots, S 4.3° W
13. 215 knots, N 75° E   14. 67 mph, if the sun is due west
15. (a) $g \sin 25°$ (b) 2.4 sec   16. 60°
17. $9.75 \times 10^{-2} e^2$, directed from proton toward electrons along line making 14.25° angle with line from proton to nearer electron, and angle arccos $(\frac{4}{5}) - 14.25°$ with line to farther electron.

Sec. 1-6

4. 0, 10   5. 1; 1, $-i$, -1, i
6. Identity element is 0° rotation. Inverse to a rotation through angle θ is the rotation through angle $-\theta$. The rotations can be represented by their angles.

Sec. 1-7

1. $(8,2)$ 2. $(1.37, -.37)$ 3. 117 knots, 277°

Sec. 1-8

7. $\mathbf{A} + \mathbf{B} + \mathbf{C} = 0$. The vectors must form a closed triangle all pointing in the same sense around the triangle.
8. Straight line through $\mathbf{A}$ in the direction of $\mathbf{B}$
10. Sphere of radius r and center $\mathbf{A}$

Sec. 1-9

1. A^2 4. $\mathbf{R} \cdot \mathbf{n} - p$ 5. $(\mathbf{r} - \mathbf{a})^2 = \rho^2$ 7. Sphere, center at $\mathbf{a}/2$, radius $a/2$

8. $A - (A \cdot B/B^2)B$ **9.** $\left(\dfrac{A - B}{|A - B|} + \dfrac{C - B}{|C - D|} \right) \div \left| \dfrac{A - B}{|A - B|} + \dfrac{C - B}{|C - B|} \right|$

Sec. 1-11

2. 100   **5.** $l = -AB \cos \theta, \ m = A^2$

Sec. 1-12

1. $(r - r_1) \cdot (r_2 - r_1) \times (r_3 - r_1) = 0$ **2.** 0   **3.** $2B \times A$

Sec. 1-13

1. $(A \times B \cdot D)C - (A \times B \cdot C)D$. $(C \times D \cdot A)B - (C \times D \cdot B)A$. It has the direction of the intersection of a plane parallel to A and B with a plane parallel to C and D.
4. $A \times B \cdot C = 0$ **5.** $A \times B \cdot C \times D = 0$ **6.** $(A \times B) \times (C \times D) = 0$

Sec. 1-14

3. $-2i - 2j - 3k$ **4.** 1   **5.** 4   **6.** $(i - j + 2k)/\sqrt{6}$
7. $-(2i + j + 2k)/3$ **8.** $\arccos(-\sqrt{2}/3)$
9. $(2i + j + 2k)/9 + (7i - 10j - 2k)/9$ **10.** $(i - 3j - 2k)/\sqrt{14}$
11. $\arccos(2/(\sqrt{14} \sqrt{17}))$ **12.** $(13i - j + 8k)/\sqrt{234}$ **13.** $(4i + j + 3k)/3$
14. $r = (2 - t)i + (1 - 2t)j + (2 - 2t)k$ **15.** $x - y + 2z + 2 = 0$
16. $-4/\sqrt{6}$. Yes.   **17.** $\sqrt{26}$ **19.** 6
21. $\left[\dfrac{1}{\sqrt{5}} i + \left(\dfrac{2}{\sqrt{5}} + \dfrac{2}{\sqrt{13}} \right) j - \dfrac{3}{\sqrt{13}} k \right] \left(2 + \dfrac{8}{\sqrt{65}} \right)^{-\frac{1}{2}}$ **22.** Right-handed

Sec. 1-15

2. $i/4, j/3, k/2$ **3.** $i - k, -i + j, k$
4. $(9i - j + 4k)/31, (-i + 7j + 3k)/31, (12i + 9j - 5k)/31$

Sec. 2-1

5. Region, contained between two spheres   **6.** Region, interior of an ellipsoid
7. Neither open nor closed region
8. Neither open nor closed region; no interior points
9. Discrete set of points lying on circular helix   **10.** Region, half plane
11. Region, interior of circle   **12.** Two regions
13. Discrete set of points spiraling in toward origin   **14.** No interior points
15. Region   **16.** Sphere. Region between two concentric spheres. Circle in plane.

Sec. 2-2

9. $\lim (f/g) = 0$ **10.** $1 + y$. Approach is uniform.
11. y. Approach is uniform.   **12.** $1/y$. Approach is not uniform.
13. $\lim_{y \to \infty} f = 0$ $0 \le x \le 1$ **14.** $\lim_{y \to \infty} f = \begin{cases} 0 & 0 < x \le 1 \\ 1 & x = 0 \end{cases}$

Sec. 2-4

3. $1/xy$ $0 < x \le 1, 0 < y \le 1$

Sec. 2-5

6. $(f/g)' = (gf' - fg')/g^2$
9. Slope of chord equals slope of arc at appropriate point
10. Distance from chord to arc along normal to x axis

Sec. 2-7

3. To the law of the mean

Sec. 3-2

3. $i + \cos x\, j - \sin x\, k$ **4.** $-32k$ **8.** $dA = (dA/dt)\, \Delta t$
9. $|dA/dt| = [(dA_1/dt)^2 + (dA_2/dt)^2 + (dA_3/dt)^2]^{1/2}$

$$dA/dt = \frac{d}{dt}\,(A_1^2 + A_2^2 + A_3^2)^{1/2}$$

Sec. 3-3

2. r/r **3.** $nr^{n-2}r$ **4.** $n(x^2 + y^2 + z^2)^{(n-2)/2}(x i + y j + z k)$
8. $(4i - 3j + k)/\sqrt{26}$
9. Take cross product of vectors normal to surfaces and unitize the resulting vector
10. $(i + j - k)/\sqrt{3}$

Sec. 4-1

1. (a) $2\rho,\ -\rho,\ -\rho$ (b) $4\rho/\sqrt{5}$ (c) 0 **2.** 3 **3.** $\beta\rho$

Sec. 4-2

1. 3 **2.** 12 **3.** 0

Sec. 4-3

1. 48

Sec. 4-4

1. 0 **2.** $4ab$ **3.** $-2\pi M$

Sec. 4-5

1. $-i - j - k$

Sec. 4-7

1. $-i - j - k$ **2.** $-ye^z i - ze^x j - xe^y k$ **3.** 0

Sec. 5-2

4. Correct answer is: $\dfrac{\partial \Phi}{\partial r}\, i_1 + \dfrac{1}{r_0}\dfrac{\partial \Phi}{\partial \theta}\, i_2 + \dfrac{\partial \Phi}{\partial z}\, i_3$, which is obtained by taking into account *all* contributions to the surface integral.

5. $\dfrac{\partial \Phi}{\partial r}\, i_1 + \dfrac{1}{r}\dfrac{\partial \Phi}{\partial \theta}\, i_2 + \dfrac{1}{r \sin \theta}\dfrac{\partial \Phi}{\partial \phi}\, i_3$

Sec. 5-3

1. $\dfrac{1}{r}\dfrac{\partial}{\partial r}\,(rA_1) + \dfrac{1}{r}\dfrac{\partial A_2}{\partial \theta} + \dfrac{\partial A_3}{\partial z}$

2. $\dfrac{1}{r^2}\dfrac{\partial}{\partial r}\,(r^2 A_1) + \dfrac{1}{r \sin \theta}\dfrac{\partial}{\partial \theta}\,(A_2 \sin \theta) + \dfrac{1}{r \sin \theta}\dfrac{\partial A_3}{\partial \phi}$

Sec. 5-4

2. $\dfrac{1}{r}\begin{vmatrix} i_1 & ri_2 & i_3 \\ \partial/\partial r & \partial/\partial \theta & \partial/\partial z \\ A_1 & rA_2 & A_3 \end{vmatrix}$ **3.** $\dfrac{1}{r^2 \sin \theta}\begin{vmatrix} i_1 & ri_2 & r \sin \theta\, i_3 \\ \partial/\partial r & \partial/\partial \theta & \partial/\partial \phi \\ A_1 & rA_2 & r \sin \theta\, A_3 \end{vmatrix}$

Sec. 7-1

1. The z axis, consisting of the rays $\theta = 0$ and $\theta = \pi$, is singular, since ϕ is indeterminate along this line.

$$
\begin{aligned}
x &= r \sin \theta \cos \phi & r &= (x^2 + y^2 + z^2)^{\frac{1}{2}} \\
y &= r \sin \theta \sin \phi & \theta &= \arctan (\sqrt{x^2 + y^2}/z) \\
z &= r \cos \theta & \phi &= \arctan (y/x)
\end{aligned}
$$

2. The z axis is singular in that for points on it the polar angle is indeterminate.

$$
\begin{aligned}
x &= r \cos \theta & r &= (x^2 + y^2)^{\frac{1}{2}} \\
y &= r \sin \theta & \theta &= \arctan (y/x) \\
z &= z & z &= z
\end{aligned}
$$

3. (a) The u_1 surfaces are elliptic cylinders. The u_2 surfaces are hyperbolic cylinders. The u_1 and u_2 surfaces have a common pair of focal lines. The u_3 surfaces are planes. The system is orthogonal.

(b)
$$
\begin{aligned}
x &= cu_1u_2 \\
y &= c[(u_1^2 - 1)(1 - u_2^2)]^{\frac{1}{2}} \\
z &= u_3
\end{aligned}
$$

4. (a) The u_1 surfaces are right parabolic cylinders, opening along the positive x direction, and with the z axis as a common focal line. The u_2 surfaces are similar to the u_1 surfaces, but open along the negative x direction. The u_3 surfaces are planes. The system is orthogonal.

(b)
$$
\begin{aligned}
x &= (u_2^2 - u_1^2)/2 \\
y &= u_1u_2 \\
z &= -u_3
\end{aligned}
$$

5. (a) The u_1 surfaces are right-circular cylinders, the traces of which in the plane $z = 0$ form a family of circles with centers on the x axis, and whose intersections with the x axis divide the points $(a,0,0)$ and $(-a,0,0)$ harmonically. The u_2 surfaces are right-circular cylinders, the traces of which in the plane $z = 0$ form the family of circles passing through $(a,0,0)$ and $(-a,0,0)$. The u_3 surfaces are planes. The system is orthogonal.

(b)
$$
\begin{aligned}
x &= \frac{a \sinh u_1}{\cosh u_1 - \cos u_2} \\
y &= \frac{a \sin u_2}{\cosh u_1 - \cos u_2} \\
z &= u_3
\end{aligned}
$$

6. (a) The u_1 surfaces are confocal ellipsoids of revolution. The u_2 surfaces are the two-sheeted hyperboloids of revolution confocal with the u_1 surfaces. The u_3 surfaces are half planes emanating from the x axis. The system is orthogonal.

(b)
$$
\begin{aligned}
x &= cu_1u_2 \\
y &= c[(u_1^2 - 1)(1 - u_2^2)]^{\frac{1}{2}} \cos u_3 \\
z &= c[(u_1^2 - 1)(1 - u_2^2)]^{\frac{1}{2}} \sin u_3
\end{aligned}
$$

7. (a) The u_1 surfaces are oblate spheroids. The u_2 surfaces are one-sheeted hyperboloids of revolution. The u_3 surfaces are half planes emanating from the y axis. The system is orthogonal.

(b)
$$x = cu_1u_2 \sin u_3$$
$$y = c[(u_1^2 - 1)(1 - u_2^2)]^{1/2}$$
$$z = cu_1u_2 \cos u_3$$

8. (a) The u_1 surfaces are paraboloids of revolution, common focus at the origin, and positive x axis as axis. The u_2 surfaces are paraboloids of revolution, common focus at the origin, and negative x axis as axis. The u_3 surfaces are half planes emanating from the x axis. The system is orthogonal.

(b)
$$x = (u_2^2 - u_1^2)/2$$
$$y = u_1u_2 \cos u_3$$
$$z = u_1u_2 \sin u_3$$

9. (a) The u_1 surfaces are confocal ellipsoids. The u_2 surfaces are one-sheeted hyperboloids confocal with the u_1 surfaces. The u_3 surfaces are two-sheeted hyperboloids confocal with the u_1 and u_2 surfaces. The system is orthogonal.
(b) Set $g(a) = (u_1 + a^2)(u_2 + a^2)(u_3 + a^2)$. Then
$$x = \pm [g(a)/(b^2 - a^2)(c^2 - a^2)]^{1/2}$$
$$y = \pm [g(b)/(c^2 - b^2)(a^2 - b^2)]^{1/2}$$
$$z = \pm [g(c)/(a^2 - c^2)(b^2 - c^2)]^{1/2}$$

10. The u_1 surfaces are rectangular hyperbolic cylinders asymptotic to the planes $x^2 - y^2 = 0$. The u_2 surfaces are rectangular hyperbolic cylinders asymptotic to the planes $xy = 0$. The u_3 surfaces are planes. The system is orthogonal.

11. The u_1 and u_3 surfaces are orthogonal sets of planes. The u_2 surfaces are congruent parabolic cylinders opening along the plane $x = 0$ in the negative y direction. The plane $x = 0$ is singular in that the u_1 and u_2 surfaces are parallel there. The system is not orthogonal.

12. The u_1 and u_3 surfaces are the planes $x = $ constant and $z = $ constant respectively. The u_2 surfaces are the planes through the z axis. The plane $x = 0$ is singular. The system is not orthogonal.

13. The coordinate surfaces are three sets of parallel planes, but the system is not orthogonal. The system is left-handed.

Sec. 7-2

3. $i_1 = e_1 = \cos \theta\, i + \sin \theta\, j$
$i_2 = e_2 = - \sin \theta\, i + \cos \theta\, j$
$i_3 = e_3 = k$
$|\partial r/\partial r| = 1 \qquad |\partial r/\partial \theta| = r \qquad |\partial r/\partial z| = 1$

Sec. 7-3

1. $u_1 = r$ **2.** $u_1^2 \sin u_2 = r^2 \sin \theta$ **3.** $c^2(u_1^2 - u_2^2)[(u_1^2 - 1)(1 - u_2^2)]^{-1/2}$
4. $u_1^2 + u_2^2$ **5.** $a^2(\cosh u_1 - \cos u_2)^{-2}$
6. Prolate case: $c^3(u_1^2 - u_2^2)$
  Oblate case: $c^3u_1u_2(u_1^2 - u_2^2)[(u_1^2 - 1)(1 - u_2^2)]^{-1/2}$
7. $u_1u_2(u_1^2 + u_2^2)$ **8.** Set $f(u) = (u + a^2)(u + b^2)(u + c^2)$. Then
$$d = (u_1 - u_2)(u_1 - u_3)(u_2 - u_3)/8[-f(u_1)f(u_2)f(u_3)]^{1/2}$$
9. $1/2 \sqrt{u_1^2 + 4u_2^2}$ **10.** $1/2 \sqrt{u_1 - u_2}$ **11.** $u_1 \sec^2 u_2$ **12.** $-\frac{1}{3}$
13. $\nabla r = \cos \theta\, i + \sin \theta\, j$
$\nabla \theta = (- \sin \theta\, i + \cos \theta\, j)/r$
$\nabla z = k$

14.　$\nabla r = \sin\theta\cos\phi\,\mathbf{i} + \sin\theta\sin\phi\,\mathbf{j} + \cos\theta\,\mathbf{k}$

　　　$\nabla\theta = (\cos\theta\cos\phi\,\mathbf{i} + \cos\theta\sin\phi\,\mathbf{j} - \sin\theta\,\mathbf{k})/r$

　　　$\nabla\phi = (-\sin\phi\,\mathbf{i} + \cos\phi\,\mathbf{j})/r\sin\theta$

15.　$\nabla u_1 = (-u_1\mathbf{i} + u_2\mathbf{j})/(u_1{}^2 + u_2{}^2)$

　　　$\nabla u_2 = (u_2\mathbf{i} + u_1\mathbf{j})/(u_1{}^2 + u_2{}^2)$

　　　$\nabla u_3 = -\mathbf{k}$

Sec. 7-4

1.　$z\cos\theta\,\mathbf{i}_1 - z\sin\theta\,\mathbf{i}_2$

In Exercises 2 through 9 the $g_{\alpha\beta}$ vanish for $\alpha \neq \beta$. The values of g_{11}, g_{22}, g_{33} are given in that order in the answers listed below.

2.　$1, r^2, 1$　　**3.**　$c^2(u_1{}^2 - u_2{}^2)/(u_1{}^2 - 1),\ c^2(u_1{}^2 - u_2{}^2)/(1 - u_2{}^2),\ 1$

4.　$u_1{}^2 + u_2{}^2,\ u_1{}^2 + u_2{}^2,\ 1$　　**5.**　$a^2(\cosh u_1 - \cos u_2)^{-2},\ a^2(\cosh u_1 - \cos u_2)^{-2},\ 1$

6.　$c^2(u_1{}^2 - u_2{}^2)/(u_1{}^2 - 1),\ c^2(u_1{}^2 - u_2{}^2)/(1 - u_2{}^2),\ c^2(u_1{}^2 - 1)(1 - u_2{}^2)$ for the prolate case.　For the oblate case $g_{33} = c^2 u_1{}^2 u_2{}^2$

7.　$u_1{}^2 + u_2{}^2,\ u_1{}^2 + u_2{}^2,\ u_1{}^2 u_2{}^2$

8.　$(u_1 - u_2)(u_1 - u_3)/4f(u_1),\ (u_2 - u_3)(u_2 - u_1)/4f(u_2),\ (u_3 - u_1)(u_3 - u_2)/4f(u_3)$

9.　$1/4\sqrt{u_1{}^2 + 4u_2{}^2},\ 1/\sqrt{u_1{}^2 + 4u_2{}^2},\ 1$

10.　$g_{11} = (1 + 4u_1 - 4u_2)/4(u_1 - u_2),\ g_{22} = 1/4\,(u_1 - u_2),\ g_{33} = 1,$

　　　$g_{12} = 1/4(u_2 - u_1),\ g_{13} = g_{23} = 0$

11.　$g_{11} = \sec^2 u_2,\ g_{22} = u_1{}^2\sec^4 u_2,\ g_{33} = 1,\ g_{12} = u_1\sec^2 u_2\tan u_2,\ g_{13} = g_{23} = 0$

12.　$g_{11} = \tfrac{2}{3} = g_{22},\ g_{33} = \tfrac{1}{3},\ g_{12} = \tfrac{1}{3},\ g_{13} = g_{23} = 0$

17 through 28.　$g = d^2$.　Cf. answers to Exercises 1 through 12, Sec. 7-3.

Sec. 7-5

1.　$u_1\,du_1\,du_2\,du_3 = r\,dr\,d\theta\,dz$

　　　$du_1{}^2 + u_1{}^2\,du_2{}^2 + du_3{}^2 = dr^2 + r^2\,d\theta^2 + dz^2$

2.　$c^2(u_1{}^2 - u_2{}^2)\,du_1\,du_2\,du_3/[(u_1{}^2 - 1)(1 - u_2{}^2)]^{1/2}$

　　　$c^2\dfrac{u_1{}^2 - u_2{}^2}{u_1{}^2 - 1}\,du_1{}^2 + c^2\dfrac{u_1{}^2 - u_2{}^2}{1 - u_2{}^2}\,du_2{}^2 + du_3{}^2$

3.　$(u_1{}^2 + u_2{}^2)\,du_1\,du_2\,du_3$

　　　$(u_1{}^2 + u_2{}^2)(du_1{}^2 + du_2{}^2) + du_3{}^2$

4.　$a^2(\cosh u_1 - \cos u_2)^{-2}\,du_1\,du_2\,du_3$

　　　$a^2(\cosh u_1 - \cos u_2)^{-2}(du_1{}^2 + du_2{}^2) + du_3{}^2$

5.　Prolate case:

　　　$c^3(u_1{}^2 - u_2{}^2)\,du_1\,du_2\,du_3$

　　　$c^2\dfrac{u_1{}^2 - u_2{}^2}{u_1{}^2 - 1}\,du_1{}^2 + c^2\dfrac{u_1{}^2 - u_2{}^2}{1 - u_2{}^2}\,du_2{}^2 + c^2(u_1{}^2 - 1)(1 - u_2{}^2)\,du_3{}^2$

　　　Oblate case:

　　　$c^3 u_1 u_2(u_1{}^2 - u_2{}^2)[(u_1{}^2 - 1)(1 - u_2{}^2)]^{-1/2}\,du_1\,du_2\,du_3$

　　　$c^2\dfrac{u_1{}^2 - u_2{}^2}{u_1{}^2 - 1}\,du_1{}^2 + c^2\dfrac{u_1{}^2 - u_2{}^2}{1 - u_2{}^2}\,du_2{}^2 + c^2 u_1{}^2 u_2{}^2\,du_3{}^2$

6.　$u_1 u_2(u_1{}^2 + u_2{}^2)\,du_1\,du_2\,du_3$

　　　$(u_1{}^2 + u_2{}^2)(du_1{}^2 + du_2{}^2) + u_1{}^2 u_2{}^2\,du_3{}^2$

7.　$(u_1 - u_2)(u_1 - u_3)(u_2 - u_3)\,du_1\,du_2\,du_3/8[-f(u_1)f(u_2)f(u_3)]^{1/2}$

　　　$\dfrac{(u_1 - u_2)(u_1 - u_3)}{4f(u_1)}\,du_1{}^2 + \dfrac{(u_2 - u_3)(u_2 - u_1)}{4f(u_2)}\,du_2{}^2 + \dfrac{(u_3 - u_1)(u_3 - u_2)}{4f(u_3)}\,du_3{}^2$

8.　$du_1\,du_2\,du_3/2\sqrt{u_1{}^2 + 4u_2{}^2}$

　　　$(du_1{}^2 + 4\,du_2{}^2)/4\sqrt{u_1{}^2 + 4u_2{}^2} + du_3{}^2$

9. $du_1\, du_2\, du_3/2\, \sqrt{u_1 - u_2}$

$$\frac{1 + 4u_1 - 4u_2}{4(u_1 - u_2)}\, du_1{}^2 + \frac{1}{4(u_1 - u_2)}\, du_2{}^2 + du_3{}^2 + \frac{1}{2(u_2 - u_1)}\, du_1\, du_2$$

10. $u_1 \sec^2 u_2\, du_1\, du_2\, du_3$

$\sec^2 u_2\, du_1{}^2 + u_1{}^2 \sec^4 u_2\, du_2{}^2 + du_3{}^2 + 2u_1 \sec^2 u_2 \tan u_2\, du_1\, du_2$

11. $du_1\, du_2\, du_3/3$

$(2\, du_1{}^2 + 2\, du_2{}^2 + du_3{}^2 + 2\, du_1\, du_2)/3$

12. $dS_{\alpha\beta} = (\partial\mathbf{r}/\partial u_\alpha) \times (\partial\mathbf{r}/\partial u_\beta)\, du_\alpha\, du_\beta$ **13.** $dS = r \sin\theta\, d\theta\, d\phi\, \mathbf{i}_1$

Sec. 7-7

9. $2\sqrt{u_1 - u_2}\left(\dfrac{\partial}{\partial u_1}\left(\dfrac{A_1}{\sqrt{1 + 4(u_1 - u_2)}}\right) + \dfrac{\partial A_2}{\partial u_2}\right) + \dfrac{\partial A_3}{\partial u_3}$

10. $\dfrac{1}{u_1 \sec u_2}\dfrac{\partial}{\partial u_1}(u_1 A_1) + \dfrac{1}{u_1 \sec^2 u_2}\dfrac{\partial A_2}{\partial u_2} + \dfrac{\partial A_3}{\partial u_3}$

11. $[(\partial A_1/\partial u_1) + (\partial A_2/\partial u_2) + \sqrt{2}\,(\partial A_3/\partial u_3)]\,\sqrt{3/2}$

Sec. 7-9

9. $\sqrt{u_1 - u_2}\left\{\dfrac{\partial}{\partial u_1}\left[\dfrac{1}{\sqrt{u_1 - u_2}}\left(\dfrac{\partial\Phi}{\partial u_1} + \dfrac{\partial\Phi}{\partial u_2}\right)\right]\right.$

$\left. + \dfrac{\partial}{\partial u_2}\left[\dfrac{1}{\sqrt{u_1 - u_2}}\left(\dfrac{\partial\Phi}{\partial u_1} + (1 + 4u_1 - 4u_2)\dfrac{\partial\Phi}{\partial u_2}\right)\right]\right\} + \dfrac{\partial^2\Phi}{\partial u_3{}^2}$

10. $\dfrac{1}{u_1}\dfrac{\partial}{\partial u_1}\left(u_1\dfrac{\partial\Phi}{\partial u_1}\right) - \dfrac{\cos u_2 \sin u_2}{u_1}\dfrac{\partial^2\Phi}{\partial u_1\, \partial u_2} - \dfrac{\cos^2 u_2}{u_1}\dfrac{\partial}{\partial u_2}\left(\tan u_2\dfrac{\partial\Phi}{\partial u_1}\right)$

$$+ \dfrac{\cos^2 u_2}{u_1}\dfrac{\partial^2\Phi}{\partial u_2{}^2} + \dfrac{\partial^2\Phi}{\partial u_3{}^2}$$

11. $2(\partial^2\Phi/\partial u_1{}^2) - 2(\partial^2\Phi/\partial u_1\, \partial u_2) + 2(\partial^2\Phi/\partial u_2{}^2) + 3(\partial^2\Phi/\partial u_3{}^2)$

Sec. 7-10

1. Use $h_\alpha = \sqrt{g_{\alpha\alpha}}$, and the answers for Exercises 2 through 8 of Sec. 7-4.

Sec. 8-1

3. (a), (c) **6.** $r^2/2$ **7.** $e^x \sin(yz)$

Sec. 8-2

2. Rays from the origin **3.** The circles, $x^2 + y^2 = a^2$, $z = b$

4. The rectangular hyperbolas, $xy = a$, $z = b$

6. Streamlines: $(x/x_0) = (y/y_0)^{3t^2}$, $(z/z_0) = (y/y_0)$

Trajectories: $x_0 e^{t^3}\mathbf{i} + y_0 e^t\mathbf{j} + z_0 e^t\mathbf{k}$

7. Streamlines: $(x - x_0)/2t = y - y_0$, $z = z_0$

Trajectories: $(t^2 + x_0)\mathbf{i} + (t + y_0)\mathbf{j} + z_0\mathbf{k}$

Sec. 8-3

1. (b), (c)

2. $\mathbf{C} = (yz - 2x^2 yz + \partial K/\partial y)\mathbf{j} + (x - x^2 y^2 + \partial K/\partial z)\mathbf{k}$, where K is a function of y and z but not of x.

Sec. 8-4

11. $\nabla'\phi(P') = -(1/4\pi) \int\limits_{\substack{\text{all} \\ \text{space}}} a\nabla'(1/R) \, dV$

$$= (1/4\pi) \int a\nabla(1/R) \, dV$$

$$= (1/4\pi) \int (\nabla(a/R) - \nabla a/R) \, dV$$

Let V be a sphere about the origin as center and of radius r sufficiently large that P' lies within V. Then

$$\int\limits_{\substack{\text{all} \\ \text{space}}} \nabla(a/R) \, dV = \lim_{r \to \infty} \int_V \nabla(a/R) \, dV$$

$$= \lim_{r \to \infty} \oint\limits_{\substack{\text{bdy} \\ \text{of } V}} (a/R) \, d\mathbf{S} = 0$$

since $a = O(1/r^3)$ as $r \to \infty$. Hence

$$\nabla'\phi(P') = -(1/4\pi) \int (\nabla a/R) \, dV$$

$$\nabla'^2\phi(P') = -(1/4\pi) \int \nabla a \cdot \nabla'(1/R) \, dV$$

$$= (1/4\pi) \int\limits_{\substack{\text{all} \\ \text{space}}} \nabla a \cdot \nabla(1/R) \, dV$$

Now let K be a small sphere of radius ρ about P' as center. Then

$$\int\limits_{\substack{\text{all} \\ \text{space}}} \nabla a \cdot \nabla(1/R) \, dV = \lim_{\rho \to 0} \int\limits_{\substack{\text{all} \\ \text{space} \\ -K}} \nabla a \cdot \nabla(1/R) \, dV$$

$$= \lim_{\rho \to 0} \left[\int_K a\nabla(1/R) \cdot d\mathbf{S} - \int\limits_{\substack{\text{all} \\ \text{space} \\ -K}} a\nabla^2(1/R) \, dV \right]$$

$$= \lim_{\rho \to 0} \int_K a \, dS/\rho^2$$

$$= 4\pi a$$

using the fact that $\nabla^2(1/R)$ vanishes for all points other than P'. Thus, finally

$$\nabla'^2\phi = a$$

Sec. 8-7

1. $-\dfrac{1}{8\pi r^4} \int_V a\rho^3(5 \cos^3 \theta - 3 \cos \theta) \, dV$ **3.** $\dfrac{m}{4\pi r^3} (2 \cos \Theta \, \mathbf{i}_1 + \sin \Theta \, \mathbf{i}_2)$

4. $r = r_0 \sin^2 \Theta/\sin^2 \Theta_0$, $\Phi = \text{constant}$

5. Let P be the position of q, and let $r = PP'$. Then

$$\phi(P') = -\frac{m}{4\pi}\left[\frac{d}{dl}\left(\frac{1}{r}\right)\right]_{l=0}$$

where $m = \lim ql$.

6. Let P be the position of m, let $r = PP'$, and let Θ be the angle between $\theta = 0$ and PP'. Then

$$\phi(P') = -\frac{p}{4\pi}\left[\frac{d}{dl}\left(\frac{\cos\Theta}{r^2}\right)\right]_{l=0}$$

where $p = \lim lm$.

8. Let

$$r(l) = x'\mathbf{i} + y'\mathbf{j} + (z' - l)\mathbf{k}$$

where (x',y',z') are the coordinates of P'. Using superscript zero to denote a unit vector, one has

$$\phi(P') = -\frac{p}{4\pi}\left[\frac{d}{dl}\left(\frac{\mathbf{m}^0 \cdot \mathbf{r}^0}{r^2(l)}\right)\right]_{l=0}$$

where $p = \lim lm$.

INDEX